CW00386383

Mathematics

TWO

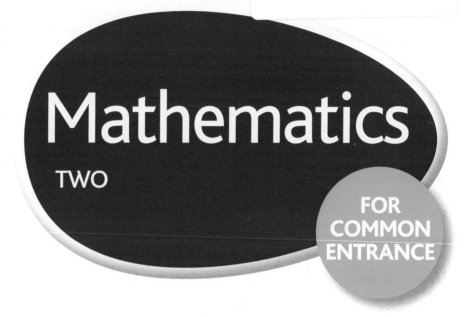

FOR COMMON ENTRANCE

Serena Alexander

GALORE PARK

AN HACHETTE UK COMPANY

About the author

Serena Alexander has taught mathematics since 1987, originally in both maintained and independent senior schools. From 1990 she taught at St Paul's School for Boys, where she was Head of mathematics at their Preparatory School, Colet Court, before moving first to Newton Prep as Deputy Head and then to Devonshire House as Head. She is now an educational consultant, with a focus on mathematics, and an ISI reporting inspector and in addition she helps to run regular mathematics conferences for prep school teachers.

Serena has a passion for maths and expects her pupils to feel the same way. After a lesson or two with her, they normally do!

The publishers would like to thank the following for permission to reproduce copyright material:

Photo credits p1 © Rocky89 – iStockphoto via Thinkstock **p18** © The Print Collector / Alamy **p51** © philipimage – Fotolia.com **p54** © Danita Delimont – Getty Images **p59** © Walter Rawlings – Getty Images **p76** © Ingram Publishing via Thinkstock **p80** © nuttawutphet – Fotolia.com **p92** © age fotostock / Alamy **p114** © Vankad – Fotolia.com **p118** © Zinco79 – iStockphoto via Thinkstock **p153** © PeteerS – iStockphoto via Thinkstock **p159** © Martin Poole – Digital Vision via Thinkstock **p173** © morrowlight – iStockphoto via Thinkstock **p267** © Richard Griffin – iStockphoto via Thinkstock

p239 © British Crown Copyright and/or database rights. Reproduced by permission of the Controller of Her Majesty's Stationery Office and the UK Hydrographic Office (www.ukho.gov.uk).

Every effort has been made to trace all copyright holders, but if any have been inadvertently overlooked the publishers will be pleased to make the necessary arrangements at the first opportunity.

Although every effort has been made to ensure that website addresses are correct at time of going to press, Galore Park cannot be held responsible for the content of any website mentioned in this book. It is sometimes possible to find a relocated web page by typing in the address of the home page for a website in the URL window of your browser.

Hachette UK's policy is to use papers that are natural, renewable and recyclable products and made from wood grown in sustainable forests. The logging and manufacturing processes are expected to conform to the environmental regulations of the country of origin.

Orders: please contact Bookpoint Ltd, 130 Milton Park, Abingdon, Oxon OX14 4SB. Telephone: +44 (0)1235 827827. Lines are open 9.00a.m.–5.00p.m., Monday to Saturday, with a 24-hour message answering service. Visit our website at www.galorepark.co.uk for details of other revision guides for Common Entrance, examination papers and Galore Park publications.

ISBN: 978 1 4718 4677 9

© Serena Alexander 2015

First published in 2015 by

Galore Park Publishing Ltd,

An Hachette UK Company

Carmelite House

50 Victoria Embankment

London EC4Y 0DZ

www.galorepark.co.uk

Impression number   10 9 8 7 6 5 4

Year   2019

All rights reserved. Apart from any use permitted under UK copyright law, no part of this publication may be reproduced or transmitted in any form or by any means, electronic or mechanical, including photocopying and recording, or held within any information storage and retrieval system, without permission in writing from the publisher or under licence from the Copyright Licensing Agency Limited. Further details of such licences (for reprographic reproduction) may be obtained from the Copyright Licensing Agency Limited, Saffron House, 6–10 Kirby Street, London EC1N 8TS.

Cover photo © Ruiponche - Fotolia

Illustrations by Integra Software Services Pvt. Ltd

Some illustrations by Graham Edwards were re-used. The publishers will be pleased to make the necessary arrangements with regard to these illustrations at the first opportunity.

Typeset in India

Printed in India

A catalogue record for this title is available from the British Library.

Contents

Introduction

This book is for pupils working towards their 13+ ISEB Common Entrance. It is intended for pupils in Year 8 who will be taking either Level 1 or Level 2 papers at the end of the year. It may also be suitable for pupils in earlier years who will eventually be sitting either Level 3 Common Entrance or Scholarship papers. It has been written in line with the National Curriculum and the ISEB syllabus.

In certain chapters the work covered in *Mathematics for Common Entrance One* is briefly revised before the topic is extended. Other topics are new and have a full introduction. There are extension exercises at the end of each chapter to encourage the more enthusiastic.

There is an emphasis on sound number work and, where relevant, efficient use of a calculator and sound calculator methods are covered. In each exercise there are clear examples showing how pupils should set out their work, in order to develop mathematical reasoning skills. As in *Mathematics for Common Entrance One*, the word problems are set in relevant contexts for 12-13 year olds: the mathematics of pocket money increases, the cost of computer games and the pricing of a school trip are all covered.

Activities, including puzzles and investigations provide ideas for more open-ended work on statistics and practical work on geometry. Some of these can be explored further by using a suitable computer programme.

The National Curriculum for Mathematics reflects the importance of spoken language in pupils' development across the whole curriculum – cognitively, socially and linguistically. These tasks are essential in developing pupils' mathematical vocabulary and presenting a mathematical justification, argument or proof. Teachers should ensure pupils build secure foundations by using discussion to diagnose understanding and to correct any misconceptions.

Notes on features in this book

Words printed in **blue and bold** are keywords. All keywords are defined in the Glossary at the end of the book.

Example

Worked examples are given throughout to aid understanding of each part of a topic.

Exercise

Exercises are provided to give pupils plenty of opportunities to practise what they have learned.

Extension Exercise

Some exercises contain questions that are more challenging. These extension exercises are designed to stretch more able pupils.

Summary Exercise

Each chapter ends with a summary exercise, containing questions on all the topics in the chapter.

Useful rules and reminders are scattered throughout the book.

Activity

The National Curriculum for Mathematics reflects the importance of spoken language in pupils' development across the whole curriculum – cognitively, socially and linguistically. Activities to develop these skills are interspersed between the chapters. These are essential for developing pupils' mathematical vocabulary and presenting a mathematical justification, argument or proof.

1 Working with numbers

In the animal kingdom many species demonstrate the ability to recognise numbers, especially the number of young they have. Many birds have a good sense of number. If a nest contains four eggs, a predator might take one away without the bird deserting the nest, but when two are removed the bird generally abandons the rest. A bird can distinguish two from three. This ability seems to be instinctive and not learned.

Very early civilisations demonstrated the same ability to recognise numbers but most did not have words for numbers larger than two. Instead they used words such as *flocks* of sheep, *heaps* of grain, or *lots* of people. There was little need for a numeric system until groups of people formed clans, villages and settlements and began a system of bartering and trade that in turn created a demand for currency.

In the days before pencil and paper, people used hand signals as an official system.

It is now generally accepted that the decimal numerals derive from a form that was developed in India and transmitted via Arab culture to Europe, undergoing a number of changes on the way. Several different ways of writing numbers evolved in India before it was possible for the existing decimal numerals to be combined with the place-value principle of the Babylonians. This led to the number system in use today.

The decimal number system – a summary

Place value

The **value** of any **digit** in a number depends on its **place** or position within that number.

This number is three hundred and seventy-two million, five hundred and six thousand and nine.

HM	TM	M	HTh	TTh	Th	H	T	U
3	7	2	5	0	6	0	0	9

You would generally write this with a small space between the hundreds and the thousands and another small space between the thousands and the millions.

372 506 009

A **proper fraction** is a part of a whole. **Decimal fractions** are separated from whole numbers by the **decimal point**.

This number is five thousand, four hundred and twelve and thirty-five thousandths.

Th	H	T	U •	t	h	th
5	4	1	2 •	0	3	5

All these numbers are greater than nought or zero, but some numbers are less than zero. These are **negative numbers**.

You can show positive and negative numbers on the number line.

Mental strategies

Sometimes, when you need to add, subtract, multiply or divide, you can do it in your head. Sometimes you need to use pencil and paper. As calculations become more complex, you may need to use a **calculator**.

You may be tempted to use a calculator for every calculation you do but you will not always have one available, for example, when you are shopping or on holiday. Make sure that you can complete calculations in your head *and* on paper.

The inverse

Many people find it easier to add or multiply, rather than subtract or divide. Remember that subtraction is the **inverse** of addition and division is the inverse of multiplication.

Think again about **number bonds**. When you know one, you know at least three more.

As $138 + 75 = 213$ then $75 + 138 = 213$

and $213 - 75 = 138$

and $213 - 138 = 75$

also $38 + 175 = 213$

and $213 - 38 = 175$

and $213 - 175 = 38$

As $15 \times 7 = 105$ then $7 \times 15 = 105$

and $105 \div 15 = 7$

and $105 \div 7 = 15$

also $5 \times 21 = 105$ You can rearrange the factors:

and $105 \div 21 = 5$ $15 \times 7 = 5 \times 3 \times 7 = 5 \times 21$

and $105 \div 5 = 21$

Examples

Given that $34 \times 15 = 510$, write down the value of:

(i) $510 \div 15$ (ii) $510 \div 17$ (iii) 3.4×0.15

(i) $510 \div 15 = 34$ Rearrange factors to give $34 \times 15 = 17 \times 2 \times 15$

                                                     $= 17 \times 30$

(ii) $510 \div 17 = 30$

(iii) $3.4 \times 0.15 = 34 \div 10 \times 15 \div 100$

                 $= 510 \div 1000$

                 $= 0.510$

                 $= 0.51$

You could also use the rules for multiplying by decimals.

The total number of digits after the decimal points in the question is the same as the total number of digits after the decimal point in the answer.

3.4×0.15 has three digits altogether after the decimal points so the answer will be 0.510 but you do not need to write the last 0 in your final answer. Unless you are asked to give the answer to 3 significant figures or 3 decimal places in this case.

> You do not need to include the final 0 as leaving it out does not change the value of the number, but you need to keep it in while you complete the calculation.

1 Given that $167 + 45 = 212$, write down the value of:

(a) $212 - 167$ (b) $212 - 145$ (c) $2.12 - 1.67$

2 Given that $19 \times 35 = 665$, write down the value of:

(a) $665 \div 19$ (b) $665 \div 35$ (c) 1.9×3.5

3 Given that $203 - 154 = 49$, write down the value of:

(a) $203 - 49$ (b) $149 + 54$ (c) $2.03 - 0.49$

4 Given that $240 \div 16 = 15$, write down the value of:

(a) $240 \div 15$ (b) 15×16 (c) 1.5×1.6

5 Given that $175 + 192 = 367$, write down the value of:

(a) $367 - 192$ (b) $367 - 75$ (c) $3.67 - 1.92$

6 Given that $24 \times 28 = 672$, write down the value of:

(a) $672 \div 24$ (b) 48×14 (c) 2.4×0.28

7 Given that $508 - 196 = 312$, write down the value of:

(a) $508 - 312$ (b) $312 + 296$ (c) $3.12 + 1.96$

8 Given that $144 \div 45 = 3.2$, write down the value of:

(a) $144 \div 3.2$ (b) 45×32 (c) 3.2×4.5

9 Given that $45 \times 24 = 1080$, write down the value of:

(a) $1080 \div 45$ (b) $108 \div 24$ (c) 7.2×1.5

10 Given that $1890 \div 54 = 35$, write down the value of:

(a) $189 \div 35$ (b) 18×105 (c) 6×3.15

Estimating

Consider the calculation 419×27

First, **estimate** the answer by **rounding** 419 to the nearest hundred and 27 to the nearest ten.

$$419 \approx 400 \qquad 27 \approx 30$$

Then: $419 \times 27 \approx 400 \times 30$

$$\approx 12\,000$$

There are three zeros altogether. You can think of this as:

$$4000 \times 3 = 12\,000$$

As this is a whole number, you cannot leave out any of the zeros.

> When estimating calculations, first collect the 0s and then multiply the numbers.

> When estimating numbers, keep the estimation simple. Aim to have each estimated value as one digit followed by zeros.

Example

Estimate the value of 3195×350

$$3195 \times 350 \approx 3000 \times 400$$

$$\approx 1\,200\,000$$

$3195 \approx 3000$ but $350 \approx 400$ as 350 is exactly halfway between 300 and 400, so you round up.

Now consider division.

Examples

(i) Estimate the answer to $579 \div 19$

$$579 \div 19 \approx 600 \div 20$$

$$\approx 30$$

Divide 600 first by 10 to get 60 then by 2 to get 30

(ii) Estimate the answer to $4136 \div \approx 485$

$$4136 \div 485 \approx 4000 \div 500$$

$$\approx 8$$

Divide 4000 first by 100 to get 40 then by 5 to get 8

You could divide both the numbers in the calculation by ten or one hundred. First cross off the zeros, making sure you cross off the same number of zeros in each number. Then complete the resulting calculation.

$$400 \div 20 = 20 \qquad 4000 \div 500 = 8$$

You can do this only with division.

Exercise 1.2

Estimate the answer to each calculation.

1 32×218

2 $399 \div 24$

3 79×450

4 $729 \div 17$

5 43×623

6 $4372 \div 246$

7 450×242

8 $650 \div 79$

9 1432×628

10 $6350 \div 47$

11 125×734

12 $1925 \div 534$

13 4200×499

14 $4200 \div 499$

15 636×99

16 $3612 \div 99$

17 48×863

18 $587 \div 26$

19 $8432 \div 428$

20 $9999 \div 475$

Now use a calculator to work out the exact answers to check the accuracy of your estimates. Were your estimates the same as your partner's?

More estimating

Sometimes it is not worth giving an exact answer to a calculation, because the values are constantly changing. One example is in questions about population sizes.

> **Example**
>
> If the population of London is 6 767 500 and the population of Belfast is 301 600, how many times larger is the population of London than that of Belfast?
>
> The population of London is approximately 6 800 000 and of Belfast it is approximately 300 000.
>
> So the population of London is 6 800 000 ÷ 300 000 = 22.7 or 23 times larger than that of Belfast.

Exercise 1.3

1 The population of Coventry is roughly four times as big as the population of Jersey. Given that the population of Jersey is 80 212, estimate the population of Coventry.

2 The population of the Isle of Wight is about one-sixth of the population of Glasgow. Given that the population of Glasgow is 733 784, estimate the population of the Isle of Wight.

3 Estimate the number of seconds in one year.

4 Given that there are 1760 yards in a mile, roughly how many yards are there in 496 miles?

5 There are 23 boys in my form. To eat comfortably they each need a width of 65 cm at the dining table. Estimate the minimum perimeter of a dining table that will seat the whole class. Give some suitable dimensions, in metres, for the length and width of the table.

6 A recent survey showed that the average weekly pocket money in my class of 24 was £1.78 (to the nearest penny). Estimate the total amount of pocket money the class receives altogether.

7 The school photocopier uses 45 packets of 500 sheets of paper in one term. There are 11 weeks in the term. The photocopier is used for five days every week and there are nine working hours in a day. Estimate the number of sheets used in one hour.

8 The school photographer is coming to take each pupil's photograph. There are 443 pupils in the school. It takes, on average, 3 minutes to photograph each pupil. Estimate the number of hours that the photographer needs to spend at the school.

9 My teacher is writing our school reports. She says that she has to write reports for nine classes. There are, on average, 19 pupils in each class. She says it takes her about 12 minutes to write each report. Estimate the number of hours my teacher spends writing our reports.

10 I have just finished a really good book. There were 298 pages in the book and about 12 words a line on 30 lines on each page. I read the book in a total of 8 hours and 40 minutes. Estimate my reading speed in number of words per minute.

Calculation strategies

Multiplication

There are some techniques that can help you when you need to multiply.

Using last digits

Sometimes looking at the last digit can be useful.

Example

Multiply: 26×19

Firstly make a good estimate. $25 \times 20 = 500$ would be good in this case.

Then multiply the last two digits together $6 \times 9 = 54$

Now you know that the product of 26×19 is approximately 500 and must end in a 4

There are two possibilities, 504 or 494, close to 500   (Those numbers ending in 4 either side of your estimate 500)

Do a mental calculation to decide: $26 \times 19 = 26 \times 20 - 26 \times 1$
$$= 520 - 26$$
$$= 494$$

If your estimate was less accurate, then you may need to look at other, less close, possible answers, such as 514 or 484

Exercise 1.4

1 Write down the last digit only of each product.

(a) 23×45 (d) 36×27

(b) 34×98 (e) 47×22

(c) 21×65 (f) 99×38

2 Only one of the three choices is correct. Work out which one it is. Then use estimation and the last digits to state the reason why the other two are incorrect.

(a) $31 \times 99 =$ (b) $29 \times 42 =$

    (i)   3069   (i)   818

    (ii) 2699   (ii) 1029

    (iii) 2708   (iii) 1218

(c) $31 \times 58 =$

    (i) 1058

    (ii) 1798

    (iii) 1218

(d) $78 \times 52 =$

    (i) 4056

    (ii) 456

    (iii) 35016

(e) $72 \times 51 =$

    (i) 3616

    (ii) 3492

    (iii) 3672

(f) $99 \times 39 =$

    (i) 2718

    (ii) 3861

    (iii) 4081

3 Use your calculator to check the answers to the six multiplications above.

4 The class teacher has displayed some number tiles to show the answers to some multiplications but the number tiles have fallen off the wall. Use estimating and the last digit rule to make the calculations work.

(a) $37 \times 25 =$ (The tiles are 2, 5, 9)

(b) $29 \times 78 =$ (The tiles are 2, 2, 2, 6)

(c) $45 \times 87 =$ (The tiles are 1, 3, 5, 9)

(d) $32 \times 49 =$ (The tiles are 1, 5, 6, 8)

(e) $29 \times 58 =$ (The tiles are 1, 2, 6, 8)

(f) $81 \times 61 =$ (The tiles are 1, 4, 4, 9)

Multiplication by factors

Sometimes, when you are multiplying difficult numbers, it can be useful to break the number into its **factors** and multiply by them.

A **factor** is a number that divides exactly into another number.
3 and 4 are factors of 12

Example

Multiply: 48×15

$$48 \times 15 = 48 \times 5 \times 3 \qquad 15 = 5 \times 3 \quad \text{Multiply by 5 first so that the product will end in 0}$$

$$= 240 \times 3$$

$$= 720$$

Division

Using factors

Just as for multiplication, it can be useful to break the number into its factors when you are dividing. This enables you to divide by smaller numbers.

Example

Divide: $336 \div 24$

$$336 \div 24 = 336 \div 4 \div 6 \qquad 24 = 4 \times 6 \quad \text{Divide by 4 first as this is easier.}$$
$$= 84 \div 6$$
$$= 14$$

Exercise 1.5

Use what you know about addition, subtraction, multiplication and division to sharpen your mental arithmetic skills in this exercise. See how quickly you can complete them all in your head without written working. Only write down the answer.

1 Copy and complete these additions.

(a) $15 + 82 =$ _____

(b) $36 + 43 =$ _____

(c) $28 + 71 =$ _____

(d) $24 + 53 =$ _____

(e) $65 + 24 =$ _____

(f) $25 + 39 =$ _____

(g) $18 + 73 =$ _____

(h) $57 + 36 =$ _____

(i) $29 + 64 =$ _____

(j) $46 + 35 =$ _____

2 Now copy and complete these multiplications.

(a) $6 \times 9 =$ _____

(b) $7 \times 8 =$ _____

(c) $3 \times 15 =$ _____

(d) $17 \times 2 =$ _____

(e) $4 \times 26 =$ _____

(f) $17 \times 5 =$ _____

(g) $3 \times 19 =$ _____

(h) $12 \times 9 =$ _____

(i) $9 \times 13 =$ _____

(j) $25 \times 7 =$ _____

3 Now copy and complete these.

(a) $35 + 15 =$ _____

(b) $27 - 18 =$ _____

(c) $166 + 223 =$ _____

(d) $168 - 49 =$ _____

(e) $123 + 337 =$ _____

(f) $356 - 129 =$ _____

(g) $532 + 119 =$ _____

(h) $281 - 59 =$ _____

(i) $364 + 259 =$ _____

(j) $507 - 169 =$ _____

4 Now try division: think of the inverse.

(a) $108 \div 12 =$ _____

(f) $275 \div 25 =$ _____

(b) $144 \div 6 =$ _____

(g) $135 \div 15 =$ _____

(c) $132 \div 4 =$ _____

(h) $315 \div 9 =$ _____

(d) $125 \div 5 =$ _____

(i) $1050 \div 25 =$ _____

(e) $375 \div 5 =$ _____

(j) $1440 \div 18 =$ _____

5 Here is a mixture of questions.

(a) $156 + 76 =$ _____

(f) $402 - 123 =$ _____

(b) $457 - 268 =$ _____

(g) $19 \times 11 =$ _____

(c) $25 \times 9 =$ _____

(h) $308 \div 44 =$ _____

(d) $170 \div 5 =$ _____

(i) $35 \times 15 =$ _____

(e) $145 + 567 =$ _____

(j) $706 - 358 =$ _____

Mixed operations

You can add, subtract, multiply and divide, but there are times when you need to do at least two of these in one calculation.

The rule is: 'multiplication and division before addition and subtraction' and also: 'complete any calculation in brackets first, followed by any **index** numbers'.

You can use the mnemonic **BIDMAS** to remember the **order of operations**.

Brackets, **I**ndices, **D**ivide, **M**ultiply, **A**dd, **S**ubtract.

Remember that **indices** are index numbers or **powers**.

$3^4 = 3 \times 3 \times 3 \times 3$

$\qquad = 81$

> 4 is the index number and indicates you multiply 3^2 by 3^2

Example

Calculate: $1 + 3 \times 7$

$1 + 3 \times 7 = 1 + 21$

$\qquad\qquad = 22$

> You must do the multiplication before the addition.

Exercise 1.6

Remember the BIDMAS rule when calculating the answers to these questions.

1 $3 + 5 \times 4$

2 $72 \div 9 - 4 \times 2$

3 $(3 + 5) \times 4$

4 $3 + 15 \div 3$

5 $3^2 + 2^3 - 2 \times 3$

6 $25 - 3 \times 7$

7 $45 \div 5 - 3 \times 2$

8 $3 \times (4 - 1)^2$

9 $(8 + 4)^2 \div (5 - 2)^2$

10 $(8 - 5)^2 \times (5 - 2)^2$

◯ Rounding

You know that it can often be convenient to use approximate or **rounded** numbers in everyday situations. For example, when discussing attendance at a rock festival, it is generally acceptable to give an **estimate** of the number of people who attended.

It can also be useful to round **decimal fractions**. For example, when a joiner is building furniture, it is unlikely that measurements will be accurate to more than one place of decimals. Look at this number line.

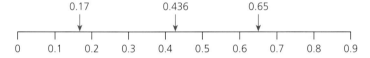

You can see that 0.17 lies between 0.1 and 0.2 but is nearer to 0.2

$$0.17 = 0.2 \text{ (to 1 d.p.) or } 0.17 \approx 0.2$$

Similarly, 0.436 lies between 0.4 and 0.5 but is nearer to 0.4

$$0.436 = 0.4 \text{ (to 1 d.p.)}$$

Note that 0.65 lies exactly halfway between 0.6 and 0.7 so the rule is to round up.

$$0.65 = 0.7 \text{ (to 1 d.p.)}$$

The steps are the same as for whole numbers.

1 Find the **digit in** the place that you are rounding to.

2 Look at the digit **to the right of it**.

3 If it is 5, 6, 7, 8 or 9, round your digit up.

4 If it is 0, 1, 2, 3 or 4, leave your digit as it is.

5 Remove all the digits after the rounded digit.

> The symbol $\approx$ means 'is approximately equal to'.

Examples

(i) Round 45 627 to the nearest: (a) ten thousand (b) hundred.

    (a) 45 627 = 50 000 to the nearest ten thousand

       The digit to the right of forty thousand is 5 so round up.

    (b) 45 627 = 45 600 to the nearest hundred

       The digit to the right of six hundred is 2 so round down.

(ii) Round 3.5139 to: (a) 3 decimal places (b) 1 decimal place.

    (a) 3.5139 = 3.514 (to 3 d.p.)

       The digit to the right of 3 thousandths is 9 so round up.

    (b) 3.5139 = 3.5 (to 1 d.p.)

       The digit to the right of 5 tenths is 1 so round down.

Exercise 1.7

1 Round each number to the nearest: **(i)** ten thousand **(ii)** hundred.

  (a) 13 569   **(c)** 2 434 709   **(e)** 29 003

  (b) 346 512   **(d)** 95 035   **(f)** 199 999

2 Round each number to: **(i)** 1 decimal place **(ii)** 3 decimal places.

  (a) 0.1754   **(c)** 5.0006   **(e)** 19.0919

  (b) 24.0255   **(d)** 25.9137   **(f)** 13.299 99

3 Round each number to the nearest: **(i)** million **(ii)** thousand.

  (a) 14 653 412   **(c)** 6 175 919   **(e)** 9 599 900

  (b) 19 856 095   **(d)** 17 500 055   **(f)** 6 940 890

4 Round each number to: **(i)** the nearest whole number **(ii)** 2 decimal places.

  (a) 5.1923   **(c)** 13.7192   **(e)** 9.605

  (b) 0.945   **(d)** 1.7359   **(f)** 2.1999

5 What is the smallest whole number that can be written as 3 million to the nearest million?

6 What is the largest whole number that can be written as 5000 to the nearest thousand?

7 What is the smallest whole number that can be written as 199 to the nearest whole number?

8 What is the largest number that can be written as 450 to the nearest 10?

9 What is the smallest number that can be written as 9.09 to two decimal places?

10 What is the largest number that can be written as 0.9 to one decimal place?

Range of values

You know that the **inequality** symbol $<$ means **less than** and $>$ means **more than**.

You need also to know that:

- $\leqslant$ is a combination of $<$ and $=$ and means **less than or equal to**
- $\geqslant$ is a combination of $>$ and $=$ and means **greater than or equal to**.

You can use these symbols to describe ranges of values.

Consider a whole number, n, such that $n < 8$

Then the value of n could be 7, 6, 5, 4, 3 ...

Consider another whole number, n, such that $n \leqslant 8$

Then the value of n could be 8, 7, 6, 5, 4, 3 ...

Consider another whole number, n, such that $n > 5$

Then the value of n could be 6, 7, 8, 9, ...

Consider another whole number, n, such that $n \geqslant 5$

Then the value of n could be 5, 6, 7, 8, 9, ...

You can show the possible values on a number line.

> Note that the solid circle means that the **value is included**, so the symbol is $\leqslant$ or $\geqslant$
>
> The open circle means that the **value is not included**, so the symbol is $<$ or $>$

Exercise 1.8

1 Write the range of whole numbers shown on each number line.

(a)

(b)
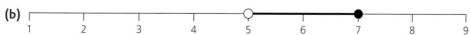

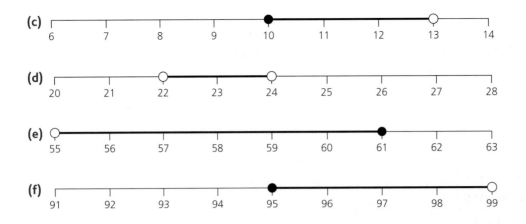

In questions 2–8, draw a suitable number line to show the range of values for a number, n.

2 $n > 5$ and $n \leqslant 8$

3 $n \geqslant 9$ and $n < 12$

4 $n > 15$ and $n \leqslant 20$

5 $n < 28$ and $n \geqslant 25$

6 $n > 15$ and $n < 18$

7 $n \geqslant 95$ and $n < 98$

8 $n < 55$ and $n \geqslant 51$

Extension Exercise 1.9

In these questions write down the calculation correctly, using brackets if necessary. Then complete the calculation, remembering the BIDMAS rule.

1 Take 4, add 7 and then multiply the answer by 6. What is your answer?

2 Take 36, divide it by 9 and subtract the answer from 15. What is your answer?

3 Take 36 divided by 9 from 28 divided by 4

4 What is the value of ten squared divided by 5 less six squared divided by four?

5 I have 9 conkers. I give 5 of them away and then I lose half of the rest. How many conkers do I have left?

6 My mother is 34. If I halve her age and then take away 5, I have my age. How old am I?

7 I am 12. If I take the square of my age and then divide it by 2, I have my grandpa's age. How old is grandpa?

8 My sister is 21. If you divide her age by 3 and then square the answer, you have my mother's age. How old is my mother?

9 I have 2 hens. Fluffy laid six eggs a week for five weeks and Clucky laid eight eggs a week for four weeks. Who laid more eggs and by how many?

10 I take the square of my little sister's age and divide it by my age, you get my brothers age. If I am 12, how old are my brother and my sister? Work out what possible ages my sister could be first.

> You may be able to answer these in your head but the challenge is to write out the calculation carefully first.

Summary Exercise 1.10

1 Write the value of A, B, C and D on this number line.

2 Round these numbers to:

  (i) the nearest ten

  (ii) the nearest thousand.

  (a) 45 909   **(b)** 346 435

3 Round these numbers to:

  (i) the nearest whole number

  (ii) two decimal places.

  (a) 13.045   **(b)** 33.499

4 Given that $971 - 346 = 625$, write down the value of:

  (a) $971 - 625$ **(b)** $325 + 646$ **(c)** $6.25 + 3.46$

5 Given that $28 \times 65 = 1820$, write down the value of:

  (a) $1820 \div 28$ **(b)** $182 \div 65$ **(c)** 0.28×6.5

6 Estimate the answers.

  (a) 547×29 **(c)** $7700 \div 44$

  (b) 1635×541 **(d)** $4945 \div 399$

7 The class teacher is using some number tiles to show the answers to some multiplications. Use estimating and the last digit rule to make the calculations work.

  (a) $17 \times 45 =$ (The tiles are 5, 6, 7)

  (b) $27 \times 48 =$ (The tiles are 1, 2, 6, 9)

  (c) $46 \times 39 =$ (The tiles are 1, 4, 7, 9)

8 Copy and complete these calculations.

  (a) $124 + 56 =$ _____   **(e)** $157 + 398 =$ _____

  (b) $458 - 214 =$ _____   **(f)** $601 - 187 =$ _____

  (c) $35 \times 4 =$ _____   **(g)** $17 \times 13 =$ _____

  (d) $160 \div 5 =$ _____   **(h)** $448 \div 56 =$ _____

9 Copy and complete these calculations.

(a) $5 \times 7 + 63 \div 7$ (b) $5 \times (7 + 63) \div 7$

10 Matron works out that of the 365 pupils in the school, the 158 boys each need six different pairs of socks but the girls need only five different pairs of socks. Does matron find that the boys have more socks than the girls or the girls than the boys, and by how many?

Activity: Dice games

1 Up to 20

For any number of players

Roll three dice.

Use the three scores to make as many numbers as possible – no more than 20 though!

To make the numbers, you combine the three scores with $+$, $-$, $\times$, $\div$ and brackets.

For example: if you rolled 3, 4 and 6:

$$3 + 4 - 6 = 1 \qquad 3 \times (6 - 4) = 6$$

$$3 \times (4 \div 6) = 2 \qquad 4 + 6 - 3 = 7$$

$$3 + 6 - 4 = 5 \qquad 4 \times (6 - 3) = 12 \text{ and so on.}$$

2 Find the factors

For two players and two dice

The first player calls a number between 1 and 30

The second player rolls the two dice.

If either score or any combination of the scores make a factor of the number called, then the second player wins; if not, the first player wins.

In this game if you throw a 1 and a 5, you can say it is 15

The winner plays first in the next round.

Once a number has been called, you cannot call it again.

The overall winner is the winner of the final (30th) round.

In that last game you will see there are quite a lot of strategies to help you win the game. Some numbers are bound to have a factor and others are not. Is it better to call these earlier or later?

3 Highest number

For two players

Each of you is going to make a four-digit number so outline four squares each.

Player 1

Player 2

Player 1 rolls the die. He can choose to write the number rolled in one of his four boxes or to pass it to player 2, and player 2 has to write it in her box.

Player 2 then rolls the die. Again, she can choose to write the number rolled in one of her four boxes or to pass it to player 1, and player 1 has to write it in his box.

Keep going until all the boxes are filled. The player with the largest four-digit number wins. For the next round player 2 has the first roll of the die.

After playing the game a few times, discuss the strategies you have discovered with your partner. See if you both agree.

2 Back to Babylon

How many miles to Babylon? Three score miles and ten.

Can I get there by candlelight? Aye, and back again.

If your feet are nimble and light, You'll get there by candlelight.

■ Tower of Babel, Babylon, Peter Brueghel

Why would anyone want to go to Babylon? In its heyday Babylon was the centre of the civilised world, ruled over by King Nebuchadnezzar. He built the glorious *Hanging Gardens of Babylon*, one of the wonders of the ancient world.

For mathematicians, Babylonians are interesting because they used a numerical system like our own, but based on the number 60 instead of 10

Why choose 60? Think again about some of the things that you know about numbers – this will give you a clue.

◯ Factors and multiples

The numbers that divide exactly into another number are its **factors**.

For example: 3 and 6 are **factors** of 12

Numbers that are the result of multiplying a number (or factor) by a whole number are **multiples** of the number.

For example: 12 is a multiple of 6 and is also a multiple of 12, 4, 3, 2, and 1

When you learnt your times tables, you were studying factors and multiples.

When whole numbers are involved:

● multiples give the result of a multiplication

● factors are the result of a division.

As $7 \times 8 = 56$ then 56 is a multiple of 7 and of 8

Then $56 \div 7 = 8$ and 7 and 8 are factors of 56

The rules of divisibility

● A number can be divided by 2 if it is even.

● A number can be divided by 3 if the **sum** of its digits is a multiple of 3

● A number can be divided by 4 if the number formed by its last two digits can be divided by 4

● A number can be divided by 5 if it ends in 5 or 0

● A number can be divided by 6 if it is even and its **digit sum** (sum of its digits) is a multiple of 3

● A number can be divided by 9 if its digit sum is a multiple of 9

● A number can be divided by 10 if it ends in 0

There are rules of divisibility for 7, 8 and 11 but they are more complicated. It is better just to be good at these times tables and to be able to divide by 7, 8 and 11

Example

Is 6 a factor of: (i)   1341   (ii)   2142?

(i)   The digit sum of 1341 is: $1 + 3 + 4 + 1 = 9$

     9 is a multiple of 3, so 1341 is divisible by 3

     But 1341 is odd, so 6 is not a factor of 1341

(ii)   The digit sum of 2142 is: $2 + 1 + 4 + 2 = 9$

     9 is a multiple of 3, so 2142 is divisible by 3

     2142 is even, so 6 is a factor of 2142

Finding factors

If you need to find all the factors of a number, consider them in pairs.

Start with 1 and write down all the **factor pairs**, until you get the same pairs of factors in reverse order.

Example

Find all the factors of 45

The next factor pair is 9 × 5 which is the same as 5 × 9 so stop the list here.

The factors of 45 are: 1, 3, 5, 9, 15 and 45

Exercise 2.1

1 Which of these numbers have 6 as a factor? Write them down.

(a) 216   (c) 425   (e) 12324

(b) 480   (d) 614

2 Which of these numbers are multiples of 9?

(a) 216   (c) 617   (e) 19368

(b) 891   (d) 6138

3 Which of these numbers have 7 as a factor?

(a) 7   (c) 77   (e) 91

(b) 27   (d) 717

4 Which of these numbers are multiples of 11?

(a) 88   (c) 292   (e) 2574

(b) 121   (d) 374

5 List all the factors of each number.

(a) 17   (c) 71   (e) 101

(b) 37   (d) 83

6 List all the factors of each number.

(a) 1   (c) 64   (e) 144

(b) 25   (d) 9

7 List all the factors of each number.

   (a) 10   **(c)** 24   **(e)** 100

   (b) 16   **(d)** 60

8 What is special about 60?

9 Look again at the numbers in question 5 and question 6. What do you notice?

Prime numbers and prime factors

A number that has exactly two factors, itself and 1, is a **prime number**.

Remember that 1 is **not** a prime number because it does not have two factors.

The first five prime numbers are 2, 3, 5, 7 and 11

Now $12 = 3 \times 4$ and $4 = 2 \times 2$, so $12 = 2 \times 2 \times 3$

When you write 12 as $2 \times 2 \times 3$, you are writing it as the **product of its prime factors**. You would normally use **index numbers** to write repeated factors.

Look at this number.

$243 = 3 \times 3 \times 3 \times 3 \times 3 = 3^5$ This is the **prime factorisation** of 243

243 has only one prime factor, which is 3, but the factor 3 is repeated to produce 243

The small raised 5 is an index number and it indicates how many 'lots' of 3 are multiplied together.

Therefore you can write 12 as $12 = 2^2 \times 3$. This is the prime factorisation of 12

A number can be factorised into a product of prime numbers in only one way. This is known as the **unique factorisation property**.

The method used above is useful for finding prime factors of smaller numbers.

For larger numbers it is better to use successive division by prime numbers. Always start with the smallest.

Examples

(i) Write 1287 as the produce of its prime factors.

Start by finding its prime factors.

	3	1	2	8	7
	3		4	2	9
1	1		1	4	3
1	3			1	3
					1

The digit sum is 18 and so 1287 can be divided by 3

The digit sum is 15 and so 429 can be divided by 3

143 cannot be divided by 5 or by 7 but can be divided by 11

13 is a prime number.

$$1287 = 3 \times 3 \times 11 \times 13$$
$$= 3^2 \times 11 \times 13$$

(ii) Write 786 as the product of its prime factors.

			2	7	8	6
			3	3	9	3
	1	3	1	1	3	1
						1

786 is an even number and so can be divided by 2

The digit sum is 15 so 393 can be divided by 3

131 cannot be divided by 3 or 5 or 7 or 11 or 13, so it must be prime.

$$786 = 2 \times 3 \times 131$$

Exercise 2.2

1 List all the prime numbers from 1 to 50

2 Which of these are prime numbers?

(a) 87   (b) 91   (c) 107   (d) 207   (e) 231

3 Write each number as the product of its prime factors.

(a) 16   (b) 40   (c) 120   (d) 28   (e) 100

4 Each number is written as a product of prime factors in index form.

What are the numbers?

(a) 2×3^2 (c) $2^3 \times 3^2 \times 5$ (e) $2^3 \times 5^2 \times 11$

(b) $2^2 \times 3^2$ (d) $2^2 \times 3^2 \times 5^2$

5 (i) Write the first five multiples of each number.

(a) 3   (b) 6   (c) 12

(ii) Write each of the given numbers as products of its prime factors.

What do you notice?

6 Use successive division to write each number as the product of its prime factors.

(a) 252   (c) 798   (e) 6215

(b) 1155   (d) 11475

7 Write down the largest number that is a factor of:

(a) both 24 and 45   (b) both 40 and 56   (c) both 100 and 120

8 Write down the smallest number that is a multiple of:

(a) both 8 and 10   (b) both 16 and 20   (c) both 20 and 25

The answers to question 7 are the **highest common factors** (HCF) of the two numbers.

The answers to question 8 are the **lowest common multiples** (LCM) of the two numbers.

You can deduce them simply for smaller numbers, but for larger numbers it helps to look at the prime factors.

Examples

(i) Find the highest common factor of 315 and 210

$$315 = 9 \times 35 \qquad\qquad 210 = 10 \times 21$$
$$= 3 \times 3 \times 5 \times 7 \qquad\qquad = 2 \times 3 \times 5 \times 7$$

You can see that 3 and 5 and 7 are factors of both numbers. Therefore the HCF of 315 and 210 is $3 \times 5 \times 7 = 105$

(ii) Find the lowest common multiple of 315 and 210

$$315 = 9 \times 35 \qquad\qquad 210 = 10 \times 21$$
$$= 3 \times 3 \times 5 \times 7 \qquad\qquad = 2 \times 3 \times 5 \times 7$$
$$\text{LCM of 315 and 210} = 3 \times (3 \times 5 \times 7) \times 2$$
$$= 315 \times 2$$
$$= 630$$

> You must include all the prime factors of one number, as well as any extra prime factors in the other.

Another way of looking at HCFs and LCMs is to put all the factors of the numbers into a **Venn diagram**.

Look carefully at where the factors have been written within the different regions in the diagram.

The HCF is the product of the factors in the dark overlapping area: $3 \times 5 \times 7 = 105$

The LCM is the product of all the factors:
$2 \times 3 \times 3 \times 5 \times 7 = 630$

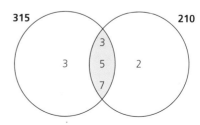

1 Work out the highest common factor of each pair of numbers.

(a) 24 and 144

(b) 132 and 198

(c) 144 and 180

(d) 224 and 504

(e) 400 and 640

(f) 630 and 882

2 Work out the lowest common multiple of each pair of numbers.

(a) 12 and 45

(b) 60 and 144

(c) 60 and 72

(d) 224 and 504

(e) 400 and 640

(f) 630 and 882

3 Consider the numbers from 1 to 100

(a) What is the largest number that is a multiple of both 3 and 7?

(b) What is the smallest number that is a multiple of both 8 and 6?

(c) What is the largest number that has 3 as a factor?

(d) What is the largest number that has 6 as a factor?

(e) What is the largest number that has both the numbers 3 and 5 as factors?

(f) Which numbers have only two factors?

(g) Which numbers have an odd number of factors?

(h) Which is the largest number that is a factor of 360?

(i) How many numbers contain the digit 7?

(j) How many numbers contain the digit 0?

Square numbers and their roots

Think again about index numbers.

$$3 \times 3 = 3^2$$

You can display 3^2 as a square array or pattern of dots, with three dots in each of three rows.

You say 3^2 as 'three squared'.

Numbers that can be drawn as a square pattern of dots are **square numbers**.

$$3^2 = 3 \times 3 = 9$$

Then the **square** root of 9 is 3

You write this as $\sqrt{9} = 3$

Notice the special sign for a square root.

Exercise 2.4

1 Draw a dot pattern to show each number.

(a) $4^2 = 16$ (b) $2^2 = 4$ (c) $6^2 = 36$

2 Without drawing dot patterns, work out the value of each number.

(a) 7^2 (b) 9^2 (c) 11^2

3 List all the square numbers from 1 to 100, in order.

4 Look at this sequence of numbers.

0, 3, 8, 15, 24, 35, ...

(a) Continue the pattern for three more terms.

(b) Compare with your sequence of square numbers. What do you notice?

5 Look at this sequence of numbers.

3, 6, 11, 18, 27, 38, ...

(a) Continue the pattern for three more terms.

(b) Compare with your sequence of square numbers. What do you notice?

6 Use this rule to generate a number sequence.

Start with 0

Add 1 and write down your answer.

Add 3 to that number. Write down that answer.

Continue adding successive odd numbers until you have 10 numbers.

Describe these numbers.

You will look again at this pattern, when you have learnt some more about algebra.

7 Imagine a square of 49 dots. How many dots are there on one side of the square?

This number is the square root of 49

8 Find the square root of each number.

(a) 16   (b) 4   (c) 36

9 Evaluate each square root.

(a) $\sqrt{100}$

(b) $\sqrt{81}$

(c) $\sqrt{1}$

(d) $\sqrt{25}$

(e) $\sqrt{64}$

(f) $\sqrt{144}$

> **Evaluate** means to find the value of.

10 The Babylonians studied square numbers and used them in their mathematics. In particular, they noticed there were special groups of three squares, in which two of the squares added up to the third. Try to find two such groups of three in your list of square numbers.

11 Now look at one of your groups of three squares. Write down the three square roots associated with your squares. Draw two triangles in which the sides are the same lengths, in centimetres, as the square roots. Measure the largest angle in each. What do you notice?

This phenomenon has long been attributed to the Greek mathematician Pythagoras because he brought the knowledge to Europe. However, it is interesting to see that in fact the Babylonians got there first!

Cubes and their roots

Just as $3 \times 3 = 3^2$ is called '3 squared', there is a special name for 3^3

You can display $3 \times 3 \times 3 = 3^3$ as a **cube** with sides of three units.

The number $3 \times 3 \times 3 = 3^3$ is **three cubed.** The small raised 3 is the index number.

$$3 \times 3 \times 3 = 27$$

From this, you can see that 27 is a **cube number.**

Then the **cube root** of 27 is 3

You write this as $\sqrt[3]{27} = 3$

The special sign for a cube root is like the sign for a square root, but has a small 3 in front of it.

Exercise 2.5

1 Evaluate each number.

   (a) 2^3 **(b)** 3^3 **(c)** 4^3

2 Copy and complete this table, with values of n from 1 to 12

n	n^3
1	1
2	8
...	
12	

3 Write down the cube root of each number.

   (a) 8   **(b)** 125   **(c)** 1000

4 Evaluate these cube roots.

   (a) $\sqrt[3]{64}$ **(c)** $\sqrt[3]{216}$ **(e)** $\sqrt[3]{512}$

   (b) $\sqrt[3]{729}$ **(d)** $\sqrt[3]{343}$

5 Write down two numbers that are both a square number and a cube number.

6 When you looked at the squares, you found some groups of three in which two of them added up to the third. Can you do that with cubes?

Perhaps question 6 is something you might try on a rainy day. If you do find two different cubes that add up to a third cube, then you will make mathematical history! This is the starting point for a more general theorem now known as **Fermat's last theorem.**

◯ Triangular numbers

You know that you can represent square numbers as square patterns of dots.

You can also arrange dots into triangles, either like this:

or like this:

The numbers represented by the dots are triangular (or triangle) numbers.

Whichever way you arrange the dots, the numbers they represent make the same number sequence.

$1 = 1$

$1 + 2 = 3$

$1 + 2 + 3 = 6$

Try exploring the interesting properties of triangular numbers. You can call them T numbers and write them down like this.

$T_1 = 1$

$T_2 = 1 + 2 = 3$

$T_3 = 1 + 2 + 3 = 6$

$T_4 = 1 + 2 + 3 + 4 = 10$

Exercise 2.6

1 Copy the sequence above and continue it until you have calculated the first ten triangular numbers.

2 Write your ten triangular numbers out in a row, spaced well apart. Beneath them, write the sum of each pair, like this.

1   3   6   10   ...

   4   9   ...   and so on.

What do you notice about your pairs?

You could draw a picture, like this.

The black dots are the fourth triangular number, T_4, which is 10

The white dots are the third triangular number, T_3, which is 6

Notice that T_4 fits neatly with T_3 to make a square and that $10 + 6 = 16$ which is 4^2

3 Draw some more pairs of triangular numbers that fit together to make squares.

Write down what you find, like this.

$T_1 + T_2 = 1 + 3 = 4 = 2^2$

$T_2 + T_3 = 3 + 6 = 9 = 3^2$

4 Multiply each triangular number by 9 and add 1

Write it like this: $9 \times T_1 + 1 = 9 \times 1 + 1 = 10 = T_4$

$9 \times T_2 + 1 =$

What do you notice?

5 Continue your list of triangular numbers as far as T_{15}

Now make a list of the digits in the units column.

What do you notice?

6 Find the digit sum of each triangular number and from this the digital root.

What do you notice?

> To find the **digital root** of a number, add its digits and keep adding until you are left with a single digit. For example, for 45 the digit sum is 9, so the digital root is 9, but for 66 the digit sum is 12, so add again to get 3, which will be the digital root.

7 Multiply each triangular number by 8 and add 1

What do you notice?

Write it like this: $8 \times T_1 + 1 = 8 \times 1 + 1 = 9$

$$8 \times T_2 + 1 =$$

8 In this diagram, two triangular numbers of the same size have been put together to make a rectangle.

What can you say about the base and height of the rectangle?

Draw some more pairs of triangular numbers fitted together to make rectangles. What do you notice about the base and height?

9 Multiply together the lengths of the sides, then divide your answer by 2

What do you notice?

10 Without drawing, use this fact to calculate the value of each of these triangular numbers.

(a) T_{10} (b) T_{20} (c) T_{100}

Extension: More about using factors

Using factors to multiply

If you were asked to multiply 125×23 you could use long multiplication. However, some multiplication calculations are easier than others. For example, you may not know your 23 times table but you should know your 8 and 3 times tables.

You also know that $8 \times 3 = 24$, and $24 - 1 = 23$

You can use this information to work out the answer.

> **Example**
>
> Multiply: 125×23
>
> $125 \times 23 = 125 \times (24 - 1)$
>
> $= 125 \times (8 \times 3 - 1)$
>
> $= 125 \times 8 \times 3 - 125 \times 1$
>
> $= 1000 \times 3 - 125$
>
> $= 3000 - 125$
>
> $= 2875$

This might look like a lot of work, but you can do some of the stages in your head, so you only need to write down the complicated working.

Notice that $125 \times 8 = 1000$

It is worth remembering that the numbers 25 and 125 are factors of 1000

You can also break the multiplier into factors.

> **Example**
>
> Multiply: 75×24
>
> $75 \times 24 = 75 \times 8 \times 3$ Multiply by 8 first as $75 \times 8 = 600$ this makes
>
> $= 600 \times 3$ the second multiplication easier.
>
> $= 1800$

Using factors to find square roots and cube roots

The square numbers can be written as 1^2, 2^2, 3^2, 4^2, ...

This is because they are $1 \times 1 = 1$, $2 \times 2 = 4$, $3 \times 3 = 9$, $4 \times 4 = 16$ ...

Thus 4 is the square root of 16 (which is 4×4)

  3 is the square root of 9 (3×3)

  2 is the square root of 4 (2×2) ...

If you write square numbers (also called perfect squares) as products of their prime factors, you can find their square roots.

Try it with an easy one.

  $36 = 2 \times 2 \times 3 \times 3 = (2 \times 3) \times (2 \times 3)$

Thus the square root of 36 is $2 \times 3 = 6$

You can write this as
$$\sqrt{36} = \sqrt{2 \times 3 \times 2 \times 3}$$
$$= \sqrt{2 \times 2} \times \sqrt{3 \times 3}$$
$$= 2 \times 3$$
$$= 6$$

You can use this method to find out if any number is a perfect square.

You can use a similar method to find cube roots.

Example

Find the cube root of 3375

	3	3	3	7	¹5
	3	1	¹1	²2	¹5
	3		3	7	¹5
	5		1	¹2	²5
	5			2	²5
	5				5
					1

$3375 = 3 \times 3 \times 3 \times 5 \times 5 \times 5$
$ = 3^3 \times 5^3$
$\sqrt[3]{3375} = 3 \times 5 = 15$

Extension Exercise 2.7

1 Complete these multiplication tables up to 10

$1 \times 25 = 25$	$1 \times 125 = 125$	$1 \times 225 = 225$
$2 \times 25 = 50$	$2 \times 125 = 250$	$2 \times 225 = 450$
$3 \times 25 = \underline{}$	$3 \times 125 = \underline{}$	$3 \times 225 = \underline{}$ ...

2 Copy and complete this multiplication.

$24 \times 19 = 24 \times (20 - 1)$
$ = 24 \times 20 - 24 \times 1$ 19 is one less than 20, so multiply 24 by 20
and then take away one lot of 24
$ = \underline{} - \underline{}$
$ = \underline{}$

3 Complete these multiplication calculations in the same way.

(a) 25×19 (c) 43×29 (e) 51×225

(b) 32×19 (d) 41×25 (f) 125×62

> Look carefully at each multiplier. You may need to use addition rather than subtraction.

4 Now try these, by dividing the second number into two factors.

(a) 25×24 (c) 55×27 (e) 215×18

(b) 35×48 (d) 105×64 (f) 65×28

5 Write each number as the product of its prime factors and then find its square root.

(a) 144   (c) 1296   (e) 1225

(b) 2025   (d) 900   (f) 1764

6 Write each number as the product of its prime factors and then find its cube root.

(a) 1728   (c) 5832   (e) 13 824

(b) 2744   (d) 42 875   (f) 46 656

7 Write the numbers in each multiplication as products of their prime factors and then find the square root of each product.

(a) 28×28 (c) 12×27 (e) 525×189

(b) 56×14 (d) 72×50 (f) 220×55

> You do not need to do the multiplications, just write the numbers as products of their prime factors.

8 Find the cube roots of these products in the same way.

(a) 18×12 (c) 98×28 (e) $147 \times 42 \times 12$

(b) 56×49 (d) $21 \times 9 \times 49$ (f) $56 \times 63 \times 21$

Summary Exercise 2.8

1 Which of these numbers are multiples of 6? Write them down.

(a) 226   (c) 1434   (e) 231

(b) 234   (d) 132   (f) 9000

2 Write down which of the numbers in question 1 can be divided by:

(i) 5   (ii) 9   (iii) 7

3 List all the factors of each number.

(a) 64   (b) 24   (c) 300

4 Consider these numbers.

7   10   4   32   25

From the numbers given above write down one that is:

(a) a prime number   (d) a square number.

(b) a factor of 16   (e) the cube root of 64

(c) a multiple of 8   (f) a triangular number.

5 Write each number as the product of its prime factors.

(a) 48   (b) 196   (c) 315

6 Evaluate each expression.

(a) $2^2 \times 3^3$ (b) $2^3 \times 5^2$ (c) $2^2 \times 3 \times 5^2$

7 Find the highest common factor of both 144 and 196

8 Find the lowest common multiple of both 24 and 56

9 Draw the first four triangular numbers and calculate the value of the seventh.

10 Calculate:

(a) 72×19 (c) the cube root of $200 \times 9 \times 15$

(b) 15×36 (d) the square root of 3136

Activity: The number game

You should now know a lot about numbers. Before you move on, here are some puzzle games for you to play. Warm up by trying to answer these questions. All the answers are numbers less than 100.

1 I am thinking of a number. It is a prime number and it is even. What is my number?

2 I am thinking of a number. It is a multiple of three and a factor of 12, but is not 12 or 3. What is my number?

3 I am thinking of a number. It is a square number that is less than 50 and the sum of its digits is 13. What is my number?

4 I am thinking of a number greater than 50 and it is a prime number.

   Its last digit is 3, and the sum of the digits is 10. What is my number?

5 My number is a factor of 455 and 693, but is not 1. What is my number?

6 My number is the highest multiple of 3 and 4 that is less than 100. What is my number?

7 My number is a triangular number that is divisible by 11. What is my number?

8   My number is a factor of 60, but is not a multiple of 5, or a square number, or a prime number. What is my number? (There are two possible answers.)

9   My number is a prime number between 25 and 75, and the sum of its digits is a square number. What is my number?

10   My number is a square number and a triangle number. What is my number?

Now that you have warmed up, it is time to play the game.

You and your opponent both need some 1–100 squares. Here's how to play.

1   Think of a number. Write it above your first 1 to 100 square. Your opponent will do the same.

2   The youngest player asks the first question in the first game. After that, take it in turns.

3   Now ask a question. As in the warm-up questions, you should ask a question that will give you some information about your opponent's number. The answer may only be 'yes' or 'no'. Whatever the answer to your question, you should be able to eliminate many of the numbers on your square.

Possible questions could be:

Is your number even? (If the answer is 'yes', cross out all odd numbers.)

Is it a multiple of 3? (If 'yes', cross out all numbers that are not multiples of 3)

Is it prime? (If 'no', cross out all primes.)

Does it contain the digit 7? (If 'yes', cross out all numbers not containing the digit 7)

4   Keep asking questions until you get the answer 'no'. Then it is your opponent's turn.

5   Your opponent can ask you questions until your answer is 'no', then it is your turn again.

6   As you eliminate numbers, you should end up with a very small selection remaining that have not been crossed out. When you reach this stage, your final question(s) might be something like:

Is your number 37?

7   The winner is the first player to work out the opponent's number.

Written calculations

It is excellent to be able to calculate accurately in your head but you also need to be able to work out the answers to harder calculations on paper.

By now, you should be able to add, subtract, multiply and divide numbers, including those with decimal fractions. Take a look at these worked examples and then see how quickly you can complete the exercise.

Addition

Example

Add: 4.109 + 274 + 14.75

	H	T	U	•	t	h	th
			4	•	1	0	9
	2	7	4	•	0	0	0
+		1	4	•	7	5	0
	2	9	2	•	8	5	9
			1				

When you first write the numbers in the frame there will probably be gaps in some of the columns and not all numbers may have decimal points. Write the decimal points and 0s in before you start your addition.

Subtraction

Example

What is the difference between 7.026 and 19?

	T	U	•	t	h	th
	1	$^8\cancel{9}$	•	$^9\cancel{0}$	$^9\cancel{0}$	$^1 0$
−		7	•	0	2	6
	1	1	•	9	7	4

First, write the decimal point and the zeros after 19, to give 19.000 and keep the size of the number correct.

Always check your answer by doing the inverse addition mentally: 11.974 + 7.026 = 19

> The difference is the answer to a subtraction.

35

Multiplication

Example

Multiply: 5.27×8 Estimate: $5 \times 8 = 40$, you will need an extra column.

T	U	•	t	h
	5	•	2	7
		×		8
4	2	•	1	6
	2		5	

Remember to put the carried numbers under the line.

Division

Division is the one of the four operations that may not give an exact answer. Consider $153 \div 4$

4 does not go exactly into 153. It gives a whole number, the **quotient**, and another number is left over, the **remainder**.

$$153 \div 4 = 38 \text{ r } 1$$

The remainder can be written as a number, as above, or as **fraction** or as a decimal.

$$153 \div 4 = 38\frac{1}{4} = 38.25$$

Example

Divide: $3147 \div 4$ Estimate: $3000 \div 4 = 750$

	Th	H	T	U	
		7	8	6	r 3
4	3	³1	³4	²7	

$3 \div 4 = 0 \text{ r } 3$, carry 3

$31 \div 4 = 7 \text{ r } 3$ Write 7 in the answer line and carry 3

$34 \div 4 = 8 \text{ r } 2$ Write 8 in the answer line and carry 2

$27 \div 4 = 6 \text{ r } 3$

$3147 \div 4 = 786 \text{ r } 3$

$ = 786\frac{3}{4}$

The other way of dealing with remainders is to write down a decimal point followed by extra zeros and keep dividing.

Example

Divide: $3147 \div 4$

	Th	H	T	U	•	t	h
		7	8	6	•	7	5
4	3	³1	³4	²7	•	³0	²0

Write a 0 in the tenths column and carry the 3

$30 \div 4 = 7 \, r \, 2$

Write 7 in the answer line, add a 0 in the hundredths column and carry the 2

$20 \div 4 = 5$

$3147 \div 4 = 786.75$

Write 5 in the answer line.

Sometimes you will be instructed to round your answer.

Example

Calculate $415 \div 7$. Give your answer correct to 1 decimal place.

	H	T	U	•	t	h	
		5	9	•	2	8	r 4
7	4	⁴1	⁶5	•	²0	⁶0	

You must keep dividing until you have at least 2 decimal places before you can round to 1 decimal place.

$415 \div 7 = 59.3$ (to 1 d.p.)

Exercise 3.1

1 Find the sum of four hundred and sixty-eight, two thousand and seventy-five and sixteen.

2 Find the difference between four thousand, two hundred and forty and two thousand, one hundred and seventy-six.

Complete these calculations. Show any remainders as decimals.

3 $245 + 12\,460 + 956$

4 $6004 - 1258$

5 $402.4 + 0.45 + 36.7$

6 $90.09 - 3.75$

7 1417×8

8 $3836 \div 7$

9 $3428 \div 4$

10 2536×7

11 3.52×9

12 $97.2 \div 9$

13 42.8×8

14 $1.428 \div 7$

15 6.098×6

16 $1575 \div 6$

17 3.218×5

18 $1305 \div 4$

19 4.735×8

20 $9003 \div 8$

Before you write the answers to these problems, consider what you need to do with the remainder – round up or round down?

21 214 children are supposed to go on a school trip in five buses. When the buses leave they are all full. As many children as possible have gone and there are equal numbers of children on each bus. Oh no! How many children are left behind?

22 The school cook bakes 148 cakes and arranges as many of them as possible neatly on six plates. Each plate has the same number of cakes. The cook eats the rest. How many cakes does he eat?

23 In our school dining room there are six long tables and 250 chairs. Five of the tables have the same number of chairs and one table has a few less. How many chairs does the one table have around it?

24 There are 214 pupils in my school, in nine classes. There is the same number of pupils in most of the classes, but the top two classes each have one fewer. How many pupils are in the top two classes?

Multiplying and dividing by multiples of 10

You have been practising multiplying by a number of units. You can use the same method to multiply by **powers of 10** (tens, hundreds, thousands...) and also **multiples** of powers of 10

When you are multiplying by a multiple of 10, you know that the answer will be bigger than if you were just multiplying by 10. The same idea apples when you multiply by a multiple of 100

> A **multiple** is the answer to a multiplication. 2, 4, 6, 8, ... are multiples of 2

Example

Multiply: 4.8×400

Estimate: $4.8 \times 400 \approx 5 \times 400$
≈ 2000

Th	H	T	U	•	t
			4	•	8
	×	4	0		0
1	9	2	0	•	0
	3				

Write the 0s from the 400 in the units and tenths columns, to show that you have multiplied by 100, and then multiply by 4

$4.8 \times 400 = 1920$

There is no need to write the .0 at the end of the answer.

3   Written calculations

When dividing by multiples of 10 you need to divide by ten, a hundred, a thousand or other multiple of 10 before setting up the frame.

Example

Divide: 14.2 ÷ 500

$$14.2 ÷ 500 = 14.2 ÷ 100 ÷ 5 = 0.142 ÷ 5$$

U	•	t	h	th	tth
	0	•	0	2	8	4

| 5 | 0 | • | 1 | ¹4 | ⁴2 | ²0 |

Write another 0 at the end, to work out the exact answer.

$$14.2 ÷ 500 = 0.0284$$

Exercise 3.2

Complete these calculations.

1   24×20

2   $2800 ÷ 20$

3   32×400

4   $8560 ÷ 80$

5   45×60

6   $46\,800 ÷ 600$

7   39×300

8   $495\,000 ÷ 5000$

9   126×50

10   $41\,300 ÷ 70$

11   1.53×60

12   $214 ÷ 200$

13   24.5×800

14   $68.5 ÷ 50$

15   0.316×900

16   $3.04 ÷ 80$

17   64.2×700

18   $21.4 ÷ 500$

19   4.57×900

20   $4.05 ÷ 6000$

Multiplying and dividing by a decimal

You have been multiplying and dividing by whole numbers, but what happens if there is a decimal in the multiplier or divisor?

Multiplying

Consider 4.6×0.2

You know that $0.2 = \dfrac{2}{10}$

$$= 2 ÷ 10$$

Therefore $4.6 \times 0.2 = 4.6 \times 2 \div 10$ Multiply by the number and then
$\qquad\qquad\qquad = 9.2 \div 10$ divide by the multiple of 10

$\qquad\qquad\qquad = 0.92$

Compare your answer to $46 \times 2 = 92$

4.6×0.2 is $\dfrac{1}{100}$ of 46×2 because $4.6 = \dfrac{46}{10}$ and $0.2 = \dfrac{2}{10}$

This gives a simple rule for multiplying with decimals.

Example

Multiply: 3.2×0.05

Estimate: $3 \times 0.05 = 0.15$

$\qquad\qquad 32 \times 5 = 160$

$\qquad 3.2 \times 0.05 = 0.160$ Three digits after the decimal points in the question,
$\qquad\qquad\qquad\qquad\qquad$ three digits after the decimal point in the answer.

$\qquad\qquad\qquad = 0.16$ Do not write the last 0

Dividing

How many halves are there in 4?

The answer is 8

$\qquad$ As $\dfrac{1}{2} = 0.5$ we can write the calculation as $4 \div 0.5$ or $\dfrac{4}{0.5}$

Before we do the division we are going to multiply 0.5 by a power of
ten to make it a whole number. To keep the fraction equivalent we
must multiply 4 by the same power of ten:

$\qquad 4 \div 0.5 = \dfrac{4 \times 10}{0.5 \times 10}$

$\qquad\qquad\quad = 40 \div 5$

$\qquad\qquad\quad = 8$

$\qquad$ Check your answer: $8 \times 0.5 = 4$

Examples

(i) Divide: $2.4 \div 0.6$

$\qquad 2.4 \div 0.6 = \dfrac{2.4}{0.6} \times \dfrac{10}{10}$

$\qquad\qquad\quad = \dfrac{24}{6}$ $\qquad 0.6 \times 10 = 6$

$\qquad\qquad\quad = 4$

$\qquad$ Check: $4 \times 0.6 = 2.4$

(ii) Divide: $60 \div 0.005$

$\qquad 60 \div 0.005 = \dfrac{60}{0.005} \times \dfrac{1000}{1000}$

$\qquad\qquad\qquad = \dfrac{60\,000}{5}$

$\qquad\qquad\qquad = 12\,000$

$\qquad$ Check: $12\,000 \times 0.005 = 60$

You can do simple division by decimals in your head but always check your answer.

> **Example**
>
> Divide: $4 \div 0.2$
>
> $4 \div 0.2 = 40 \div 2$
> $ = 20$
>
> Check: $0.2 \times 20 = 4$

Exercise 3.3

Complete these calculations.

1 0.4×0.7

2 $3.2 \div 0.8$

3 0.8×0.5

4 $24 \div 0.3$

5 1.2×0.7

6 $0.0014 \div 0.07$

7 1.21×0.05

8 $210 \div 0.3$

9 1.2×1.5

10 $180 \div 0.006$

Use a frame if you cannot do these in your head.

11 1.55×1.2

12 $1.05 \div 0.6$

13 $0.000\,24 \div 0.03$

14 $0.063 \div 0.09$

15 $1.35 \div 0.06$

16 $4.5 \div 0.005$

17 0.056×0.05

18 $0.0036 \div 0.9$

19 9.105×0.6

20 $0.000\,12 \div 0.6$

Long multiplication

What happens when you want to multiply 152×23?

You can split the calculation like this.

$$152 \times 23 = 152 \times (3 + 20)$$

$$= 152 \times 3 + 152 \times 20$$

Now you could put these numbers into frames and complete the different parts of the calculation. There are three stages.

Stage (i) 152×3 Stage (ii) 152×20 Stage (iii) $152 \times 3 + 152 \times 20$

In long multiplication, though, you combine all of these into one calculation.

Example

Multiply: 1876 × 49   Estimate: 2000 × 50 = 100 000

HTh	TTh	Th		H	T	U	
		1		8	7	6	
×					4	9	
	1	6_7		8_6	8_5	4	× 9
	7_3	5_3		0_2	4	0	× 40
	9	1		9	2	4	
	1			1			

You will need HTh and TTh columns.

Next to each row, write down what you are multiplying.

The carried numbers from the multiplications are in these rows.

The carried numbers from the addition are in this row.

1876 × 49 = 91 924

Exercise 3.4

Do these without using a calculator. Show all your working.

1 35 × 24

2 67 × 36

3 45 × 27

4 163 × 54

5 248 × 48

6 125 × 17

7 1244 × 26

8 3325 × 72

9 5207 × 69

10 8716 × 78

For these questions, complete the long multiplication first and then write the answer with the decimal point in the correct place.

11 3.6 × 5.2

12 4.8 × 0.75

13 6.5 × 0.084

14 12.2 × 3.4

15 45.2 × 4.2

16 2.14 × 0.52

17 3.12 × 0.14

18 2.08 × 0.35

19 1.07 × 0.036

20 5.6 × 1.08

21 The school cook orders 36 boxes of crisps. There are 24 packets of crisps in a box. How many packets of crisps are there in all?

22 The school has bought 42 new maths textbooks. There are 356 pages in each book. How many pages are there altogether?

23 32 pupils are going on the skiing trip to Switzerland. The cost is £625 per child. What is the total cost?

24 How many seconds are there in 4 hours?

25 If there are 14 pounds in a stone, what is the total mass, in pounds, of a man who weighs 14 stones 8 pounds?

In the UK people used to be weighed in stones and pounds; in the USA they use only pounds.

Long division

For **long division**, you use exactly the same principle as for short division, but with bigger numbers, and you work down the page.

Example

Divide: 5451 ÷ 23

		Th	H	T	U
			2	3	7
2	3	5	4	5	1
		4	6		
			8	5	
			6	9	
			1	6	1
			1	6	1
			–	–	–

$$23$$
$$\times 3$$
$$\overline{69}$$

$$23$$
$$\times 7$$
$$\overline{161}$$

> If you cannot work out the multiplication in your head write it down neatly on the right.

Exercise 3.5

Use long division to complete these calculations. The first five have no remainders, but the last five may have.

1 646 ÷ 17

2 667 ÷ 23

3 855 ÷ 19

4 882 ÷ 42

5 851 ÷ 37

6 1870 ÷ 24

7 3684 ÷ 36

8 5995 ÷ 31

9 2972 ÷ 27

10 8730 ÷ 39

For these you should eliminate the decimal in the divisor first, by multiplying by a power of 10

11 7.65 ÷ 0.17

12 37.8 ÷ 2.7

13 0.406 ÷ 0.29

14 8.4 ÷ 0.35

15 4.94 ÷ 1.9

16 0.567 ÷ 0.45

17 5.22 ÷ 3.6

18 0.729 ÷ 0.54

19 5.772 ÷ 0.037

20 0.5922 ÷ 0.047

Now try some word problems.

21 Form 7X won the house-points competition and now have a box of 323 chocolates to share. There are 19 pupils in 7X. How many chocolates does each pupil get?

22 48 pupils are going on an outing to the Isle of Wight. Altogether, they have paid £1632. How much money has each pupil paid?

23 The 23 pupils in Form 7Z have to have an eye test. Each test takes the same amount of time and altogether the tests take 299 minutes. How long does each eye test take?

24 36 cans of cola cost £27. How much does one can of cola cost?

25 A ream of paper contains 500 sheets. For our geography project our teacher shares out one ream equally among 24 of us. How many sheets do we get each? How many sheets are left over?

 Problem solving

You can now add, subtract, multiply and divide, both in your head and by using pencil and paper. Answer the questions in the next exercise in any way you wish, but take care to write down all your working.

Example

If 12 doughnuts cost £3, what is the cost of one doughnut?

If you do the calculation in your head, write:

£3.00 ÷ 12 = £0.25   or   300p ÷ 12 = 25p

If you work it out in a frame, write:

		H	T	U		
			2	5		
1	2	3	0	⁶0		

Make sure that you include the correct unit of measurement with the number. In this case, it is p for pence, as the cost of one doughnut is 25p.

One doughnut costs 25p

> If the question is a sentence your answer should be a short phrase or sentence.

Exercise 3.6

1 I spend 96p on eight sticks of liquorice. What is the cost of one stick?

2 I spend £6 on 24 pencils. What is the cost of one pencil?

3 There are 16 ounces in a pound and 14 pounds in a stone. How many ounces are there in a stone?

4 Ash have 217 more house points than Beech. If Beech have 357, how many house points do Ash have?

5 Taking part in the school Christmas production are 104 members of the choir, 9 readers and 27 musicians. How many people are there in total?

6 On a school trip 255 pupils are accompanied by 17 teachers. All the teachers have the same number of pupils in their groups. How many pupils are there in each group?

7 For a science project I need six 4 m lengths of string and eight 5 m lengths of string. How much string is that altogether?

8 Our whole class needs to buy 1332 m of string. If string comes in balls holding 24 m, how many balls do we need to buy?

9 At the school fair the cake stall sold 38 big cakes at £3 each and 75 little cakes at 24p each. How much money did the stall make in total?

10 I reckon that I spend 75 minutes, five nights a week, on homework. In a school year of 34 weeks how many minutes is that in all? How many hours is that?

11 A recipe says that I need 1500 g of flour to make 12 cakes. How many grams do I need to make 1 cake? How many grams do I need to make 36 cakes?

12 There is a special prize for winning 300 house points. I reckon I can get 12 house points a week. How many weeks will it take me to get 300 house points?

13 There are 1000 g in a kilogram. I use 455 g from a 2 kg bag of sugar. How much sugar is left in the bag?

14 (a) I am counting up the money from the tombola at the end of the school fair. There are 24 £1 coins, seven £2 coins, six £5 notes, 14 £10 notes, three £20 notes and one £50 note. How much money is there in total?

   (b) I exchange all the money for as many £20 notes as possible. How many £20 notes do I have now?

15 The school put aside £20 000 for new computers. In the summer they bought 24 computers at £699 each. How much money did they have left?

Using a calculator

For more complicated calculations it is important to do the parts of the calculation in the correct order, especially if you are using a calculator.

Example

Work out: $\dfrac{42.84}{19.61-13.49}$.

First, estimate the answer.

$$\dfrac{42.84}{19.61-13.49} \approx \dfrac{42}{6} = 7$$

Method 1: Using the memory button on your calculator

Enter ⟨1⟩⟨9⟩⟨.⟩⟨6⟩⟨1⟩⟨−⟩⟨1⟩⟨3⟩⟨.⟩⟨4⟩⟨9⟩ and press the ⟨=⟩ button.

Put the answer (6.12) into the memory. Then clear the screen.

Now enter ⟨4⟩⟨2⟩⟨.⟩⟨8⟩⟨4⟩ and ⟨÷⟩ then ⟨RCL⟩ and ⟨M+⟩ to get the answer: 7

> Usually there is a ⟨Min⟩ or ⟨M+⟩ button.

Method 2: Using brackets

Think of the calculation as being:

$42.84 \div (19.61 - 13.49)$

Enter the characters in that order, using your brackets keys.

⟨4⟩⟨2⟩⟨.⟩⟨8⟩⟨4⟩⟨÷⟩⟨(⟩⟨1⟩⟨9⟩⟨.⟩⟨6⟩⟨1⟩
⟨−⟩⟨1⟩⟨3⟩⟨.⟩⟨4⟩⟨9⟩⟨)⟩⟨=⟩

You should get the answer 7

This is usually the better method to use.

> Refer to your calculator instruction manual if this does not work.

Extension Exercise 3.7

These questions involve a mixture of addition, subtraction, multiplication and division. Use the rules of BIDMAS and solve them without using a calculator. Write any non-exact answers as decimals, correct to 2 decimal places.

1 $\dfrac{4.8+7.2}{6}$

2 $\dfrac{5.6+9.4}{1.6+1.4}$

3 $\dfrac{76}{9.1+9.9}$

4 $\dfrac{27.2-13.7}{12.4-7.9}$

5 $(1.46 + 2.54)^2 \div 2$

6 $14 \div (0.354 + 1.646)$

7 $28 - 3.6 \div 0.9 \times 6$

8 $24 \times 3 - 144 \div 36$

9 $4.5 + 2.5 \times 0.55 \div 0.11$

10 $(3.8 + 4.2)^3 \div (0.5 \times 8)^2$

11 Now check your answers with your calculator.

Summary Exercise 3.8

1 Calculate the answers to these, either in your head or in a frame. Remember to write down your working.

   (a) $173 + 312$ (c) 56×3

   (b) $738 - 125$ (d) $406 \div 7$

2 Calculate the answers to these.

   (a) 3600×200 (c) $120 \times 110\,000$

   (b) $42\,000 \div 600$ (d) $56\,000 \div 70$

3 Use frames to calculate carefully the answers to these questions. Estimate the answer first.

   (a) $4.878 + 56.7 + 0.17 + 517$ (c) 1.37×7

   (b) $7.003 - 6.715$ (d) $4.25 \div 5$

4 Calculate the answers to these. You will need to write in extra zeros to complete your division. If the answer is not exact, give it correct to 2 decimal places.

   (a) $1.4 \div 5$ (c) $1.7 \div 7$

   (b) $2.3 \div 8$ (d) $17.1 \div 6$

5 Calculate the answers to these.

   (a) 1.2×0.4 (c) $4.5 \div 0.09$

   (b) 3.6×0.07 (d) $0.87 \div 0.6$

6 Calculate the answers.

   (a) 145×23 (c) 1546×47

   (b) $2352 \div 42$ (d) $665 \div 38$

7 The school cook bakes 367 potatoes and roasts 196 potatoes. How many potatoes does he cook?

8 48 pupils are going to France. They all give Mr Muddle their spending money. He collects €1680 in total. If all the pupils give him the same amount, how much money does each pupil give him?

9 I have to work out how many words I have written for my history essay. I estimate that I write 13 words on a line and that there are 48 lines on a page. If I have covered one and a half pages, roughly how many words have I written?

10 If 96 parents each pay £19.50 for a ticket to the school play, how much money do they pay in total?

Activity: Babylonian numbers

It is easy to think that because we still use Roman numerals, the Romans were the earliest civilisation to use a number system, but this is not true. Many early civilisations had their own different systems. One of the most sophisticated and oldest was developed by the Babylonians about 5000 years ago. The first mathematics can be traced to the ancient country of Babylon (which lies in modern day Iraq), during the third millennium B.C.

The Babylonians recorded their mathematics on clay tablets. These were baked dry by the sun and then preserved, which is why we can study them today.

Like most early systems the numbers from one to nine were formed by a succession of simple marks, easily made with a stick in the soft clay.

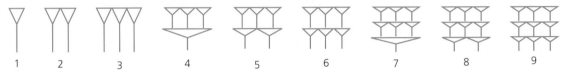

Note the way the numbers 1, 2 and 3 were one size stroke, 4, 5, 6 a little smaller and 7, 8, 9 smaller again.

The tens were grouped with a different shape.

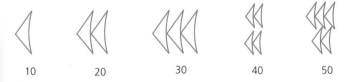

The Babylonians did not count in tens over 60 because their system was based on sixty. Ours, on the other hand, is based on 10

The biggest difference between the Babylonian system and those of the Greek and Roman civilisations was that it, like our own, used place value to show larger numbers.

Look at these numbers.

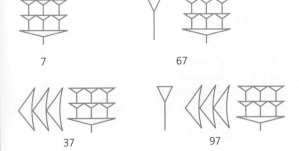

> The 1 on the left is in the 60 column so you have
> $1 \times 60 + 7 = 67$

> The 1 on the left is in the 60 column, so you have
> $1 \times 60 + 30 + 7 = 97$

1 Copy each of these Babylonian numbers and write its value, as a decimal number, next to it.

(a)

(c)

(e)

(b)

(d)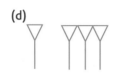

(f)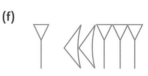

The numbers you should have written down in question 1 were (not necessarily in this order): 63, 14, 59, 83, 126, 4. If you did not get them all go and check your answers again.

2 Now get out your stick and clay tablet, and write these down in Babylonian numbers. No sticks and tablets? It might be better to use pencil and paper!

(a) 6   (c) 56   (e) 75   (g) 127
(b) 26   (d) 64   (f) 92   (h) 142

Consider 142, the highest number you have looked at so far.

You should have drawn:

You have $2 \times 60 + 20 + 2 = 142$

Look at the number:

$4 \times 60 + 50 + 7 = 297$

3 Now work out these even larger numbers.

(a)

(d)

(b)

(e)

(c)

(f)

The numbers you should have written down were (not necessarily in this order):
344, 1292, 359, 184, 3296, 179

If you did not get them all, check your answers again.

4   Now write these down in Babylonian numbers.

(a) 306   (c) 2364   (e) 3216   (g) 1204

(b) 2472   (d) 1317   (f) 2781   (h) 3599

For your last answer you should have drawn:

$$59 \times 60 + 59 = 3540 + 59 = 3599$$

The next number after this would be 3600 which is 60×60 or 60^2

To write 3681 you would have to work out:

$$1 \times 3600 + 1 \times 60 + 21$$

and then write:

5   Now try these.

(a)    (c)

(b)    (d)

6   Now write these down in Babylonian numbers.

(a) 3666   (b) 7297   (c) 4876   (d) 5999

These numbers are written in Cuneiform script. If you had been to school 5000 years ago, this is how you would have learnt to write your numbers, using the 14 different Cuneiform numerals. (Like many early civilisations there was no symbol for 0, they just left a blank.)

7   You can see that the Babylonians were very enthusiastic about the number 60 which they also used for their system of measurement. 5000 years later which Babylonian measures do we still use?

4 Measurement and the metric system

Britain, like many other countries, uses the **metric system** for most units of measure, although long distances are still measured in **miles**, the older imperial unit. Strange though it may seem, measures were the subject of heated political debate in the nineteenth century. In 1874, William Rankine, a British engineer, wrote a poem, *The Three Foot Rule*, which includes this verse:

Some talk of millimetres, and some of kilograms,
And some of decilitres, to measure beer and drams;
But I'm a British workman, too old to go to school,
So by pounds I'll eat, and by quarts I'll drink, and I'll work by my three-foot rule.

The traditional measures used in Britain evolved over centuries. Britain as a nation was involved heavily in trade and so the measures it used became standard and, by the end of the eighteenth century, were used by both Britain and America.

In France, on the other hand, there was no standardisation. It has been estimated that France had about 800 different names for measures at this time and, taking into account different values used in different towns, around 250 000 different-sized units.

In 1790 France was in the middle of a revolution but their National Assembly was determined to make improvements. It was agreed that a new measurement system based on a length from nature should be adopted. The system should have decimal subdivisions, and all measures such as area, volume and mass (rather than weight) should be linked to the fundamental unit of length.

Over the next century the European countries, and their colonies, adopted the new units, but Britain and America resisted. It was only in 2009 that shops in Britain were no longer required to give the length, weight and volume of goods in both **metric units** and imperial units although many still do.

Metric units

Length is measured in **metres** (m).

10 mm	= 1 centimetre (cm)
100 cm	= 1 metre (m)
1000 millimetres (mm)	= 1 metre (m)
1000 metres	= 1 kilometre (km)

Mass is measured in **grams** (g).

1000 milligrams (mg)	= 1 gram (g)
1000 grams	= 1 kilogram (kg)
1000 kg	= 1 tonne (t)

Capacity or **volume** is measured in **litres** (l).

1000 cubic centimetres (cm^3)	= 1 litre (l)
1000 millilitres (ml)	= 1 litre (l)
100 centilitres (cl)	= 1 litre (l)

> Capacity is linked to volume, although capacity is more generally used for fluid measures, such as milk and oil, and volume for solid measures, such as bricks.
>
> Capacity is the amount a container can hold. Volume is the amount taken up by a substance. A jug may have capacity of one litre but contain milk of volume $\frac{1}{2}$ litre.

To convert between a basic unit and its multiples or subunit you need to divide or multiply by 10, 100 or 1000. It helps if you always write down the basic conversion fact before you start. Make sure you read the units in the question carefully; this will help you to avoid making careless mistakes.

Examples

(i) Write 54 cm in metres.

100 cm = 1 m

1 cm = 0.01 m   Divide by 100 and multiply by 54

54 cm = 0.54 m

(ii) Write 35 kg in grams.

1 kg = 1000 g   Multiply by 1000

Therefore 35 kg = 35 000 g

Exercise 4.1

1 Write these lengths in metres.

   (a) 25 cm   (b) 480 mm   (c) 5.3 km   (d) 258 cm

2 Write these masses in grams.

   (a) 25 kg   (b) 3750 mg   (c) 0.625 kg   (d) 3.6 t

3 Write these capacities in litres.

   (a) 220 ml   (b) 3634 ml   (c) 2.8 cl   (d) 5 ml

4 Write these lengths in centimetres (cm).

   (a) 24 mm   (b) 2.7 km   (c) 35 m   (d) 0.07 m

5 Write these masses in kilograms (kg).

   (a) 350 g   (b) 4.5 t   (c) 25 mg   (d) 7.5 g

6 Write these capacities in millilitres (ml).

   (a) 1.4 l   (b) 0.35 l   (c) 45 cl   (d) 0.7 cl

7 Write these in mm.

   (a) 3.2 cm   (b) 4.5 m   (c) 0.7 m   (d) 0.4 km

8 Write these in mg.

   (a) 3.2 g   (b) 5.5 g   (c) 165 g   (d) 0.06 kg

9 Write these in km.

   (a) 3.5 m   (b) 4050 m   (c) 320 000 cm

Calculating with quantities

When you calculate with quantities, always make sure that they are all in the same units before you start. This means that you may need to change some units.

Example

Add: 1.2 m + 23 cm + 15 mm. Give your answer in centimetres (cm).

$$1 \text{ m} = 100 \text{ cm} \qquad 10 \text{ mm} = 1 \text{ cm}$$

$$1.2 \text{ m} = 120 \text{ cm} \qquad 15 \text{ mm} = 1.5 \text{ cm}$$

$$1.2 \text{ m} + 23 \text{ cm} + 15 \text{ mm} = 120 \text{ cm} + 23 \text{ cm} + 1.5 \text{ cm}$$

$$= 144.5 \text{ cm}$$

> Remember to start by writing down the basic conversion facts.
>
> When all your quantities are in the same units then do the calculation.

Exercise 4.2

1 Add: 5 m + 672 cm + 65 mm. Give your answer in centimetres (cm).

2 Add: 3500 g + 1.7 kg + 375 mg. Give your answer in grams (g).

3 Subtract: 0.678 km − 4525 cm. Give your answer in metres (m).

4 Multiply: 375 ml × 8. Give your answer in litres (l).

5 Divide: 2 km ÷ 8. Give your answer in metres (m).

6 Divide: 5.7 t ÷ 12. Give your answer in grams (g).

7 I need 12 lengths of rope. Each length must be 75 cm long. How many metres of rope should I buy?

8 Our class is making chocolate crispies for the summer fair. I don't have any cocoa, so I have to go and buy some. 12 crispies need 45 g of cocoa. How much cocoa should I buy to make 240 crispies?

9 I need to buy 2.4 kg of raisins, but raisins come in bags of 150 g. How many bags do I need to buy?

10 I have a plank that is 2.2 m long. I cut it into five equal pieces with four cuts, but I lose 1.5 mm of wood with each cut. How long are my five pieces of plank, in centimetres?

11 I am making concrete in my science lesson. I mix 4 kg of sand with 1.2 kg of cement and 600 g of water. I pour the concrete into four equal-sized moulds. What is the mass of concrete in each mould?

12 I add 4 cupfuls of raspberry flavouring and 2 cupfuls of banana flavouring to a 4-litre carton of milk. I pour the resulting milkshake into 10 glasses. If each glass contains 475 ml, how much is in one cupful?

Imperial units

How did it all begin?

The Greeks developed the **foot** as their fundamental unit of length. Legend has it that this Greek unit was based on an actual measurement of Hercules' foot.

People measured a **yard** of cloth as the distance between the end of the outstretched arm and the chin.

The Romans measured their **pace** steps at about $2\frac{1}{2}$ feet. 1000 double paces formed a **mile**.

It is useful to know the common imperial units in everyday use.

Length

12 inches (in) = 1 foot (ft)

3 ft   = 1 yard (yd)

1760 yards   = 1 mile (m)

Mass

16 ounces (oz)   = 1 pound (lb)

14 lb   = 1 stone (st)

2240 pounds (lb) = 1 ton (t)

Capacity (volume)

2 pints (pt) = 1 quart (qt)

8 pints (pt) = 1 gallon (gal)

Exercise 4.3

Give any non-exact answers as fractions.

1 Write these lengths in inches.

  (a) 2 feet   (b) $\frac{1}{2}$ ft   (c) 1 yard   (d) $1\frac{1}{2}$ ft

2 Write these lengths in feet.

  (a) 2 yards   (b) $\frac{2}{3}$ yd   (c) 9 in   (d) 27 in

3 Write these lengths in yards.

  (a) 72 in   (b) 12 feet   (c) 1 ft   (d) $\frac{1}{8}$ mile

4 Write these distances in miles.

  (a) 880 yd   (b) 110 yd   (c) 2640 yd   (d) 5280 feet

5 Write these in ounces.

  (a) 4 lb   (b) 2.5 lb   (c) $\frac{1}{2}$ lb   (d) 1 ton

6 Write these in pounds.

  (a) 4 oz   (b) 24 oz   (c) $\frac{1}{8}$ ton   (d) $2\frac{1}{2}$ stone

7 Write these in stones.

    (a) 7 lb   **(b)** 84 lb   **(c)** $\frac{1}{10}$ ton   **(d)** 448 oz

8 Write these capacities in pints.

    (a) 2 quarts   **(b)** $\frac{1}{2}$ gallon   **(c)** 5 gallons   **(d)** $\frac{1}{4}$ quart

9 Write these capacities in quarts.

    (a) 1 pt   **(b)** 5 pints   **(c)** 3 gallons   **(d)** $\frac{1}{2}$ gallon

10 Write these in gallons.

    (a) 60 pints   **(b)** 2 pints   **(c)** 1 quart   **(d)** $\frac{1}{2}$ quart

11 I add 12 ounces of raisins to half a pound of flour. What is the total mass, in:

    (a) ounces   **(b)** pounds?

12 I add 9 inches to $1\frac{1}{2}$ feet and then add that to 1 yard. What is the total length in:

    (a) inches   **(b)** feet?

13 I pour 4 pints of juice into 2 gallons of water and then add a quart of ginger beer. What is the total volume in:

    (a) pints   **(b)** gallons?

14 1 gallon of water has a mass of 10 lb.

    (a) What is the mass of 1 pint of water?

    (b) How many gallons of water have a total mass of 1 ton?

Exercise 4.4

1 Find a tape measure that is marked in inches (in). Measure your height, your girth (the distance around your body at navel height), the height of a door. Now measure them again, using metric units.

2 Find some weighing scales that are marked in pounds (lb) and stones. Weigh yourself. Now weigh yourself in kilograms (kg). Weigh some other things as well.

3 Find a pint glass and a litre container. Fill the pint glass and pour the contents into the litre container.

4 From your experiments work out some rough equivalent comparisons of metric and imperial units, for example 1 foot ≈ 30 cm.

Now see how your comparisons compare to the ones used in this book.

1 metre ≈ 39 inches
(or 3 feet and 3 inches)   Multiply by $3\frac{1}{4}$

1 kilometre $= \frac{5}{8}$ mile   Multiply by 5 divide by 8

1 kilogram = 2.2 pounds   Add $\frac{1}{10}$ and multiply by 2

1 litre = 1.75 pints   Multiply by 7 and divide by 4

1 foot = 0.3 metres   Multiply by 3 and divide by 10

1 mile $= 1\frac{3}{5}$ kilometres   Multiply by 8 and divide by 5

1 pound = 0.45 kilograms   Divide by 2 and subtract $\frac{1}{10}$

1 pint = 0.6 litres   Multiply by 3 and divide by 5

Exercise 4.5

1 Imperial units have been used in this story. Rewrite it, using metric units.

(a) Connie was going shopping for her mother. She walked two miles into the village. Connie bought 2 lb of potatoes and 8 oz of mushrooms.

(b) Connie walked 100 yards down the road to the haberdashery shop. There, she bought 3 yards of blue ribbon and 5 feet of knicker elastic.

(c) Connie was tired and the shopping was heavy and so she stopped at the sweet shop and bought 4 ounces of wine gums.

2 Metric units have been used in this story. Rewrite it, using imperial units.

(a) Digby bicycled 4 km to the shops where he bought a 2 kg weight and 6 weights of 300 g.

(b) Digby also bought 200 m of fishing twine and 50 cm of string.

(c) Digby was thirsty and so he also bought a 500-ml bottle of water.

3 Write some stories of your own and give them to a friend to rewrite.

Summary Exercise 4.6

1 Copy and complete these statements.

(a) 1.3 g = _____ mg   (c) 7.2 km = _____ m

(b) 53 mm = _____ m   (d) 0.072 ml = _____ l

2 (a) Add: 4.5 m + 450 cm + 36 mm = _____ cm

(b) Add: 4.2 t + 56 kg + 765 g = _____ kg

(c) Divide: 5 l ÷ 8 = _____ ml

(d) Multiply: 240 mg × 5 = _____ kg

3 I am the dining-room monitor. I fill up all the cups on my table from a 2-litre jug of water. If I can fill up 8 cups from one full jug, how much water goes in each cup?

4 I make a cake with 1.2 kg of flour, 450 g of sugar, 450 g of butter and 4500 mg of cocoa. What is the total mass of these ingredients?

5 To raise money for charity, I run 2.2 km every day for five days. Harry runs the same total distance as I do, but in four days. How many metres more does Harry run each day than I do?

6 Copy and complete these conversions.

(a) 5 lb = _____ oz

(b) 3 quarts = _____ pt

(c) 2 tons = _____ lb

(d) 15 in = _____ ft

(e) 4 yards = _____ in

(f) $1\frac{1}{2}$ gallons = _____ pt

7 (a) Add: 3 gallons + 2 pints + 1 quart = _____ pints.

(b) Add: 24 oz + $2\frac{1}{2}$ lb + $\frac{1}{2}$ stone = _____ lb.

8 (a) What is the metric equivalent of:

(i) 3 lb   (ii) 5 pints   (iii) 10 feet?

(b) What is the imperial equivalent of:

(i) 4 kg   (ii) 5 litres   (iii) 240 km?

Activity: Design a poster

It is not always easy to remember the imperial–metric equivalents. Pictures can help!

Choose length, mass or capacity.

Divide a sheet of A3 into four quarters.

In each quarter draw a picture of a common object and write the appropriate imperial and metric *equivalent units* next to it.

330 ml

0.6 pint

4   Measurement and the metric system

5 Fractions

Some early number systems were not based on 10 but on 60. It is likely that 60 was used as a base because it has so many factors.

With a symbol-based number system, division was not simple, but using fractions with a base of 60 was very common.

In Ancient Egypt, scribes created tables with calculations of fractions. They used these tables as references, so that temple personnel could carry out the fractional divisions on food and supplies.

This is a wall painting of Egyptian scribes recording the harvest in the 18th dynasty 1543–1292 B.C. from the Tomb of Menna, Egypt.

You are becoming as used to calculating with fractions as the Ancient Egyptians were. You are already familiar with equivalent fractions, mixed numbers and simplifying. Here is a quick review of these and some other terms.

Simple fractions

Numerator and denominator
The number at the bottom of a fraction is the **denominator**. It tells you how many parts the whole is divided into. The number on the top is the **numerator**. It tells you how many of these parts you have.

$$\frac{numerator}{denominator}$$

Equivalent fractions

Equivalent fractions are fractions that have the same value.

$$\frac{1}{2} \quad = \quad \frac{4}{8}$$

You can draw diagrams to show equivalent fractions, or you can work them out numerically by multiplying or dividing the numerator and denominator by the same number.

Example

Fill in the missing number to make these fractions equivalent.

$$\frac{5}{8} = \frac{}{24} \qquad\qquad 8 \times 3 = 24$$

$$\frac{5}{8} = \frac{5 \times 3}{8 \times 3} \qquad\qquad \text{Multiply the 5 by 3}$$

$$= \frac{15}{24}$$

Simplifying fractions

To simplify a fraction, you divide the numerator and denominator by the same **factor**. You continue to do this until you have the smallest possible numbers.

Example

Simplify: $\frac{18}{24}$

$$\frac{18}{24} = \frac{\overset{3}{\cancel{18}}}{\underset{4}{\cancel{24}}} \qquad\qquad \text{The highest common factor of 18 and 24 is 6, so divide both numbers by 6}$$

$$= \frac{3}{4}$$

You can see that 2 and 3 are also **common factors** of 18 and 24. You may not always recognise the highest common factor (HCF) straight away but there is no reason why you cannot **cancel** more than once.

$$\frac{18}{24} = \frac{9}{12} = \frac{3}{4}$$

When there are no more common factors the fraction is in its **lowest terms** or **simplest form**.

Writing one value as a fraction of another

When you write one value as a fraction of another, always give the answer in its lowest terms.

Example

Write 25p as a fraction of £2

£2 = 200p

Always change your quantities to the same units first.

The fraction is $\frac{25}{200} = \frac{1}{8}$

Comparing and ordering fractions

To compare or order fractions, write them in terms of their **lowest common denominator**. This is the LCM of the denominators of all the fractions.

Example

Write these fractions in order, smallest first.

$\frac{5}{6}$ $\frac{3}{4}$ $\frac{7}{12}$

$\frac{5}{6} = \frac{10}{12}$ $\frac{3}{4} = \frac{9}{12}$ $\frac{7}{12}$

12 is the lowest common multiple of 6, 4 and 12 so it is the lowest common denominator for these fractions.

The correct order is $\frac{7}{12}, \frac{3}{4}, \frac{5}{6}$

When ordering or comparing fractions remember that:

< means less than $\frac{3}{4} < \frac{5}{6}$ and > means greater than $\frac{3}{4} > \frac{7}{12}$

Exercise 5.1

1 Replace the stars to make these fractions equivalent. Note that the star represents a different number in each case.

(a) $\frac{3}{4} = \frac{*}{12}$ (b) $\frac{2}{7} = \frac{*}{14}$ (c) $\frac{4}{9} = \frac{*}{27}$ (d) $\frac{5}{6} = \frac{15}{*}$

2 Write each fraction in its lowest terms.

(a) $\frac{10}{12}$ (b) $\frac{15}{18}$ (c) $\frac{8}{48}$ (d) $\frac{14}{56}$ (e) $\frac{60}{100}$

3 Draw four 5 cm by 6 cm rectangles in your book. Use one of the rectangles to illustrate each fraction.

(a) $\frac{7}{30}$ (b) $\frac{4}{15}$ (c) $\frac{5}{6}$ (d) $\frac{1}{10}$

4 Write the first quantity as a fraction of the second, giving your answer in its simplest form.

(a) 50p as a fraction of a £1

(b) 24 as a fraction of 60

(c) 48 as a fraction of 360

(d) 350 g as a fraction of a kilogram

(e) 35p as a fraction of £5

(f) 36 cm as a fraction of 1 m

(g) 125 cm as a fraction of 4 m

(h) 750 ml as a fraction of 2 litres

5 Copy and complete these statements.

(a) $\frac{3}{8} = \frac{}{40}$ $\frac{2}{5} = \frac{}{40}$

(b) Which is larger, $\frac{3}{8}$ or $\frac{2}{5}$?

6 Use the same method as in Q5. Write > or < between each pair of fractions.

(a) $\frac{3}{8}$ and $\frac{5}{8}$

(b) $\frac{3}{4}$ and $\frac{2}{3}$

(c) $\frac{5}{6}$ and $\frac{7}{8}$

(d) $\frac{3}{7}$ and $\frac{5}{12}$

(e) $\frac{4}{9}$ and $\frac{3}{7}$

(f) $\frac{3}{5}$ and $\frac{5}{9}$

7 I poured myself a drink from a 2-litre bottle of cola. My glass holds 125 ml. What fraction of the whole bottle is there in 1 glass?

8 I have saved up £15 towards a jacket costing £75. What fraction of the £75 have I saved?

9 I cut 12 m of string from a ball that holds 45 m. What fraction of the string have I cut off?

10 We have driven 350 km. The length of our total journey is 480 km. What fraction of our journey have we still to go?

Mixed numbers and improper fractions

All the fractions you have looked at so far have been proper fractions because they are less than 1 but you often use fractions with whole numbers attached.

● I am twelve and a half years old.

● It is quarter past two.

These are mixed numbers because they are a mixture of whole numbers and fractions. You can turn mixed numbers into fractions, to get **improper fractions**.

They are called improper fractions because the numerator is bigger than the denominator and the fraction is 'top heavy'.

Examples

(i) Write $\frac{25}{6}$ as a mixed number.

$$\frac{25}{6} = 4\frac{1}{6} \qquad\qquad 25 \div 6 = 4 \text{ remainder } 1$$

(ii) Write $2\frac{1}{4}$ as an improper fraction.

$$2\frac{1}{4} = \frac{9}{4} \qquad\qquad 4 \times 2 + 1 = 9$$

Exercise 5.2

1 Write each mixed number as an improper fraction.

(a) $1\frac{3}{5}$ (e) $6\frac{5}{9}$ (i) $4\frac{3}{11}$

(b) $2\frac{4}{7}$ (f) $7\frac{3}{8}$ (j) $5\frac{7}{12}$

(c) $4\frac{1}{11}$ (g) $6\frac{5}{7}$ (k) $6\frac{4}{9}$

(d) $6\frac{3}{4}$ (h) $5\frac{6}{7}$ (l) $8\frac{5}{9}$

2 Write these improper fractions as mixed numbers.

(a) $\frac{13}{2}$ (e) $\frac{13}{5}$ (i) $\frac{32}{5}$

(b) $\frac{11}{3}$ (f) $\frac{35}{7}$ (j) $\frac{58}{7}$

(c) $\frac{22}{7}$ (g) $\frac{19}{4}$ (k) $\frac{91}{8}$

(d) $\frac{36}{5}$ (h) $\frac{39}{10}$ (l) $\frac{125}{11}$

Adding and subtracting fractions

Adding fractions

You can add fractions only if they have the **same denominator**.

You can add $\frac{1}{10} + \frac{3}{10}$ to get $\frac{4}{10}$ because the denominator (10) is the same in both fractions.

However, you cannot add $\frac{3}{10} + \frac{5}{12}$ directly because you cannot add tenths to twelfths.

You have to write both fractions as equivalent fractions. It is sensible always to use the **lowest** common denominator.

In this example the lowest common multiple of 10 and 12 is 60, so multiply the top and the bottom of each fraction to make 10 up to 60 ($\times$ 6) and 12 up to 60 ($\times$ 5)

$$\frac{3}{10} = \frac{3 \times 6}{10 \times 6} = \frac{18}{60} \text{ and } \frac{5}{12} = \frac{5 \times 5}{12 \times 5} = \frac{25}{60}$$

Now you can complete the fraction addition.

Example

Add: $\frac{3}{10} + \frac{5}{12}$

$$\frac{3}{10} + \frac{5}{12} = \frac{18}{60} + \frac{25}{60}$$

$$= \frac{18 + 25}{60}$$

$$= \frac{43}{60}$$

When you need to add mixed numbers, add the whole numbers first and then the fractions.

Example

Add: $3\frac{1}{8} + 2\frac{11}{12}$

The lowest common denominator of 8 and 12 is 24

$$3\frac{1}{8} + 2\frac{11}{12} = 5\frac{3}{24} + \frac{22}{24}$$

$$= 5\frac{3 + 22}{24}$$

$$= 5\frac{25}{24}$$

You now have a mixed number with an improper fraction.

$$= 6\frac{1}{24}$$

As $\frac{25}{24} = 1\frac{1}{24}$ add the 1 to the 5 to make 6

> When adding fractions, remember to put the answer in its simplest form. If the answer is an improper fraction, such as $\frac{13}{12}$, write it as a mixed number: $1\frac{1}{12}$

Exercise 5.3

1. $\frac{2}{5} + \frac{1}{4}$

2. $\frac{1}{7} + \frac{3}{5}$

3. $\frac{2}{3} + \frac{1}{5}$

4. $\frac{5}{6} + \frac{3}{5}$

5. $\frac{2}{15} + \frac{4}{9}$

6. $\frac{3}{10} + \frac{3}{8}$

7. $\frac{5}{6} + \frac{3}{4}$

8. $\frac{5}{6} + \frac{3}{10}$

9. $\frac{5}{12} + \frac{3}{8}$

10. $\frac{3}{4} + \frac{5}{14}$

11. $1\frac{1}{5} + 3\frac{2}{3}$

12. $2\frac{1}{7} + 3\frac{3}{5}$

13. $1\frac{2}{5} + 4\frac{1}{8}$

14. $7\frac{2}{9} + 2\frac{2}{15}$

15. $5\frac{3}{8} + 3\frac{1}{16}$

16. $2\frac{4}{5} + 2\frac{2}{15}$

17. $6\frac{5}{12} + 3\frac{5}{8}$

18. $3\frac{5}{8} + 3\frac{3}{10}$

19. $5\frac{1}{12} + 3\frac{2}{3}$

20. $3\frac{3}{4} + 3\frac{2}{3}$

Subtracting fractions

To subtract fractions, follow the same basic steps as for addition. First, find the lowest common denominator, then work out the equivalent fractions and finally complete the subtraction.

Example

Subtract: $\frac{3}{5} - \frac{1}{3}$ The lowest common denominator for 3 and 5 is 15

$$\frac{3}{5} - \frac{1}{3} = \frac{9 - 5}{15}$$

$$= \frac{4}{15}$$

When you subtract one mixed number from another, try subtracting the whole numbers first and then the fractions.

Example

Subtract: $3\frac{3}{7} - 1\frac{1}{4}$ The lowest common denominator for 4 and 7 is 28

$$3\frac{3}{7} - 1\frac{1}{4} = 2\frac{12-7}{28}$$

$$= 2\frac{5}{28}$$

There will be times when a subtraction is not possible (5 – 9). Then you must borrow from the next number on the left. Remember, though, that you are not borrowing ten units – you will be borrowing 8 eighths, 12 twelfths or 16 sixteenths, depending on the fraction.

Example

Subtract: $3\frac{1}{3} - 1\frac{3}{4}$

$$3\frac{1}{3} - 1\frac{3}{4} = 2^1\frac{\overset{16}{\cancel{4}} - 9}{12}$$

$$= 1\frac{7}{12}$$

You cannot subtract 9 from 4, so change 1 unit into 12 twelfths. $4 + 12 = 16$

Exercise 5.4

1 $\frac{4}{5} - \frac{2}{3}$

2 $\frac{2}{3} - \frac{1}{4}$

3 $\frac{5}{7} - \frac{1}{6}$

4 $\frac{7}{8} - \frac{5}{6}$

5 $\frac{5}{12} - \frac{1}{4}$

6 $\frac{7}{12} - \frac{1}{5}$

7 $\frac{5}{8} - \frac{2}{5}$

8 $\frac{6}{7} - \frac{3}{4}$

9 $\frac{7}{8} - \frac{5}{6}$

10 $\frac{4}{15} - \frac{1}{6}$

11 $5\frac{2}{3} - 2\frac{2}{7}$

12 $4\frac{4}{5} - 1\frac{1}{3}$

13 $6\frac{2}{5} - 3\frac{2}{9}$

14 $5\frac{4}{9} - 1\frac{1}{3}$

15 $4\frac{4}{7} - 3\frac{1}{4}$

16 $6\frac{2}{3} - 2\frac{2}{9}$

17 $4\frac{3}{4} - 1\frac{2}{3}$

18 $7\frac{5}{6} - 3\frac{5}{8}$

19 $2\frac{4}{5} - 1\frac{2}{3}$

20 $4\frac{3}{8} - 1\frac{1}{6}$

21 $1\frac{1}{5} - \frac{2}{3}$

22 $3\frac{3}{4} - 1\frac{7}{8}$

23 $5\frac{3}{7} - 2\frac{4}{5}$

24 $2\frac{3}{5} - 1\frac{9}{10}$

25 $1\frac{1}{3} - \frac{7}{8}$

26 $2\frac{2}{7} - \frac{2}{3}$

27 $2\frac{1}{4} - 1\frac{5}{6}$

28 $4\frac{1}{9} - 2\frac{5}{6}$

29 $1\frac{2}{7} - \frac{3}{4}$

30 $5\frac{1}{6} - 1\frac{5}{8}$

A fraction of an amount

Here are some everyday examples of fractions of an amount.

Half an hour is 30 minutes. You divide 60 minutes by 2

Half a metre is 50 cm. You divide 100 cm by 2

Three-quarters of an hour is 45 minutes. You divide 60 minutes by 4 and then multiply the result by 3 to get the answer.

> When you are finding a fraction of an amount, you can replace 'of' with the $\times$ sign.

Example

Work out $\frac{1}{5}$ of 25

$\frac{1}{5}$ of $25 = \frac{1}{5} \times 25$

$\qquad = 5$

When you are working out more than one part you need to divide and then multiply. It is often simplest to cancel by a common factor, as with simplifying.

Example

Find $\frac{3}{4}$ of 1 m. Give the answer in centimetres.

$\frac{3}{4}$ of $1\,\text{m} = \frac{3}{4} \times 100\,\text{cm}$ Divide both 4 and 100 by 4 and then multiply 25 by 3

$\qquad\quad = 3 \times 25\,\text{cm}$

$\qquad\quad = 75\,\text{cm}$

1 Work out $\frac{1}{4}$ of 16

2 Work out $\frac{1}{7}$ of 35

3 Work out $\frac{1}{8}$ of 104

4 Work out $\frac{1}{9}$ of 126

5 Work out $\frac{1}{4}$ of 81

6 Work out $\frac{1}{8}$ of 74

7 Work out $\frac{3}{4}$ of 48

8 Work out $\frac{2}{3}$ of 72

9 Work out $\frac{3}{5}$ of 1 m. Give the answer in cm.

10 Work out $\frac{2}{3}$ of 1 hour. Give the answer in minutes.

11 Work out $\frac{3}{4}$ of 1 kg. Give the answer in grams.

12 Work out $\frac{5}{8}$ of 3 km. Give the answer in km and m.

13 Work out $\frac{3}{7}$ of 420

14 Work out $\frac{5}{16}$ of 240

15 Work out $\frac{3}{26}$ of 130

16 Work out $\frac{7}{18}$ of 126

17 Work out $\frac{11}{36}$ of 612

18 Work out $\frac{7}{18}$ of 216

19 Work out $\frac{7}{26}$ of 208

20 Work out $\frac{5}{34}$ of 306

Multiplying and dividing fractions

Multiplying fractions

In the last exercise, you multiplied a whole number by a fraction. You can use the same principle to multiply a fraction by a fraction.

Example

Multiply: $\frac{2}{7} \times \frac{21}{26}$

This example includes a difficult multiplication: 7×26

It is sensible to divide by any common factors before attempting the multiplication. This leads to easier calculations.

$$\frac{2}{7} \times \frac{21}{26} = \frac{\cancel{2}^{1}}{\cancel{7}_{1}} \times \frac{\cancel{21}^{3}}{\cancel{26}_{13}}$$

$$= \frac{3}{13}$$

2 divides into 2 and into 26

7 divides into 7 and into 21

Then you have 1×3 as the numerator and 1×13 as the denominator.

When you are working with mixed numbers, before you can cancel you must turn the mixed number into an improper fraction.

Example

Multiply: $1\frac{2}{7} \times 2\frac{1}{3}$

$$1\frac{2}{7} \times 2\frac{1}{3} = \frac{\cancel{9}^3}{\cancel{7}_1} \times \frac{\cancel{7}^1}{\cancel{3}_1}$$

First make the mixed numbers into improper fractions and then cancel.

$$= 3$$

You can use the same principle to multiply three or more fractions together.

Example

Multiply: $\frac{4}{5} \times \frac{10}{21} \times \frac{7}{8}$

$$\frac{4}{5} \times \frac{10}{21} \times \frac{7}{8} = \frac{\cancel{4}^1}{5} \times \frac{\cancel{10}^2}{\cancel{21}_3} \times \frac{\cancel{7}^1}{\cancel{8}_2}$$

$$= \frac{1}{3}$$

Exercise 5.6

Multiplying the fractions.

1 $\frac{2}{3} \times \frac{9}{10}$

2 $\frac{4}{5} \times \frac{15}{16}$

3 $\frac{9}{14} \times \frac{7}{12}$

4 $\frac{6}{7} \times \frac{2}{9}$

5 $\frac{20}{21} \times \frac{14}{15}$

6 $\frac{7}{10} \times \frac{5}{14}$

7 $\frac{20}{21} \times \frac{8}{9}$

8 $\frac{8}{9} \times \frac{6}{7} \times \frac{21}{22}$

9 $\frac{10}{11} \times \frac{2}{5} \times \frac{22}{25} \times \frac{5}{8}$

10 $\frac{1}{2} \times \frac{3}{4} \times \frac{5}{6} \times \frac{7}{8} \times \frac{9}{10} \times \frac{11}{12}$

11 $2\frac{1}{4} \times 2\frac{1}{3}$

12 $3\frac{1}{4} \times 2\frac{2}{5}$

13 $1\frac{1}{2} \times 1\frac{1}{3}$

14 $2\frac{1}{2} \times 3\frac{1}{3}$

15 $2\frac{3}{5} \times 3\frac{2}{3}$

16 $3\frac{1}{4} \times 2\frac{1}{3}$

17 $7\frac{7}{8} \times 4\frac{4}{9}$

18 $9\frac{3}{8} \times 8\frac{2}{5}$

19 $11\frac{1}{4} \times 12\frac{2}{5}$

20 $10\frac{8}{9} \times 3\frac{3}{14}$

21 $1\frac{1}{4} \times 2\frac{2}{3} \times 1\frac{2}{5}$

22 $2\frac{1}{2} \times 3\frac{1}{3} \times 1\frac{1}{4}$

23 $4\frac{2}{3} \times 3\frac{1}{7} \times 1\frac{1}{11}$

24 $1\frac{1}{2} \times 3\frac{4}{5} \times 1\frac{1}{4} \times 5\frac{1}{7}$

25 $1\frac{1}{2} \times 2\frac{2}{3} \times 3\frac{4}{5} \times 4\frac{5}{6}$

26 $\frac{1}{2} \times 1\frac{1}{3} \times 2\frac{1}{4} \times 3\frac{1}{5} \times 4\frac{1}{6}$

Dividing with fractions

You know from your work on **inverses** that division is the **opposite** of multiplication and therefore dividing by $\frac{1}{3}$ is the same as multiplying by $\frac{3}{1}$ or 3

Therefore the answer to $12 \times \frac{1}{3}$ is 4 because $12 \times \frac{1}{3} = 12 \div 3$

Now consider $12 \times \frac{2}{3}$

First divide by 3 and then multiply by 2

$$12 \times \frac{2}{3} = 12 \div 3 \times 2 \text{ or } 12 \div \frac{3}{2}$$

This works for all fractions, so $\div \frac{3}{4}$ is the same as $\times \frac{4}{3}$

Therefore to divide by a fraction, you multiply by the reciprocal.

> When you turn a fraction upside down the resulting fraction or integer is called the reciprocal.
>
> For example, the reciprocal of $\frac{3}{4}$ is $\frac{4}{3}$ and the reciprocal of $\frac{1}{4}$ is $\frac{4}{1}$ which is 4
>
> From this, you can see that the reciprocal of 4 is $\frac{1}{4}$

Examples

(i) Divide: $4 \div \frac{4}{5}$

$$4 \div \frac{4}{5} = \frac{4}{1} \times \frac{5}{4}$$

The reciprocal of $\frac{4}{5}$ is $\frac{5}{4}$

$$= \frac{\cancel{4}^1}{1} \times \frac{5}{\cancel{4}_1}$$

$$= 5$$

(ii) Divide: $\frac{2}{3} \div \frac{4}{9}$

$$\frac{2}{3} \div \frac{4}{9} = \frac{\cancel{2}^1}{\cancel{3}_1} \times \frac{\cancel{9}^3}{\cancel{4}_3}$$

The reciprocal of $\frac{4}{9}$ is $\frac{9}{4}$

$$= \frac{3}{2}$$

$$= 1\frac{1}{2}$$

> Take care to turn only the fraction you are dividing by upside down. The first fraction stays the same.

Just as with multiplication, when dividing with mixed numbers, you must turn them into improper fractions. If your answer is an improper fraction then you must turn it back into a mixed number in its lowest terms.

Example

Divide: $3\frac{1}{3} \div 1\frac{1}{6}$

$$3\frac{1}{3} \div 1\frac{1}{6} = \frac{10}{3} \div \frac{7}{6}$$

$$= \frac{10}{\cancel{3}_1} \times \frac{\cancel{6}^2}{7}$$

$$= \frac{20}{7}$$

$$= 2\frac{6}{7}$$

First turn the mixed numbers into improper fractions. Then multiply by the reciprocal.

Do not try to turn the mixed numbers into improper fractions and form the reciprocal in one stage. That leads to mistakes.

Exercise 5.7

1 $3 \div \frac{1}{6}$

2 $5 \div \frac{3}{10}$

3 $4 \div \frac{5}{6}$

4 $\frac{8}{9} \div \frac{2}{3}$

5 $\frac{7}{12} \div \frac{5}{9}$

6 $\frac{9}{10} \div \frac{3}{5}$

7 $\frac{24}{25} \div \frac{8}{15}$

8 $\frac{25}{36} \div \frac{5}{9}$

9 $\frac{4}{39} \div \frac{8}{13}$

10 $\frac{24}{35} \div \frac{3}{10}$

11 $2\frac{1}{4} \div 1\frac{7}{8}$

12 $2\frac{4}{5} \div 1\frac{7}{10}$

13 $2\frac{2}{3} \div 1\frac{1}{9}$

14 $3\frac{3}{4} \div 1\frac{3}{7}$

15 $4\frac{2}{7} \div 1\frac{1}{9}$

16 $4\frac{2}{5} \div 1\frac{7}{15}$

17 $3\frac{2}{3} \div 1\frac{2}{9}$

18 $4\frac{1}{5} \div 1\frac{2}{5}$

19 $5\frac{3}{4} \div 1\frac{7}{8}$

20 $4\frac{1}{6} \div 1\frac{7}{8}$

Exercise 5.8: Mixed operations

Remember BIDMAS and use it to calculate the answers to these questions.

1 $\frac{3}{8} + \frac{2}{5} \times \frac{5}{6}$

2 $\left(\frac{1}{2}\right)^2 + \frac{1}{3}$

3 $\frac{3}{8} + \frac{5}{6} \div \frac{2}{3}$

4 $\left(\frac{1}{8} + \frac{2}{5}\right) \times \frac{5}{6}$

5 $\left(\frac{1}{3}\right)^2 - \left(\frac{1}{6}\right)^2$

6 $\frac{3}{4} + \frac{2}{3} \times \frac{3}{8}$

7 $\left(\frac{1}{4} + \frac{2}{3}\right) \times \frac{3}{11}$

8 $\frac{2}{3} + \frac{3}{5} \div \frac{7}{10}$

9 $\left(\frac{2}{3} + \frac{3}{5}\right) \div \frac{7}{10}$

10 $\frac{3}{8} + \left(\frac{1}{4}\right)^2$

Solving problems with fractions

Write down all your working carefully and take care with the units.

Example

I travelled at 45 mph for 40 minutes. How far did I go?

40 minutes $= \frac{2}{3}$ hour

Distance $= 45 \times \frac{2}{3}$

$= \frac{\overset{15}{\cancel{45}}}{1} \times \frac{2}{\cancel{3}_1}$

$= 30$ miles

Extension Exercise 5.9

1 I bought a packet of toffees. Five-sixths of them were stuck together. What fraction were not stuck together?

2 I drink $\frac{7}{12}$ of a large bottle of cola and my friend drinks $\frac{2}{3}$ of a bottle of the same size. Who drinks more cola?

3 When I measure myself I find that I am 1.4 metres tall. I measure the distance from my chin to my crown and find that the height of my head is 20 cm. What fraction of my total height is made up by my head?

4 I have a new ball of string that holds eight and a half metres. I use five and five-sixths of a metre on my technology project. How much string is left on the ball?

5 In a bag of sweets one-quarter of the sweets are red, two-fifths are green and the rest are orange. What fraction of the sweets are orange?

6 Prince Absolute has to travel a distance of 8 leagues. For $2\frac{3}{8}$ leagues of the journey he travels through forest and for $1\frac{1}{5}$ leagues he travels through desert. He travels the rest of the journey across plains. How many leagues does he travel across plains?

7 I buy $\frac{3}{4}$ kg of tomatoes at £1.20 per kilogram and a cabbage weighing $\frac{3}{8}$ kg at 80p per kilogram. How much money do I spend?

8 I have a new ball of string that holds $4\frac{1}{2}$ m and I use $\frac{1}{2}$ of it. How many metres are left?

9 I have a new ball of string that holds $8\frac{1}{2}$ m and I use $3\frac{3}{8}$ m of it. How many metres are left?

10 My lunch break lasts three-quarters of an hour. I spend a third of it playing conkers. What fraction of an hour is that?

Extension Exercise 5.10

Use the four rules for addition, subtraction, multiplication and division of fractions, and remember BIDMAS when you answer these questions.

1 $\dfrac{\frac{2}{3}-\frac{4}{7}}{\frac{2}{15}}$ 2 $\dfrac{\frac{3}{4}+\frac{3}{7}}{\frac{5}{18}}$ 3 $\dfrac{1\frac{4}{7}-\frac{7}{10}}{\frac{3}{14}}$ 4 $\dfrac{\frac{7}{15}-\frac{5}{12}}{\frac{7}{8}-\frac{5}{6}}$

5 $\dfrac{\frac{2}{9}+\frac{1}{6}}{\frac{2}{9}}$ 6 $\dfrac{\frac{3}{5}+\frac{2}{7}}{\frac{4}{7}-\frac{3}{10}}$ 7 $\dfrac{2\frac{1}{3}-1\frac{4}{9}}{\frac{8}{9}}$

8 (a) The teacher asked the class to work out the sum of the series:

$\frac{1}{1}+\frac{1}{2}+\frac{1}{3}+\frac{1}{4}+\frac{1}{5}$ ... stopping when the sum was greater than $2\frac{1}{2}$

What would the final answer be?

(b) George was not paying attention. The series he was summing was:

$\frac{1}{1}+\frac{1}{2}+\frac{1}{4}+\frac{1}{8}$ ...

What was George's final answer?

Summary Exercise 5.11

1 (a) What fraction of £5 is 75p?

(b) What fraction of 3 hours is 15 minutes?

2 Write $<$ or $>$ between the fractions in each pair.

(a) $\frac{3}{5}$ \qquad $\frac{2}{3}$

(b) $\frac{11}{24}$ \qquad $\frac{17}{36}$

3 Calculate

(a) $\frac{3}{4}+\frac{5}{6}$
(b) $2\frac{3}{5}+3\frac{5}{7}$

4 Calculate

(a) $\frac{5}{8}-\frac{2}{5}$
(b) $4\frac{2}{3}-2\frac{5}{8}$

5 Find $\frac{1}{7}$ of 350

6 Find $\frac{3}{8}$ of 3 kg. Give your answer in grams.

7 Calculate

(a) $\frac{2}{5}\times\frac{15}{16}$
(b) $1\frac{1}{4}\times2\frac{2}{5}$

8 Calculate

(a) $\frac{2}{15}\div\frac{4}{5}$
(b) $3\frac{3}{4}\div1\frac{1}{9}$

9 I cut three-quarters of a metre of ribbon from a piece two and one-third metres long. What fraction of the ribbon was left?

10 Calculate

(a) $\dfrac{\frac{3}{4}+\frac{5}{6}}{\frac{2}{3}-\frac{3}{5}}$
(b) $1-\frac{1}{4}\left(1+\frac{1}{4}\left(1-\frac{1}{4}\right)\right)$

Activity: Egyptian fractions

Egyptians were able to write *any* fraction as *a sum of unit fractions* where all the unit fractions were different.

> A **unit fraction** is one that has 1 as the numerator, such as $\frac{1}{4}$

For example:

- $\frac{5}{12}=\frac{1}{3}+\frac{1}{12}$

- $\frac{7}{9}=\frac{1}{2}+\frac{1}{6}+\frac{1}{9}$

How can you work out Egyptian fractions for any fraction, such as $\frac{11}{25}$?

Fibonacci devised a method that he called the 'greedy' fraction to work out Egyptian fractions.

The greedy fraction

Imagine that your fraction is eating unit fractions. He is greedy and he starts with the largest fraction that he can, which must be $\frac{1}{2}$ or less.

You can see that $\frac{11}{25}$ is less than a half but more than a quarter.

$$\frac{11}{25} = \frac{1}{4} + ?$$

$$? = \frac{11}{25} - \frac{1}{4}$$

$$= \frac{44 - 25}{100}$$

$$= \frac{19}{100}$$

Now you can see that $\frac{19}{100}$ is just less than $\frac{1}{5}$ so lies between $\frac{1}{5}$ and $\frac{1}{6}$

$$\frac{11}{25} = \frac{1}{4} + \frac{1}{6} + ?$$

$$? = \frac{11}{25} - \frac{1}{4} - \frac{1}{6}$$

$$= \frac{132 - 75 - 50}{300}$$

$$= \frac{7}{300}$$

$\frac{7}{300}$ lies between $\frac{1}{40}$ and $\frac{1}{50}$

$$\frac{11}{25} = \frac{1}{4} + \frac{1}{6} + \frac{1}{50} + ?$$

$$? = \frac{11}{25} - \frac{1}{4} - \frac{1}{6} - \frac{1}{50}$$

$$= \frac{132 - 75 - 50 - 6}{300}$$

$$= \frac{1}{300}$$

$$\frac{11}{25} = \frac{1}{4} + \frac{1}{6} + \frac{1}{50} + \frac{1}{300}$$

Use the greedy fraction method to find Egyptian fractions for $\frac{13}{25}$, $\frac{8}{9}$, $\frac{7}{15}$ and $\frac{23}{100}$

Is there more than one solution? Check with your neighbours! Who has found the Egyptian fraction with the smallest number of unit fractions?

6 Probability

You know that some things will definitely happen and some things will definitely not happen, but some other things **might** happen. It can be useful to know how likely it is that these things could happen. After all, if there is an 80% chance of rain tomorrow, you may decide not to go to the park.

The probability scale

You often encounter **probability**, **or chance**, when you play certain games. For example:

- It is **impossible** to roll a total of 1 with two normal dice.

- It is **certain** that I will roll a total of more than 1 with two normal dice.

- If I toss a coin there is an **even chance** that I will see heads or tails.

When you toss a coin or roll a die, this is an **event**. The results of an event are its outcomes. Tossing a coin has two possible outcomes (heads or tails), rolling a normal die with six faces has six possible outcomes (1, 2, 3, 4, 5 or 6)

- If an outcome is impossible, it has a probability of 0

- If an outcome is certain, it has a probability of 1

- If an outcome has an even chance, then it has a probability of 1 in 2 or $\frac{1}{2}$
- The sum of all the probabilities of all the possible outcomes of an event is 1

You can write a probability as:

- a fraction, such as $\frac{1}{2}$
- a decimal, such as 0.5
- a **percentage**, such as 50%

You can show probabilities on a **probability scale**, like this:

or like this:

◯ More probability words

Here are some more things to remember, when you are discussing probability. If you pick from a box of chocolates, this is **unlikely** to be **at random** because you will pick your favourite flavour.

Rolling a die or taking a card out of a pack is called a **random** event as you have no control over the outcome.

You talk about taking a card **at random** because you do not know what card you will get.

When you toss a coin you will score either a head or a tail. These are **equally likely** outcomes.

All three of these are **fair** tests because you cannot control the result. This is why you might toss a coin at the start of a cricket match.

Suppose, though, that you had a pack of cards that had been prepared with only the black suits – two sets of clubs and two sets of spades. Maybe you have seen a coin that has two heads or two tails, rather than one of each.

It is possible you have heard of weighted or loaded dice, that are more likely to show a six than any other number. These examples all show **bias**, because the outcomes are not all equally likely. This is why you will often see a pack of cards, a coin or a die described as **fair**.

Die is the singular of dice. Sometimes people say 'one dice' but that is incorrect.

Exercise 6.1

1 Write down an outcome that:

(a) is impossible

(b) is possible

(c) has an even chance of happening

(d) is probable

(e) is certain.

2 Now think of your own examples of:

(a) a random event

(b) equally likely outcomes

(c) fair tests.

3 The weather forecast says that there is a 75% chance of a shower tomorrow.

(a) What would you **not** plan to do?

(b) What is the probability that there will **not** be a shower?

4 The weather forecast says that there is a 0.1 chance of a shower tomorrow.

(a) What would you plan to do?

(b) What is the probability that there will **not** be a shower?

5 The forecast says that on Tuesday there is a 1 in 2 chance of rain, on Wednesday there is a 0.25 chance of rain but on Thursday they are 99% certain that it will be a glorious day.

(a) Which would be the best day to spend outside?

(b) What is the chance of no rain on Tuesday: possible, even chance or probable?

(c) What is the chance of no rain on Wednesday: possible, even chance or probable?

6 Copy the probability scale and mark on it the probability of each of the listed outcomes. The first one is done for you.

A: I will throw a 1 with a normal die.

B: I will toss a coin and score 'heads'.

C: I will watch television tonight.

D: There will be salad for lunch.

E: Humans will land on Mars in the next decade.

F: It will rain tomorrow.

◯ Recording probabilities

There are three types of outcome, as shown in question 6 of the previous exercise:

● those over which you have control (I will watch television.)

● those about which you can make a sensible guess (Humans will land on Mars.)

● those for which you can calculate the theoretical probability. (I will toss a coin and score 'heads'.)

When you roll a die, all the outcomes are equally likely. This means that each possible outcome has a probability of $\frac{1}{6}$

Therefore, if you were rolling a die, you could write:

probability of rolling a three $P(3) = \frac{1}{6}$

You can also see that:

probability of **not** rolling a three $P(\text{not } 3) = 1 - \frac{1}{6}$

$$= \frac{5}{6}$$

When there is more than one possible outcome, you can determine the probability of any desired outcome as:

$$\frac{\text{number of favourable outcomes}}{\text{total number of possibilities}}$$

Example

A number is chosen at random from the first 10 positive integers.

What is the probability of that number:

(a) being square

(b) not being square?

The first 10 positive integers are 1, 2, 3, 4, 5, 6, 7, 8, 9, 10

The square numbers are 1, 4, 9

$$P(\text{square}) = \frac{3}{10}$$

$$P(\text{not square}) = 1 - \frac{3}{10}$$

$$= \frac{7}{10}$$

Always start by listing all the possibilities.

First find the probability of choosing a square number, then subtract the answer from 1

Games of chance

Because so many games depend on chance as well as skill, questions about probability are often based on examples involving cards and dice. Here are the basic facts you need to know about a pack of cards.

- A pack of cards has four suits (spades, hearts, diamonds and clubs) and each suit has 13 cards.

- In each suit there is an ace, the numbers 2 to 10, a jack (or knave) a queen and king.

- The knave, queen and king are **royal cards.**

- Diamonds and hearts are red, spades and clubs are black.

It is worth taking a look at a pack of cards, if you have not already done so.

Exercise 6.2

1 Suppose you throw a normal die. Write down the probability of throwing:

(a) an even number

(b) a 3

(c) a square number

(d) at least 2

(e) a number that is less than 5

2 Suppose you choose one card at random from a normal pack. Write down the probability of choosing:

(a) a club

(b) a king

(c) a royal card

(d) a red ace

(e) a black card.

(f) a card that is not an ace.

3 Suppose you choose a letter at random from the letters of the word 'MATHEMATICS'. What is the probability of:

(a) choosing a vowel

(b) not choosing a vowel?

4 I have a die with eight faces numbered from 1 to 8. Write down the probability of throwing:

(a) a 6

(b) an even number

(c) a prime number

(d) a square number

(e) a multiple of 3

(f) a composite number.

> A **composite number** is a number that has more than two factors, such as 4, 6, 9, 36

5 Look at this five-sided spinner. Write down the probability of spinning:

(a) 1

(b) 2

(c) an odd number

(d) an even number.

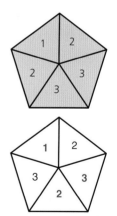

6 Look at this five-sided spinner. Notice that some numbers are red. Write down the probability of spinning:

(a) a red 2

(b) a red number

(c) a red odd number

7 A number is chosen at random from the first 20 positive integers. Write down the probability of that number:

(a) being odd

(b) being prime

(c) not being prime

(d) not being a multiple of 3

(e) not being a cube number

(f) not being a factor of 360

(g) not being a triangular number.

8 An eight-sided spinner is numbered from 1 to 8. Write down the probability of spinning a number that is:

(a) a prime number

(b) not a prime number

(c) not less than 6

(d) not more than 4

(e) at least 7

(f) less than 9

9 I have a bag of 20 coloured sweets. Four of them are red, three are brown, seven are orange and the rest are yellow. I take one out of the bag at random. Write down the probability that I pick a sweet that is:

(a) red

(b) yellow

(c) not red

(d) not orange or yellow

(e) not a colour of the rainbow.

Calculating the probability of a second event

What happens if I pick a sweet from a bag, and then I eat it? There are fewer sweets in the bag (by one) and fewer of the colour that I took (also by one).

Example

I have a bag of 20 coloured sweets. Four of them are red, three are brown, seven are orange and the rest are yellow. I take an orange sweet and then eat it. If I take another sweet out at random, what is the probability that it will be orange?

Number of orange sweets left is 6

Number of sweets now in the bag is 19   Remember to take 1 from the total, as well as from the number of orange sweets.

$P(\text{orange}) = \frac{6}{19}$

If you look back over these examples, you can see why it is better to use fractions to describe probability!

Combined events

When you are considering a **combined event**, you need to consider two options.

Example

I take a card at random from a normal pack. What is the probability that it is a red four or a black five?

Number of red fours is 2   Number of black fives is 2

$P(\text{red 4 or black 5}) = \frac{4}{52}$

$= \frac{1}{13}$

Being certain

Understanding theoretical probability can help you to calculate how many times you should do something to be certain of a definite outcome.

It is important to remember that, however many times you repeat an experiment, you cannot be sure to get any particular outcome; for example, you could roll a die one hundred times and still not score a 6. However, when you take a sweet from a bag without putting it back, then you can work out how many sweets you must take out to be sure of getting one of a particular colour.

Example

I have a bag of 20 coloured sweets. Four of them are red, three are brown, seven are orange and the rest are yellow. How many sweets must I take out of the bag at random to be sure of getting an orange one?

Number of non-orange sweets = 20 − 7

$$= 13$$

I must take 13 + 1 = 14 sweets out of the bag to be sure of getting an orange one.

> Note the difference between the theoretical probability of picking an orange sweet and the certainty of picking an orange sweet.

Exercise 6.3

1 I have a bag of 20 coloured sweets. Four of them are red, three are green, seven are orange and the rest are yellow. I eat a yellow one. I take another sweet out of the bag at random.

(a) Give the probability of my taking:

(i) a yellow sweet

(ii) a green sweet.

(b) How many sweets must I take, at random, to be certain of getting a green one?

2 I have a drawer full of 26 socks. Nine of them are grey, 11 of them are black and the rest are white.

(a) I take 1 sock out of the drawer at random. Write down the probability that it is:

(i) white   (ii) black   (iii) grey or white.

(b) In fact the first sock that I take out is white. I do not replace the sock. Write down the probability that the next sock I take is:

(i) white   (ii) grey   (iii) black or white.

(c) How many socks must I take out of the drawer to be sure of getting a pair of the same colour?

3 For the school tombola we are told that the winning tickets will be those that end with a 0 or 5. There are 500 tickets and 100 prizes.

(a) If I buy a ticket, what is the probability that I will win a prize?

(b) How many tickets must I buy in order to be sure of winning a prize?

(c) After 1 hour, 350 people have bought tickets and 40 prizes have been won. What is the probability of winning a prize now?

4 A card is selected at random from a normal pack. What is the probability that it is:

(a) an ace or a ten

(b) a red royal card

(c) a black card less than five?

5 I am playing a game of cards. I have been dealt an ace, a king and a queen and my friend has been dealt an ace, a knave and a 10

(a) What is the probability that the next card I am dealt is a knave?

(b) I am dealt a 10. What is the probability that the next card my friend is dealt is also a 10?

6 In our maths lesson, we are playing a game with a die. The teacher rolls the die and scores a 5. She rolls the die a second time.

(a) Write down the probability that she:

(i) scores a 4

(ii) scores a 5

(iii) makes a total with the first die of more than 5

(iv) makes a total with the first die of 8

(b) Which of these answers would be different if the teacher had rolled a 3 the first time? Suppose she had rolled a 1?

(c) How many times should she roll the die to be sure of getting another 5?

7 I packed four tins of soup and three tins of rice pudding to take on a camping trip but left them outside in the rain and all the labels washed off.

(a) What is the probability that the first tin that I open is rice pudding?

(b) How many tins must I open to be sure of having rice pudding?

8 In a packet of jelly beans there are five lemon beans, three orange beans, six lime beans, one vanilla bean and four strawberry beans.

(a) If I pick a bean at random what is the probability that it is:

(i) vanilla

(ii) not lime

(iii) orange or lemon?

(b) I picked a strawberry bean and ate it. What is the probability that the next bean I pick is:

(i) strawberry

(ii) not lime

(iii) orange or lemon?

Possibility space diagrams

When you toss a coin it will show either heads or tails. If you toss two coins, the first coin could show heads or tails and the second coin could also show heads or tails. This means that you could have any one of four possible combinations:

(head, head)   (head, tail)   (tail, head)   (tail, tail)

To make it easier to see all the possible outcomes, you can list all of them in a table called a possibility space diagram.

Example

What is the probability of scoring two heads when you toss two coins together?

		First coin	
		H	T
Second coin	H	(H, H)	(T, H)
	T	(H, T)	(T, T)

From the table, you can see that there are four possible outcomes, but only one of them gives two heads.

$P(H, H) = \frac{1}{4}$

> The notation $P(H, H)$ means the probability of scoring a head and a head.

1 Copy and complete this possibility space to show the possible outcomes when throwing two dice.

		First die					
		1	2	3	4	5	6
Second die	1	(1, 1)	(2, 1)	(3, 1)	(4, 1)	(5, 1)	(6, 1)
	2	(1, 2)	(2, 2)	(3, 2)	(4, 2)	(,)	(,)
	3	(,)	(,)	(,)	(,)	(,)	(,)
	4	(,)	(,)	(,)	(,)	(,)	(,)
	5	(,)	(,)	(,)	(,)	(,)	(,)
	6	(,)	(,)	(,)	(,)	(,)	(,)

Now work out the probability that, when you throw two dice, you will score:

(a) a double 6

(b) any double

(c) a total of 7

(d) a total of 4

(e) more than 6

(f) at least 5

(g) a 4 on either die.

2 The game *Catch the mouse* uses two dice. One is a normal die with numbers from 1 to 6 and the other has coloured spots on the six faces: three blue spots, two red spots and one yellow spot. Copy and complete this possibility space to show the possible outcomes when you throw the two dice together.

		Coloured die					
		B	B	B	R	R	Y
Numbered die	1	(B, 1)	(B, 1)	(B, 1)	(R, 1)	(R, 1)	(Y, 1)
	2	(B, 2)	(B, 2)	(B, 2)	(R, 2)	(,)	(,)
	3	(,)	(,)	(,)	(,)	(,)	(,)
	4	(,)	(,)	(,)	(,)	(,)	(,)
	5	(,)	(,)	(,)	(,)	(,)	(,)
	6	(,)	(,)	(,)	(,)	(,)	(,)

Work out the probability that you will score:

(a) a blue spot and a 3

(b) a yellow spot and a 3

(c) a red spot

(d) a 6

3 The game *Tell me* uses a five-sided spinner with letters on it and a four-sided spinner with colours on it.

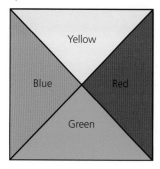 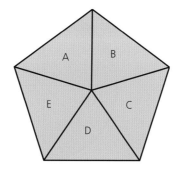

Draw a possibility space diagram showing all the possible outcomes when both spinners are spun. Write down the probability of spinning:

(a) red

(b) blue and D

4 (a) Draw a possibility space diagram showing all the possible outcomes when you throw one normal die and another die that is numbered 1, 1, 2, 2, 3, 4

(b) Use your possibility space to find the probability that you will score:

(i) a double 2

(ii) any double

(iii) a double 6

(iv) a total of 6

(v) at least 8

(vi) over 8

Extension Exercise 6.5

We have looked at events in which all outcomes had an equal chance of occurring. The two pentagonal spinners in Exercise 6.2 have 5 possible outcomes. On each spinner, two of the five outcomes are 2 and two outcomes are 3. Now look at this spinning wheel. With this wheel, two outcomes are £5 and two outcomes are £1

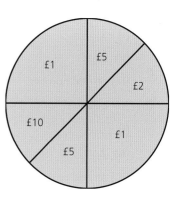

Although the wheel is divided into six sections, the sections are not all of equal size. This means that there is **not** an equal chance of picking each section.

Although two of the six sections might win £1, the probability of winning £1 is higher than $\frac{2}{6}$ (or $\frac{1}{3}$). Looking again at the spinner, you should see that, effectively, it is divided into eight equal sections and that two pairs of these sections are joined together. Looking at where the £1 labels are, you can see that the probability of winning £1 is $\frac{4}{8} = \frac{1}{2}$

1 In the circular spinner, the wheel is divided into eight equal sections, but then two pairs of sections are joined together.

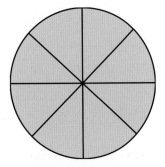

becomes:

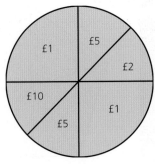

(a) Give the probability of winning:

(i) £10   (ii) £5   (iii) more than a £1

(b) If it costs £2 to have a spin of the wheel, what is the probability of winning more than you pay?

2 Look at these spinners.

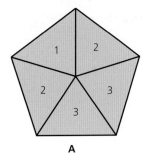

A

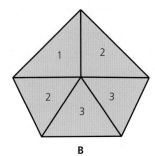

B

(a) For spinner A, write down the probability of scoring:

(i) 1

(ii) 2

(iii) an odd number.

(b) For spinner B, write down the probability of scoring:

(i) 1

(ii) 2

(iii) an odd number.

(c) I have to spin a total of 4 to win a game. Would I be better off spinning A twice, spinning B twice or spinning A and B together?

Explain your answer.

3 In a game called *Old Macdonald* I have to throw a plastic lamb. The way the lamb lands decides what move I can make next. I throw the lamb 100 times. My results are recorded in this table.

Position	Move	Tally	Frequency
On four legs	Stay still	JHT JHT JHT III	18
On right side	Move right	JHT JHT JHT JHT JHT JHT I	31
On left side	Move left	JHT JHT JHT JHT JHT JHT JHT III	38
Nose down	Move forward	JHT III	8
Tail down	Move back	JHT	5
Total			**100**

3 **(a)** If I were to throw the lamb once more, write down the probability, based on the results above, that it lands:

(i) on four legs

(ii) on its left or right side

(iii) not on a side

(iv) either tail down or nose down.

(b) If I were to throw the lamb another 100 times, would I get the same results? Explain your answer.

(c) At the same time as throwing the lamb, I throw a normal die. The die tells me how many squares to move. Draw up a possibility space diagram showing all the possible combinations of throwing the lamb and the die together.

(d) My friend Jake says that the probability of moving forward three squares is $\frac{1}{30}$ Is he right? Explain your answer. If he is wrong, what do you think the correct probability is?

Summary Exercise 6.6

1 Draw a probability scale. Show the probability of these events on the scale.

(a) There will be a cloud in the sky tomorrow.

(b) It will rain tomorrow.

(c) England will win the next football World Cup.

(d) Next year will be a leap year.

(e) I will brush my hair before I go to bed.

2 A letter is chosen from the word PROBABILITY. Write down the probability that it is:

(a) a vowel

(b) a consonant

(c) the letter P

(d) a letter with rotational symmetry.

3 A card is taken at random from a normal pack of cards. Write down the probability that it will be:

(a) a knave

(b) more than 8

(c) a red royal card

(d) a black king or a red 9

(e) a heart

(f) a knave or a heart.

4 A normal die is rolled. Write down the probability that the score will be:

(a) 5   **(b)** at least 4   **(c)** a factor of 36

5 I toss a coin and roll a die at the same time. Copy and complete this possibility space diagram to show the possible combinations.

		Die					
		1	2	3	4	5	6
Coin	H	(1, H)	(2, H)	(3, H)	(4, H)	(,)	(,)
	T	(1, T)	(2, T)	(,)	(,)	(,)	(,)

Write down the probability of throwing:

(a) a head and an odd number

(b) a tail and a number greater than 4

(c) a prime number and either a head or tail

(d) a tail and a number greater than 6

6 I roll two dice together. Both are **cubes** but their numbering is rather different. Here are the **nets** of the cubes, showing the number of dots on each face.

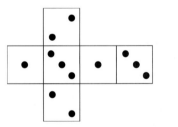 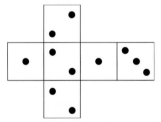

(a) Copy and complete this possibility space diagram showing the possible outcomes when both dice are rolled.

		First die					
		1	2				
	1	(1, 1)	(1, 1)	(,)	(, 1)	(, 1)	(,)
	2	(1, 1)	(1, 1)	(, 1)	(, 1)	(,)	(,)
Second die		(,)	(,)	(,)	(,)	(,)	(,)
		(,)	(,)	(,)	(,)	(,)	(,)
		(,)	(,)	(,)	(,)	(,)	(,)
		(,)	(,)	(,)	(,)	(,)	(,)

(b) What is the probability of rolling a double?

(c) What is the probability of rolling a total of 4?

(d) What is the probability of getting at least 5?

(e) What possible totals could you throw?

(f) Which is the most likely score?

7 I bought a bag of mixed Munchy bars. There were four nutty bars, three chocolate chip bars, five crispy bars and two coconut bars. I took one bar at random. Write down the probability that it was:

(a) coconut **(b)** nutty.

My little sister ate one coconut bar and one chocolate chip bar. Now, write down the probability that, if I take one bar at random, I will pick:

(c) coconut **(d)** nutty.

Activity: Design a board game

Think how you could design your own board game. Before you start, you could do some research into games. Perhaps everyone in the class could bring in an unusual game for you all to talk about.

1 What makes a good game? List all the games you enjoy. Note whether they are games of chance or games of skill, or a mixture of both.

2 For games that involve chance, write down what these elements of chance are. There may be more than one. For some games the element of chance depends on what your opponent does.

3 Decide what works best. Now create a game in which you could use two or more elements of chance. It might involve throwing one or two dice to allow you to move, and picking up some cards from time to time. You will need to put your game into a context. Here are a few ideas:

- purely mathematical on a grid of squares or hexagons

- a general knowledge game, where the question you get depends on where you land

- a race game, similar to *Ludo* or *Snakes and ladders*

- a game based on a popular book or film.

- a game with letters.

4 When you have planned your game, draw the game board accurately.

5 Write down the rules.

6 This is the clever bit! Assuming your game involves chance, what advice can you give someone about how to win the game? Does it matter who goes first? What choices could you make? Could you change the rules a little so that there is some skill as well as chance?

7 When you are happy with your game, play it. If you enjoy it, then you could try to market it – now that will involve some exciting mathematics!

7 Algebra 1: Expressions and formulae

The word **algebra** derives from the Arabic *al-jabr,* meaning literally 'the reunion of broken parts'. It gained widespread use through the title of a book *ilm al-jabr wa'l-mukabala* – the science of restoring what is missing and equating like with like – written by the mathematician Abu Ja'far Muhammad (c.800–847). He subsequently became known as *al-Khwarazmi, the man of Kwarazm* (now Khiva in Uzbekistan). He introduced the technique of writing calculations down instead of using an abacus.

Statue of the mathematician *al-Khwarazmi* the man of Kwarazm, Uzbekistan

The Arabs brought algebra from ancient Babylon, Egypt and India and finally to Europe via Italy. The first treatise on algebra was written by Diophantus of Alexandria in the third century A.D.

The rules of algebra

In *Maths for Common Entrance One* you learnt some simple rules of algebra and used them to solve equations. Here is a brief summary of what you should know.

- In algebra, you use **symbols** or **letters** to represent numbers. These are known as variables.

- You can use any letters to represent unknowns, and in textbooks they are written as *italic* letters. For example, if you use x as an unknown, you write it as a curly x, not the $\times$ that means multiply.

- You can add and subtract terms made up of the same letters, or numbers, but you cannot add unlike letters or letters to numbers.

  $a + a + a = 3a$ but $a + b = a + b$ and cannot be simplified.

- A term may be a number or an algebraic unknown, such as 3, 12, a, xy or z^2

- Terms that involve exactly the same letters are called **like terms**. So a, $2a$ and $5a$ are like terms, as are x, $3x$ and $5x$, and $2xy$, $4xy$, $7xy$. You can add or subtract like terms. This is called **gathering** or **collecting like terms**.

- When you **simplify** expressions, you do not use multiplication signs, or division signs.

  - $3 \times x = 3x$ but $1 \times x = x$

  - $x \div 3 = \frac{x}{3}$

- You use a fraction rather than a decimal to describe a variable:

  $0.2x = \frac{x}{5}$

- An **expression** is a combination of terms, such as $3x + 4y$

- You cannot solve an expression but you may be able to **simplify** it.

- An **equation** contains an equals sign: $2 + x = 6$

- You can **solve** equations.

- You should always align equals signs vertically in your working.

> You never write $1x$ or $0x$

Example

Simplify each expression.

(i) $a + a + a + a$ (ii) $3 \times b$ (iii) $6d \div 2$

(i) $a + a + a + a = 4a$ (ii) $3 \times b = 3b$ (iii) $6d \div 2 = 3d$

> To **simplify** means to write more simply.

In each of the examples, there was just one unknown but the same rules apply when you have two or more unknowns.

Example

Simplify each expression.

(i) $3a + 4b - 2a + 3b$ (ii) $3a \times 4b$ (iii) $12x \div 2y$

(i) $3a + 4b - 2a + 3b = a + 7b$

(ii) $3a \times 4b = 12ab$

(iii) $12x \div 2y = \frac{12x}{2y}$

$ = \frac{6x}{y}$

> You can simplify or cancel fractions written in algebra, just like fractions with numbers.

Exercise 7.1

Use the rules of algebra to simplify each expression.

1 $a + a + a$

2 $5 \times x$

3 $m + m + m - m$

4 $p + p + q + q$

5 $4 \times y + 3 \times y$

6 $^-0.1a$

7 $0.5 \times d$

8 $\frac{10x}{5}$

9 $a + 5 + a + 5$

10 $c - c - c - c$

11 $2a \times 3b$

12 $2p + 3q - 4p + q$

13 $m + 2n - 3n + m$

14 $4x \times 0.5y$

15 $8x \div 2y$

16 $4a + 3b + 2a - b$

17 $5m - 5 - 7m + 4$

18 $15m \div 5n$

19 $2p \times 5q$

20 $8a + 2b - 2a - 2b$

Powers of x

You know that you can use an index number to write the result of multiplying any number by itself a number of times.

$$3 \times 3 = 3^2$$

The same is true for an algebraic variable.

$$x \times x \times x = x^3 \qquad x \times x \times x \times x = x^4$$

Look at these squares.

How can you calculate their areas?

The area of the first square: $\quad 1 \times 1 = 1^2 = 1$

The area of the second square: $2 \times 2 = 2^2 = 4$

The area of the third square: $\quad 3 \times 3 = 3^2 = 9$

The area of the fourth square: $\ x \times x = x^2$

You cannot simplify x^2 any further.

It is very important not to confuse x^3 with $3 \times x = 3x$ or $x + x + x = 3x$

Make sure you understand why before you move on.

If you are not sure, then imagine the calculation when $x = 2$

$$x \times x \times x = x^3 \qquad 2 \times 2 \times 2 = 2^3 = 8$$

$$3 \times x = 3x \quad 3 \times 2 = 2 + 2 + 2 = 6$$

Can you see how important it is to understand this correctly?

You can **gather like terms** that include index numbers, just as you would gather other like terms. but you may need another stage of working.

Example

Simplify: $2 \times x \times x \times y + x \times x \times y$

$2 \times x \times x \times y + x \times x \times y = 2x^2y + x^2y$ There are two x^2y terms here, so add $2x^2y$ to the single x^2y

$\qquad\qquad\qquad\qquad = 3x^2y$

Exercise 7.2

Simplify each expression.

1 (a) $x \times x$

   (b) $x + x$

   (c) $2 \times x$

   (d) $2 \times 2 \times x$

2 (a) $x + x + x$

   (b) $3 \times x$

   (c) $x \times x \times x$

   (d) $3 \times x \times 3$

3 (a) $4 \times x$

   (b) $x \times x \times x \times x \times x$

   (c) $2 \times x \times 2 \times x$

4 (a) $a \times x$

   (b) $a \times x \times x$

   (c) $a \times a \times x$

   (d) $a \times x \times x \times a \times x$

5 (a) $b \times b$

   (b) $2 \times b \times b$

   (c) $2 \times a \times b$

   (d) $a \times b \times a \times b$

6 (a) $x \times y + x$

   (b) $x \times y + x \times x$

   (c) $x \times y + x \times y$

   (d) $x \times x + 2 \times x \times x$

7 (a) $2 \times a \times b + a \times a$

   (b) $2 \times a \times a + a \times a$

8 (a) $2 \times a \times b + a \times b \times b$

   (b) $2 \times a \times b + 3 \times a \times b$

9 (a) $s \times t \times u + s \times t \times t$

   (b) $2 \times s \times t \times t - s \times t \times t$

10 (a) $3 \times x \times y \times x - x \times x \times y$

   (b) $3 \times x \times y \times x - x \times y \times y$

Algebra and index numbers

Sometimes you need to combine expressions in algebra, for example:

$$2x^2 \times 3x^3 = 2 \times x \times x \times 3 \times x \times x \times x$$

$$= 6x^5$$

It is important not to confuse adding and multiplying.

- $a^2b + a^2b + a^2b = 3a^2b$

- $a^2b \times a^2b \times a^2b = a^6b^3$

Exercise 7.3

Simplify each expression, if possible.

1 $a \times a^2 \times a^3$

2 $3a \times 2a^2 \times a^3$

3 $3b + b^2 + 2b^3$

4 $2b^2 + b^2 + 3b^2$

5 $2ab \times a^2b \times 3ab^2$

6 $4x^2y + x^2y + 3x^2y$

7 $4xy + x^2y - xy$

8 $4xy + x^2y - xy^2$

9 $3ac \times a^2b \times 4bc$

10 $2bc + a^2b + 4ac$

Combining multiplication and division

You can **simplify** or **cancel** an **algebraic fraction** in the same way as you do a **numerical fraction**. Look for **common factors** in the numerator and denominator of an algebraic fraction, just as you do in ordinary fractions. Then cancel by dividing numerator and denominator by the same number or letter.

Example

Simplify: $3xy^2 \div 6xy$

$$3xy^2 \div 6xy = \frac{3xy^2}{6xy}$$

$$= \frac{\cancel{3}^1 \times \cancel{x} \times \cancel{y} \times y}{\cancel{6}_2 \times \cancel{x} \times \cancel{y}}$$

It is a good idea to write the expression out in full before cancelling. That helps you to avoid making mistakes.

$$= \frac{y}{2}$$

Exercise 7.4

Simplify each of these fractions.

Check that your answer is in the simplest form possible, each time.

1 $\dfrac{6ab}{2}$

2 $\dfrac{6ab}{3}$

3 $\dfrac{6ab}{12}$

4 $\dfrac{6ab}{a}$

5 $\dfrac{6ab}{b}$

6 $\dfrac{6ab}{12a}$

7 $\dfrac{6ab}{3b}$

8 $\dfrac{6ab}{ab}$

9 $\dfrac{6ab}{6ab}$

10 $\dfrac{6ab}{15ab}$

11 $3xy \div 6$

12 $12p^2 \div 6p$

13 $4n^2 \div 6n$

14 $3ab \div 6b$

15 $4mn \div 6n$

16 $20xy \div 4y$

17 $24ab \div 12b$

18 $3x^2 \div x$

19 $3x^2 \div x^2$

20 $8ab \div 2b^2$

◯ Index numbers and brackets

Sometimes it can be difficult to see exactly what the index number is referring to. Always look carefully to see if there are any brackets.

What is the difference between $2a^2$ and $(2a)^2$?

- $2a^2 = 2 \times a \times a$
- $(2a)^2 = (2a) \times (2a)$

$$= 2 \times a \times 2 \times a$$

$$= 4 \times a \times a \quad \text{or} \quad 4a^2$$

Sometimes, the index number is also indexed.

If you are confused, remember that the index number represents at least one multiplication.

Examples:

(i) $(3^2)^2 = (3^2) \times (3^2)$

$\qquad = 3 \times 3 \times 3 \times 3$

$\qquad = 3^4$

(ii) $(b^2)^3 = (b^2) \times (b^2) \times (b^2)$

$\qquad = b \times b \times b \times b \times b \times b$

$\qquad = b^6$

Exercise 7.5

Simplify each expression, if possible, and check that your answer is in its simplest form.

1 3^2

2 3×2^2

3 $(3 \times 2)^2$

4 $(3b)^2$

5 $3 \times a^2$

6 $(4x)^2$

7 $(x^2)^2$

8 $3 \times 2b^3$

9 $3(2b)^3$

10 $2(3b)^3$

Now that you can simplify an expression by adding, subtracting, multiplying and dividing, try this mixed exercise.

Exercise 7.6

Simplify each expression, if possible, and check that your answer is in its simplest form.

1 $2x + 5x$

2 $a \times a \times a$

3 $3ax - ax$

4 $\dfrac{6xy}{3}$

5 $(2b)^2$

6 $c^2x + 2c^2x - 3c^2x$

7 $a^2 \times 3a$

8 $3y \times 2y$

9 $\dfrac{ab}{a}$

10 $\dfrac{b^2}{b}$

11 $\dfrac{(2b)^2}{b}$

16 $3x + 2y - 5x - y$

12 $\dfrac{3a + 3a}{3a}$

17 $7 - 3x + 4 - 6x$

13 $\dfrac{3a \times 3a}{6a}$

18 $\dfrac{3b^2}{3b - b}$

14 $\dfrac{3a + ab - 2ab}{6b}$

19 $3a \times 2b \times 3bc$

15 $3 \times (3b)^2$

20 $\dfrac{3a \times 2b \times c}{2ab}$

Substituting variables in expressions

When you know the value of a variable, such as x, you can **substitute** for the variable to find the value of the expression.

Algebraic variables may have positive or negative values.

Therefore, before you look any further at substitution, here is a review of arithmetic with negative numbers.

Negative numbers

Do you remember these rules about negative numbers?

$3 - 5 = {}^-2$	$3 - ({}^-5) = 3 + 5$ $\qquad\qquad = 8$
${}^-3 - 5 = {}^-8$	${}^-3 - ({}^-5) = {}^-3 + 5$ $\qquad\qquad\quad = 2$
$3 + 5 = 8$	$3 + ({}^-5) = 3 - 5$ $\qquad\qquad = {}^-2$
${}^-3 + 5 = 2$	${}^-3 + ({}^-5) = {}^-3 - 5$ $\qquad\qquad\quad = {}^-8$

Exercise 7.7

Use the rules about negative numbers to answer these questions.

1 ⁻6 − 4

2 6 − 9

3 ⁻8 − (⁺6)

4 ⁻5 + (⁻3)

5 ⁻9 − (⁻4)

6 6 + (⁻2)

7 ⁻3 − (⁺5)

8 6 + (⁻6)

9 ⁻7 − (⁻3)

10 8 − 5

11 ⁻9 − 6

12 8 − 12

13 ⁻13 + (⁻5)

14 ⁻7 + (⁻14)

15 13 − (⁻9)

16 ⁻2 + (⁻7)

17 ⁻7 − (⁺8)

18 ⁻7 + 9

19 ⁻3 − 8

20 ⁻(⁻3) − (⁺8)

Multiplying and dividing with negative numbers

If $2 + 2 + 2 + 2$ is the same as $4 \times 2 = 8$

then $(^-2) + (^-2) + (^-2) + (^-2) = 4 \times (^-2) = {}^-8$

What about $(^-4) \times (^-2)$?

You know that adding ⁻4 gives the same answer as subtracting ⁺4

So $(^-4) \times (^-2) = {}^-(^+4) \times (^-2)$

$= {}^-(^-8)$

$= {}^+8$ or 8

From this you can see that multiplying any number by a negative number changes its sign.

$$4 \times {}^-2 = {}^-8 \qquad {}^-4 \times 2 = {}^-8 \qquad {}^-4 \times {}^-2 = {}^+8$$

As division is the inverse of multiplication then it follows that:

$${}^-8 \div (^-2) = 4 \qquad \text{and} \qquad {}^-8 \div 4 = {}^-2$$

This is a useful rule to remember:

negative $\times$ or $\div$ positive gives negative

negative $\times$ or $\div$ negative gives positive

Thus $4 \times (^-2) = {}^-8 \qquad (^-4) \times 2 = {}^-8 \qquad (^-4) \times (^-2) = 8$

$8 \div (^-2) = {}^-4 \qquad (^-8) \div 2 = {}^-4 \qquad (^-8) \div (^-2) = 4$

Note the use of brackets. It is not good practice to have two signs such as $\times$ and $-$ next to each other, so you can use brackets to make it clear that the raised negative ($^-$) is attached to the number and the $\times, +, -$ or $\div$ is the **operator**.

Using negative numbers with a calculator

On your calculator you should find a 'change sign' button like this $\boxed{\pm}$ or $\boxed{(-)}$.

- The $\boxed{\pm}$ button changes the sign of the number you have just entered, or the number on the screen.

- You can press the 'negative' button $\boxed{(-)}$ before a number is entered, to make it negative.

To check the calculations below, you need to follow one of these four key sequences, depending on the type of calculator you have.

	$\boxed{\pm}$	$\boxed{(-)}$
Sequence 1: $(^+4) \times (^+2)$	$\boxed{4}$ $\boxed{\times}$ $\boxed{2}$ $\boxed{=}$ 8	$\boxed{4}$ $\boxed{\times}$ $\boxed{2}$ $\boxed{=}$ 8
Sequence 2: $(^-4) \times 2$	$\boxed{4}$ $\boxed{\pm}$ $\boxed{\times}$ $\boxed{2}$ $\boxed{=}$ $^-8$	$\boxed{(-)}$ $\boxed{4}$ $\boxed{\times}$ $\boxed{2}$ $\boxed{=}$ $^-8$
Sequence 3: $4 \times (^-2)$	$\boxed{4}$ $\boxed{\times}$ $\boxed{2}$ $\boxed{\pm}$ $\boxed{=}$ $^-8$	$\boxed{4}$ $\boxed{\times}$ $\boxed{(-)}$ $\boxed{2}$ $\boxed{=}$ $^-8$
Sequence 4: $(^-4) \times (^-2)$	$\boxed{4}$ $\boxed{\pm}$ $\boxed{\times}$ $\boxed{2}$ $\boxed{\pm}$ $\boxed{=}$ 8	$\boxed{(-)}$ $\boxed{4}$ $\boxed{\times}$ $\boxed{(-)}$ $\boxed{2}$ $\boxed{=}$ 8

Now repeat the examples above, with $\div$ instead of $\times$, and check your answers.

Exercise 7.8

Complete each calculation and then use a calculator to check your answer.

1 4×3

2 $(^-24) \div 8$

3 $(^-4) \times (^-8)$

4 $(^+25) \div (^-5)$

5 $(^-3) \times (^-5)$

6 $(^-18) \div (^-6)$

7 3×8

8 $(^-72) \div 9$

9 $(^+4) \times (^-5)$

10 $(^-64) \div 8$

11 $(^-6) \times (^-9)$

12 $(^-24) \div (^+4)$

13 $6 \times (^-4)$

14 $(^+72) \div (^-6)$

15 $(^-15) \times 5$

16 $105 \div (^-5)$

17 $(^-17) \times 3$

18 $(^-108) \div (^-12)$

19 $(^+15) \times (^-8)$

20 $104 \div (^-8)$

Now you are ready for some mixed examples.

Exercise 7.9

Complete each calculation and then use a calculator to check your answer
Remember the BIDMAS rule.

1 $8 \times (^-2)$

2 $^-4 + 7$

3 $^-3 - 6$

4 $14 \div (^-2)$

5 $(^-3) - (^-4)$

6 $35 \div (^-5)$

7 $^-4 - (^-7)$

8 $^-3 + 9$

9 $(^-3) \times (^-6)$

10 $5 + (^-10)$

11 $16 - 8 - 4$

12 $(^-24) + 8 - (^-3)$

13 $36 \div (^-9) \times (^-2)$

14 $(^+5) - (^-5) + (^-10)$

15 $12 \times (^-3) \div 4$

16 $(^-12) \div (^-6) \times (^-3)$

17 $(^-2) + (^-6) - (^-3)$

18 $18 \div 2 \times (^-3)$

19 $(^-7) - 9 - (^-2)$

20 $5 + (^-7) - (^-3)$

Substitution

Given a statement such as:

the area of a rectangle of base b and height h is bh

or a **formula**, such as:

$A = bh$

you can **substitute** values of b and h into the expression bh to find the value of the area, A.

Just as in football, the letters come out and the substituted numbers take their place.

These are the simple steps for **substitution**.

1 Write down the expression.

2 **Substitute** the numbers for the letters.

3 **Calculate**.

4 Write down the **answer** with correct **units**.

Example

Given that $x = 3$, find the value of:

(i) $x + 2$

(ii) $x - 1$

(iii) $2x + 4$

(i) $x + 2 = 3 + 2$

$= 5$

(ii) $x - 1 = 3 - 1$

$= 2$

(iii) $2x + 4 = (2 \times 3) + 4$

$= 6 + 4$

$= 10$

Note the use of brackets in this example, this gives you time to think about BIDMAS.

If the variable has a negative value, take care to remember the rules you learnt earlier about negative numbers and always do any calculations in brackets first.

Example

Given that $a = 3$ and $b = {}^-5$, find the value of $a(b + a)$

$a(b + a) = 3({}^-5 + 3)$ Expression, substitute

$= 3 \times ({}^-2)$ Calculate

$= {}^-6$ Answer

Exercise 7.10

1 Find the value of each expression, given that $a = 4$

(a) $a - 2$

(b) $2a$

(c) $6 + a$

(d) $3a - 5$

2 Find the value of each expression, given that $b = {}^-3$

(a) $2b$

(b) b^2

(c) $2b^2$

(d) $(2b)^2$

3 Find the value of each expression, given that $x = 5$

(a) $2x - 2$

(b) x^2

(c) $x^2 + 1$

(d) $3x + 5$

4 Find the value of each expression, given that $y = 0$

(a) $2y$

(b) y^2

(c) $y + 4$

(d) $15 - 3y$

5 Find the value of each expression, given that $a = 1$ and $b = 2$

   (a) $a + b$ **(c)** $2a + 3b$

   (b) $b - a$ **(d)** ab

6 Find the value of each expression, given that $x = 2$ and $y = {}^-4$

   (a) $x - y$ **(c)** xy

   (b) $x + y$ **(d)** $\frac{y}{x}$

7 Find the value of each expression, given that $a = 3$ and $b = {}^-2$

   (a) $a + b$ **(c)** $2a + 3b$

   (b) $a^2 + b^2$ **(d)** ab

8 Find the value of each expression, given that $x = 5$ and $y = {}^-3$

   (a) $2x - y$ **(c)** $x^2 - y^2$

   (b) $\frac{3y}{x}$ **(d)** $3x + 5y$

9 Find the value of each expression, given that $x = 4$ and $y = {}^-4$

   (a) $x(y + x)$

   (b) $2x(3y - x)$

   (c) $(2x + y) - (x - y)$

10 Find the value of each expression, given that $a = {}^-3$, $b = 0$ and $c = 4$

   (a) $b(a + c)$

   (b) $2a(3a + c)$

   (c) $(2b + 3c) - (2a + c)$

11 Find the value of each expression, given that $x = 4.5$, $y = 0.2$ and $z = 3.1$

   (a) xy **(b)** $2xz$ **(c)** $x(2y + z)$

12 Find the value of each expression, given that $r = 30$, $s = 10$ and $t = {}^-5$

   (a) $\frac{rs}{2}$ **(b)** $\frac{r}{3} + \frac{t}{2}$ **(c)** $\frac{t(r + s)}{2}$

◯ Formulae

Now that you can substitute values into expressions, you are ready to think about **formulae**. A formula is a mathematical relationship between variables. A formula, like an equation, contains an equals sign. A formula usually has one variable on one side of the equals sign and an expression on the other.

In other words, a formula gives you a rule or expression for calculating the value of a quantity such as an area or perimeter, in terms of other variables, such as length.

Area: $A = bh$

Perimeter: $P = 2b + 2h$

Mean average: mean = $\dfrac{\text{total of all the values}}{\text{number of values}}$

Example

Find the perimeter of a rectangle of base 7 cm and height 5 cm.

$P = 2b + 2h$ Formula

$\quad = (2 \times 7) + (2 \times 5)$ Substitute

$\quad = 14 + 10$ Calculate

$\quad = 24$ cm   Answer with correct units

Exercise 7.11

Substitute the given values into each into formula.

1 Consider the formula $P = 2b + 2h$

  (a) Find the value of P when $b = 2$ and $h = 6$

  (b) Find the value of P when $b = 100$ and $h = 50$

  (c) Find the value of P when $b = 0.6$ and $h = 1.4$

  (d) Find the value of b when $P = 10$ and $h = 3$

  (e) Find the value of h when $P = 120$ and $b = 45$

2 Consider the formula $A = \dfrac{bh}{2}$

  (a) Find the value of A when $b = 4$ and $h = 5$

  (b) Find the value of A when $b = 100$ and $h = 80$

  (c) Find the value of A when $b = 0.4$ and $h = 1.5$

  (d) Find the value of b when $A = 10$ and $h = 4$

  (e) Find the value of h when $A = 150$ and $b = 30$

3 Consider the formula $A = \dfrac{h(a+b)}{2}$

  (a) Find the value of A when $a = 4$, $b = 5$ and $h = 8$

  (b) Find the value of A when $a = 20$, $b = 50$ and $h = 40$

  (c) Find the value of A when $a = 0.3$, $b = 0.55$ and $h = 1.8$

  (d) Find the value of a when $A = 20$, $h = 10$ and $b = 3$

  (e) Find the value of b when $A = 150$, $a = 30$ and $h = 5$

4 Consider the formula $X = v^2 - u^2$

(a) Find the value of X when $v = 10$ and $u = {}^-8$

(b) Find the value of X when $v = 0.4$ and $u = 0.4$

(c) Find the value of v when $X = 9$ and $u = 4$

(d) Find the value of u when $X = 25$ and $v = 13$

Writing formulae

You have seen that a formula can include more than one variable. This is useful if you need to write a formula to represent a story puzzle.

Example

I had £a and my uncle gave me £b for my birthday.

Find the value of P, the number of pounds I have now.

$$P = a + b$$

Exercise 7.12

1 My brother's age is x years and my age is y years. Write a formula for S, the sum of our ages.

2 My mother has a piece of string s metres long. She cuts off t metres and gives it to me. She is left with L metres of string. Write a formula for L.

3 There are m families in our road and each family has n children. Write a formula for C, the total number of children living in the road.

4 In my class of 24 pupils, g boys wear glasses all the time and s boys wear glasses some of the time. b boys do not need to wear glasses at all. Write a formula for b.

5 (a) What is the total cost, c pence, of y ice creams at x pence each?

(b) What is the total cost, C pounds, of y ice creams at x pence each?

6 My height increased by a centimetres last year and b centimetres this year. I am now 1.6 metres tall. Two years ago I was T m tall. Write a formula for T.

7 I buy m magazines costing p pence each. Write a formula for F, where F is the change that I get from £5

8 The total cost of a school trip is £150 for the coach hire plus £4.50 per pupil.

(a) Write a formula for C_1, the total cost, of taking p pupils.

(b) Write a formula for C_2, the cost per pupil (including the coach), of taking p pupils.

9 In a class of 24, p pupils have two pets, q pupils have one pet and the rest have no pets.

   (a) Write a formula for P, the total number of pets the pupils in the class have altogether.

   (b) What would the formula be if p pupils had no pets, q pupils had one pet and the rest had two pets?

10 A man was going to St Ives with his x wives. Each wife had y cats and each cat had z kittens, so that T in total were going to St Ives. Write a formula for T.

Exercise 7.13: Shape formulae

Sometimes you need to find unknown lengths in a shape. You can often do this by writing a formula.

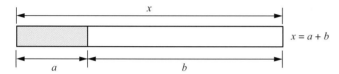

$x = a + b$

1 Write a formula for x for each of these diagrams.

   (a)

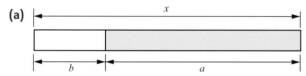

   (b)

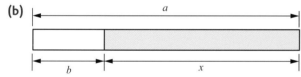

   (c)

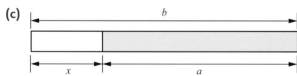

2 Write a formula for x for each of these diagrams.

   (a)

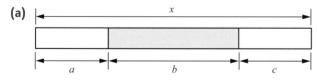

   (b)

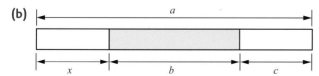

(c)

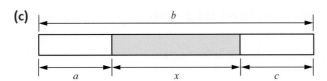

(d)

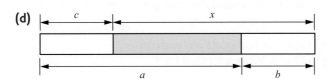

3 Write a formula for:

(a) A, the area

(b) P, the perimeter of this rectangle.

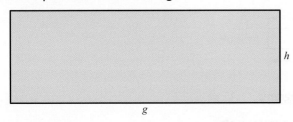

4 Write a formula for:

(a) A, the area

(b) P, the perimeter of this shape.

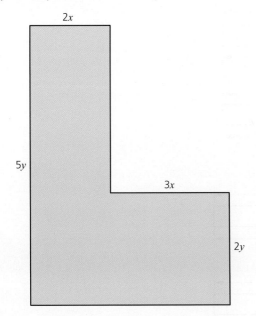

5 Write a formula for:

   (a) A, the area

   (b) P, the perimeter of this shape.

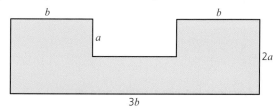

6 Write a formula for:

   (a) A, the area

   (b) P, the perimeter of this shape.

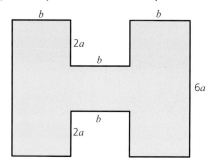

7 Write a formula for:

   (a) A, the area

   (b) P, the perimeter of this shape.

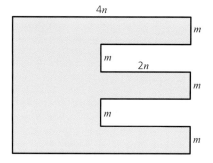

8 Draw a shape of your own that has an area of $20ab$
   Write a formula for its perimeter.

9 Draw a shape of your own that has a perimeter of $8a + 10b$
   Write a formula for its area.

Harder substitution

You must take great care when substituting into expressions with fractions.

Example

Find the value of $\frac{x+y}{z}$ given that $x = \frac{1}{2}$, $y = \frac{2}{3}$ and $z = \frac{5}{6}$

$\frac{x+y}{z} = \left(\frac{1}{2} + \frac{2}{3}\right) \div \frac{5}{6}$
Do not stack the fractions but use a $\div$ sign instead.

$= \left(\frac{3+4}{6}\right) \div \frac{5}{6}$
Add the two fractions that were in the top line, bring the division down.

$= \frac{7}{_1\cancel{6}} \times \frac{\cancel{6}^1}{5}$
Now multiply by the reciprocal of the divisor and cancel.

$= \frac{7}{5}$

$= 1\frac{2}{5}$
Finally express the answer in its lowest terms, as a mixed number if necessary.

Extension Exercise 7.14

1 Find the value of each expression, given that $x = \frac{1}{2}$, $y = \frac{1}{3}$ and $z = \frac{1}{5}$

(a) $x + y + z$

(d) $\frac{x^2 + y^2}{z^2}$

(b) $2z + (x + y)$

(e) $z(2x + y)$

(c) $x^2 + y - z^2$

(f) $\frac{xz}{2y}$

2 Find the value of each expression, given that $a = \frac{3}{5}$, $b = \frac{2}{3}$ and $c = \frac{1}{4}$

(a) $a^2 + bc$

(d) $\frac{bc}{a+b}$

(b) $a - \frac{c}{b}$

(e) $\frac{a+b}{b+c}$

(c) $\frac{2bc}{a^2}$

(f) $2ab - bc$

Now try substituting with decimals. Remember, it is important to show every stage of your working.

3 Find the value of each expression, given that $s = 2.5$, $t = 0.4$, $u = 0.7$ and $v = 0.9$

(a) $\frac{v-u}{t}$

(d) $\frac{u+v}{2s}$

(b) $u^2 + st^2$

(e) $\frac{st}{v-u}$

(c) $\frac{v^2-u^2}{2s}$

(f) $\frac{s(v-u)}{u+t}$

Summary Exercise 7.15

1 Simplify each expression.

(a) $m + m + m + m - m$

(b) $4a + 3b - 2a - 4b$

2 Simplify each expression.

(a) $b^2 + 2b^2 - b^2$

(b) $b^2 \times 2b^3 \times b$

3 Simplify each expression.

(a) $\frac{3ab}{a}$

(c) $\frac{p^2}{p}$

(b) $\frac{2xy}{12x}$

(d) $\frac{8n^3}{n}$

4 Simplify each expression.

(a) $(3a)^2$

(b) $3 \times (2a^2)$

5 Calculate the answers.

(a) $9 - 4$

(d) $(^-2) \times (^-4)$

(g) $(^-4) \div (^-4)$

(b) $^-8 - 3$

(e) $36 \div (^-4)$

(h) $6 \times (^-4)$

(c) $^-4 + (^-3)$

(f) $(^-8) \times (^+3)$

(i) $(^-2) - (^-4)$

6 (a) Find the value of each expression, given that $x = 5$

(i) $2x$

(iii) $2x^2$

(ii) x^2

(iv) $(2x)^2$

(b) Find the value of each expression, given that $x = ^-3$

(i) $2x$

(iii) $2x^2$

(ii) x^2

(iv) $(2x)^2$

7 Find the value of each expression, given that $a = 2$ and $b = ^-6$

(a) $a + b$

(c) $2ab$

(b) $a - b$

(d) $\frac{a-b}{4a}$

8 Consider the formula $P = 2a(a - b)$

    (a) Find the value of P when $a = 10$ and $b = 5$

    (b) Find the value of P when $a = 0.6$ and $b = {}^-0.4$

    (c) Find the value of b when $P = 2.8$ and $a = 1.4$

9 Write a formula for N, the total number of legs on h hens and c cows.

10 All three sides of an equilateral triangle have length a cm.

    (a) Write a formula for P, the perimeter of the triangle, in centimetres.

    (b) Write a formula for Q, the perimeter of the triangle, in metres.

11 Write a formula for P, the perimeter of this shape.

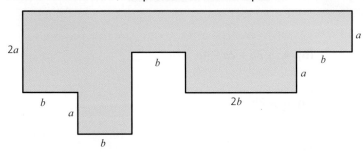

Activity: A number trick

Here is a trick you can perform on your friends. It will appear to show them that you are a mathematical genius.

Before you can do the actual trick, you must learn a clever bit of wizardry – how to multiply a number by 11 quickly.

Look at these products.

    $24 \times 11 = 264$

    $35 \times 11 = 385$

    $46 \times 11 = 506$

The first and last digits in the answer are the same as the tens and units digits in the number being multiplied by 11

The middle digit is the sum of the T and U digits in the number being multiplied by 11

Add 1 to the T digit if the sum is 10 or more.

$123 \times 11 = 1353$ $2 + 3 = 5$ and $1 + 2 = 3$

$325 \times 11 = 3575$ $2 + 5 = 7$ and $3 + 2 = 5$

$678 \times 11 = 7458$ $7 + 8 = 15$, $6 + 7 + 1 = 14$, carry the 1 and add it
                             to the 6

To multiply a three-digit number by 11, add the T and U digits to get the third digit and the H and T digits to get the second. Take care, though, when the digits add up to more than 9

Try some yourself and then you are ready for the trick.

Stage 1: Ask your friend to choose any two numbers that he or she likes, but suggest that they should not be too big because he or she will have to do some calculations with them.

(For example 16 and 23)

Stage 2: Ask your friend to write them down, one above the other, and then add them up.

1 16

2 23

3 $16 + 23 = 39$

Stage 3: Now ask your friend to add the 2nd number he or she chose to the answer in stage 2

4 $39 + 23 = 62$

Stage 4: Now he or she has to add that answer to the previous answer. Keep adding the answer just calculated to the number before it and put the new sum underneath. He should stop when he has 10 numbers written down (this should include the two numbers first chosen).

5 $62 + 39 = 101$

6 $101 + 62 = 163$

Stage 5: Ask him or her to tell you the seventh number in the column of 10 (in this case $101 + 163 = 264$) but do not look at any of the others. Tell your friend to add up all the ten numbers. Before he can work it out you can tell him that the answer is 2904. How do you do it?

The sum of all ten numbers is just eleven times the seventh number from the bottom. Go on, try it a few times and convince yourself.

Why does it work?

You can use algebra to find out how it works.

Start with A and B as the two numbers that your friend chooses.

What does your friend write next? Just $A + B$ in algebraic form.

Keep going through each stage, then add up your ten algebraic terms and you should see how it works!

8 More about numbers

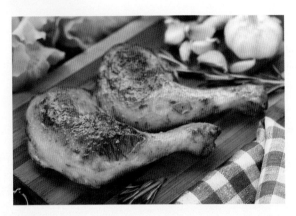

A pack of 8 chicken legs costs £5.35. What is the price of one chicken leg?

Cost of 1 chicken leg = £5.35 ÷ 8

= £0.668 75

You cannot record or use money to an accuracy of £0.668 75 so you must **round** the price to the nearest penny, or to two decimal places. This is £0.67

In this chapter you will look at other ways of rounding numbers.

Significant figures

Suppose Noah buys a plank of wood 2 m long and cuts it into seven equal lengths. How long is each piece?

Length of one piece = 2 m ÷ 7

= 0.285 714 285 m

= 28.571 43 cm

Noah only needs to give the length to an accuracy of three figures, either 0.286 m or 28.6 cm or 286 mm, because he cannot measure to any greater accuracy than that.

Notice that whatever the units: mm, cm or m, you have the same three digits. The lengths are all rounded to three significant figures.

What exactly is a significant figure? A significant figure is a digit that is part of a number and that tells you how many units, tens, hundreds, ... there are in the number.

Zeros are special. In a number such as 0.0024, where zeros come before the first non-zero digit, they are not significant. They hold the places of units, tenths and hundredths, and tell you the values of the other digits. For numbers such as 2056 or 0.205 the 0s that come after the first non-zero digit are significant.

Look at 203 455

2 is the first significant figure – it shows that the number has 2 hundred thousands

0 is the second significant figure – it shows that the number has no ten thousands

3 is the third significant figure – it shows that the number has 3 thousands.

Now look at 0.000 452

4 is the first significant figure: it shows that the number has 0.0004 or 4 ten thousandths.

5 is the second significant figure and 2 is the third.

None of the zeros before the 4 is significant as they are only there to keep the 4 in the correct place.

Exercise 8.1

1 Write down the value of the first significant figure in each of these numbers.

(a) 542

(c) 34.052

(b) 0.034

(d) 0.003 45

2 Write down the value of the second significant figure in each of these numbers.

(a) 3456

(c) 34.052

(b) 0.032 478

(d) 0.009 78

3 Write down the value of the third significant figure in each of these numbers.

(a) 2354

(c) 590 034

(b) 3.0045

(d) 0.098 876

4 Write down the value of the fourth significant figure in each of these numbers.

(a) 23 876

(c) 340 405

(b) 0.065 725

(d) 0.000 567 87

Rounding

The rules for rounding to a given number of significant figures are similar to those for rounding to the nearest ten or to the nearest two decimal places.

Look at the number 235 674 in the next example. Imagine a line drawn after the required significant figure. If the number to the right of this imaginary line is 5 or more, round the number to the left of the imaginary line up; if it is 4 or less, it stays the same.

Example

(i)   Round 235 674 to 3 significant figures.

235|674 = 236 000 (to 3 s.f.)   The third significant figure is 5, the fourth significant figure is 6 so round up.

(ii) Round 0.004 523 16 to 3 significant figures.

0.004 52|3 16 = 0.004 52 (to 3 s.f.)   The third significant figure is 2, the fourth significant figure is 3, so the third significant figure is unchanged.

> When you round, you must describe how you have rounded, for example, 'to 3 s.f.' after your rounded numbers because 235 674 ≠ 236 000

Exercise 8.2

1   Round each of these numbers to one significant figure.

(a) 245   (b) 304 567   (c) 0.0465   (d) 0.309

2   Round each of these numbers to two significant figures.

(a) 3065   (b) 946   (c) 0.0755   (d) 0.309

3   Round each of these numbers to three significant figures.

(a) 25 099   (b) 3494   (c) 0.005 893   (d) 0.460 27

4   Round each of these numbers to four significant figures.

(a) 34 599   (b) 120 519   (c) 0.035 465   (d) 0.339 452

5   Round each of these numbers to 3 significant figures.

(a) 1.999 99   (b) 24.999   (c) 0.999 99   (d) 99.999

6   Round each of these numbers to 3 significant figures.

(a) 0.050 906   (b) 305.099   (c) 0.100 490 5   (d) 55.0709

Significant figures versus decimal places

It is important that you know the difference between significant figures and decimal places. Make sure you understand this difference before you move on.

24.5 is written correct to **1 decimal place** and to **3 significant figures**.

0.005 is written correct to **3 decimal places** but to **1 significant figure**.

Exercise 8.3

1 Look at these numbers.

   (i) 516   **(ii)** 3.9   **(iii)** 34.785   **(iv)** 6.16

   (a) Write down the number of decimal places to which each is written.

   (b) Write down the number of significant figures to which each is written.

2 Look at these numbers.

   (i) 0.567   **(ii)** 0.38   **(iii)** 0.001789   **(iv)** 0.000156

   (a) Write down the number of decimal places to which each is written.

   (b) Write down the number of significant figures to which each is written.

3 Look at these numbers.

   (i) 51006   **(ii)** 3.0906   **(iii)** 34.005   **(iv)** 6.10064

   (a) Write down the number of decimal places to which each is written.

   (b) Write down the number of significant figures to which each is written.

4 Look at these numbers.

   (i) 51000   **(ii)** 0.0720   **(iii)** 34.000   **(iv)** 7.000040

   (a) Write down the number of decimal places to which each is written.

   (b) Write down the number of significant figures to which each is written.

5 The previous question included numbers with zeros as their last digits.

   (a) Give an example of a number that could be rounded to 2.40 to 3 significant figures.

   (b) Give an example of a number that could be rounded to 2.070 to 3 decimal places.

Large and small numbers

Most problems you need to solve have quite ordinary numbers but as humans explore the world of science, geography and astronomy they often come across very large numbers and very small numbers.

Consider these facts about the Earth.

The Earth is the fifth largest of the planets and is on average about 149 700 000 km from the Sun.

The total mass of the Earth is about 6 694 000 000 000 000 000 000 tonnes (6694 million million million tonnes).

The population of China was approximately 1 400 000 000 in 2014

The relative density of hydrogen is about 0.000 089 9

The distance between atoms in copper is about 0.000 000 000 34 m.

Look at your calculator. You should notice that the display can only show 8 or 10 digits. This makes it very difficult to do any calculations with very large and very small numbers such as those listed above. You need to be able to write them in a shorter form, so that you can use your calculator.

Writing these numbers in a shorter form makes it easier not only to calculate with them but also to compare their relative sizes. It is also quicker to write them in the shorter form.

Decimals as powers of ten

You know that you can write the column headings of large numbers, thousands, ten thousands, hundred thousands and so on, as powers of ten.

Hundred thousand	$= 100\,000$	$= 10 \times 10 \times 10 \times 10 \times 10$	$= 10^5$
Ten thousand	$= 10\,000$	$= 10 \times 10 \times 10 \times 10$	$= 10^4$
One thousand	$= 1000$	$= 10 \times 10 \times 10$	$= 10^3$
One hundred	$= 100$	$= 10 \times 10$	$= 10^2$
Ten	$= 10$		

> Ten could be written as 10^1 but you do not generally write the index number 1

But what happens as the numbers get smaller?

Looking at the sequence of the index numbers, 4, 3, 2, 1, the next must be 0

This gives you the definition of a number to the power 0

$n^0 = 1$ when n stands for 'any number'.

1 unit $= 1 = 10^0$

Moving to the right, after units come tenths.

1 tenth $= \dfrac{1}{10}$ or 0.1

How can you write $\dfrac{1}{10}$ as a power of ten?

Remember the sequence of index numbers:

4, 3, 2, 1, 0, …

So it follows that the next power must be $^-1$, then $^-2$ and so on.

This leads to the definition of a negative index number:

$$n^{-1} = \frac{1}{n} \qquad n^{-2} = \frac{1}{n^2} \qquad n^{-3} = \frac{1}{n^3} \qquad \dots$$

Then you can continue the column headings as:

One tenth $\quad = 0.1 \quad = \dfrac{1}{10} \qquad\qquad\qquad = 10^{-1}$

One hundredth $\quad = 0.01 \quad = \dfrac{1}{100} \quad = \dfrac{1}{10^2} \quad = 10^{-2}$

One thousandth $= 0.001 \quad = \dfrac{1}{1000} \quad = \dfrac{1}{10^3} \quad = 10^{-3} \dots$

As a quick check, notice that the number of 0s in 1000 is 3 and that reminds you that the index number is 3

Similarly, the number of 0s in 0.001 and in $\dfrac{1}{1000}$ is 3 and that reminds you that the index number is $^-3$

Example

Write these numbers as powers of 10

(i) 10 000   (ii) 0.000 001

(i) $10\,000 = 10^4$ Four 0s and no decimals so the index is 4

(ii) $0.000\,001 = 10^{-6}$ Six zeros and a decimal so the index is $^-6$

Write each of these numbers as a power of ten.

1	100 000	**5**	100 000 000	**9**	1 000 000 000
2	100	**6**	0. 000 000 001	**10**	0.000 01
3	0.01	**7**	10 000	**11**	0.1
4	0.0001	**8**	0.001	**12**	1

Writing large and small numbers

Now you can use these powers of 10 written with index numbers to write large and small numbers as a single figure multiplied by a power of 10

Example

Write each of these numbers as a single figure multiplied by a power of 10

(i) 4000   (ii) 0.007

(i) $4000 = 4 \times 1000$

$\quad\quad = 4 \times 10^3$

(ii) $0.007 = 7 \times 0.001$

$\quad\quad\quad = 7 \times 10^{-3}$

Exercise 8.5

Write each of these numbers as a single figure multiplied by a power of 10

1	200 000	**7**	0.000 009
2	0.000 002	**8**	0.000 02
3	0.3	**9**	200
4	0.005	**10**	0.000 000 000 000 8
5	0.000 000 006	**11**	5000
6	400 000 000	**12**	30 000

Remember to put the spaces in the correct position after or before each group of three digits, when there are five or more digits on either side of the decimal point.

Writing numbers in full

You can also write the abbreviated numbers out in full.

> **Example**
>
> Write these numbers out in full.
>
> (i) 3×10^4
>
> (ii) 7×10^{-5}
>
> (i) $3 \times 10^4 = 3 \times 10\,000$ 10^4 is 1 followed by four 0s.
>
> $= 30\,000$
>
> (ii) $7 \times 10^{-5} = 7 \times 0.000\,01$ 10^{-5} is five 0s and a decimal point.
>
> $= 0.000\,07$

> Remember to include the 0 when writing decimals smaller than 1
>
> For example, 0.35, not just .35 because it is easy to miss the decimal point.

Exercise 8.6

Write these numbers out in full.

1 7×10^2 5 9×10^5 9 8×10^{-5}

2 8×10^6 6 3×10 10 4×10^{-3}

3 9×10^{-1} 7 2×10^{-3} 11 6×10^6

4 5×10^2 8 7×10^7 12 2×10^{-2}

◯ Standard index form

The way of writing numbers as a number multiplied by a power of ten is called **standard index form**.

You can use the methods you have been using to write any number as the product of another number, A, and a power of ten. When A is at least 1 but less than 10, the number is in **standard index form**.

You can use algebra to write this definition as:

$A \times 10^n$ where $1 \leqslant A < 10$ and n is an integer (positive or negative).

Standard index form and the scientific calculator

Try this calculation on a scientific calculator.

4 5 0 0 0 0 × 2 5 0 0 0 0

The display showing the answer may look something like this:

1.125^{11} or 1.125×10^{11}

This is the calculator's own way of showing 1.125×10^{11} or $112\,500\,000\,000$

Now do the calculation $0.000\,004 \div 500\,000$

The answer on the display might look similar to this:

8.00^{-12} or 8×10^{-12}

This is the calculator's way of showing 8×10^{-12} or $0.000\,000\,000\,008$

Example

Write these numbers out in full.

(i) 3.4×10^3 (ii) 4.5×10^{-4}

(i) $3.4 \times 10^3 = 3.4 \times 1000$ 3 is multiplied by 1000, so the answer
              $= 3400$ will be three thousand and something, not
                                        thirty-four thousand.

(ii) $4.5 \times 10^{-4} = 4.5 \times 0.0001$

                  $= 0.000\,45$ There are four 0s (including the one before the
                                     decimal point) and then the digits 4 and 5

> When you write your answers, you must write down the calculation correctly.
>
> You must not use the same notation as the calculator, as 8^{-12} is actually $\frac{1}{8^{12}}$ and must not be confused with 8×10^{-12}

Exercise 8.7

Write these numbers out in full.

1   4.5×10^2 6 3.71×10^{-2}

2   2.3×10^3 7 4.1×10^{-3}

3   1.82×10^4 8 6.72×10^{-4}

4   7.34×10^5 9 5.45×10^3

5   9.02×10^{-1} 10 3.65×10^{-2}

Writing numbers in standard index form

Example

Write these numbers in standard index form.

(i) $230\,000$ (ii) $0.000\,305$

(i) $230\,000 \quad = 2.3 \times 100\,000$ Separate the number from the power of ten.

                  $= 2.3 \times 10^5$

(ii) $0.000\,305 = 3.05 \times 0.0001$ The number must be 1 or greater but less than 10

                     $= 3.05 \times 10^{-4}$

Exercise 8.8

Write each of these numbers in standard index form.

1 420

2 12 000

3 234 000 000

4 102 000

5 3000

6 55

7 600 000 000 000

8 19 909

9 340 000

10 5 060 000

11 0.003

12 0.004 51

13 0.000 056

14 0.000 000 705

15 0.12

16 0.009 712

17 0.105 67

18 305

19 67 900 000

20 0.000 045 56

Using standard index form

Now you can use standard index form to write answers to problems.

> **Example**
>
> Write 400 litres in millilitres.
>
> 400 litres = 400 × 1000 millilitres
>
> $\qquad\quad$ = 400 000 ml
>
> $\qquad\quad$ = 4×10^5 ml

Exercise 8.9

Give your answers in standard index form.

1 Write 4 km in millimetres.

2 Write 6 kg in grams.

3 How many seconds are there in a day?

4 Write 5 mm in kilometres.

5 What is 5 g in tonnes?

6 Write 4.24 mm in kilometres.

7 **Mega** is the prefix for one million. A megabuck is one million dollars. Write 150 megabucks as dollars, in standard index form.

8 **Micro** is the prefix for one millionth. One microsecond is one millionth of a second. Write 90 microseconds in seconds, in standard index form.

9 Dinosaurs roamed the Earth 150 million years ago. Write this number of years in standard index form.

10 **Pico** is the prefix for a million-millionth. Write 15 picoseconds as seconds in standard index form.

11 The Big Bang is supposed to have taken place 10^{10} years ago. How many years is that?

12 The total mass of the Earth is 6 694 000 000 000 000 000 000 tonnes (6694 million million million tonnes). Write this mass in standard index form.

13 The relative density of hydrogen is 0.000 089 9

Write this in standard index form.

14 In solid copper, the distance between copper atoms is about 3.4×10^{-10} m. Write this distance out in full.

◯ Powers and roots on the calculator

You know that any number can be squared:

$$5^2 = 25$$

and a square number has a square root:

$$\sqrt{36} = 6$$

Similarly, a number can be cubed:

$$4^3 = 64$$

and a cube number has a cube root:

$$\sqrt[3]{125} = 5$$

In fact any number can be raised to any power, just as you have seen for 10 in this chapter.

$$6^7 = 279 936$$

Numbers can also have larger roots:

$$\sqrt[6]{4096} = 4$$

As the numbers you are using are getting larger, it is sensible to use a calculator.

Powers

Find the button that looks like this: $x^\blacksquare$. This is the power or index button.

Now enter 6 $x^\blacksquare$ 7 =

Your calculator display should show something like 6^(7), which is how the calculator shows a power or it might show 6^7

When you press the = button you should get the answer 279 936

If you don't, look at the manual that came with your calculator.

Roots

Now find the button that looks like this √■. This is the square-root button.

Try entering √■ 1 4 4 =

You should get the answer 12

Now find the button that looks like this ■√□

This is the button for any root. You will probably need to use the Shift key.

Try entering 6 ■√□ 4 0 9 6 =

You should get the answer 4

If you don't, look at the manual that came with your calculator.

You have only been looking at positive numbers and positive roots, but the square of $^-5$ is 25

Therefore the square root of 25 ($\sqrt{25}$) can be $^+5$ or $^-5$. There is more about this in Chapter 12

Exercise 8.10

Use your calculator to find the value of each number.

1 5^5

2 3^6

3 $\sqrt[4]{625}$

4 $\sqrt[5]{16\ 807}$

5 6^5

6 3^{10}

7 4^8

8 $\sqrt[6]{117\ 649}$

9 $\sqrt[4]{6561}$

10 $\sqrt[8]{65\ 536}$

Working with decimals

All the powers and roots you have considered so far have been for whole numbers (**integers**). Decimal numbers also have powers and roots.

You know that $1.2 \times 1.2 = 1.44$

So you could write this as $1.2^2 = 1.44$

Then the inverse is $\sqrt{1.44} = 1.2$

Now look at $\sqrt{5.25}$

You can estimate that since 5 is between 4 and 9, $\sqrt{5.25}$ will be a little larger than 2

Now use your calculator to find the value of $\sqrt{5.25}$

You should fid that $\sqrt{5.25} = 2.291\,287\,847...$

The square root of 5.25 cannot be written down exactly, as a decimal. It has an infinite number of decimal places. As you cannot write them all down, you can only give the answer correct to a number of decimal places or significant figures.

> The three dots show that the number is not exact, there are more decimal places than are written here, or that your calculator can show.

Example

Calculate $\sqrt{5.25}$, giving your answer correct to three significant figures.

Estimate: $\sqrt{5.25} > 2$

From the calculator:

$\sqrt{5.25} = 2.291\,287\,847...$

$\phantom{\sqrt{5.25}} = 2.29$ (to 3 s.f.)

> Remember to write 'to 3 s.f.' after your answer.

Exercise 8.11

Estimate the answers first, then use your calculator.

1 Find the answers. Give any non-exact answers correct to 1 decimal place.

(a) $\sqrt{1.5}$ (b) $\sqrt{6.25}$ (c) $\sqrt{4.9}$ (d) $\sqrt{182.25}$

2 Find the answers. Give any non-exact answers correct to 3 significant figures.

(a) $\sqrt{11}$ (b) $\sqrt{12100}$ (c) $\sqrt{123}$ (d) $\sqrt{146.41}$

3 Find the answers. Give any non-exact answers correct to 2 decimal places.

(a) $\sqrt{38.44}$ (b) $\sqrt{46.55}$ (c) $\sqrt{132.12}$ (d) $\sqrt{106.09}$

4 Find the answers. Give any non-exact answers correct to 1 decimal place.

(a) $\sqrt[3]{625}$ (b) $\sqrt[3]{512}$ (c) $\sqrt[3]{100}$ (d) $\sqrt[3]{1728}$

5 Find the answers. Give any non-exact answers correct to 3 significant figures.

(a) $\sqrt[3]{2744}$ (b) $\sqrt[3]{12500}$ (c) $\sqrt[3]{8000}$ (d) $\sqrt[3]{10000}$

6 Find the answers. Give any non-exact answers correct to 3 significant figures.

(a) $\sqrt[4]{50\,625}$ (d) $\sqrt[7]{279\,936}$ (g) $\sqrt[5]{79.62624}$

(b) $\sqrt[3]{62\,500}$ (e) $\sqrt{1000}$ (h) $\sqrt[3]{46.656}$

(c) $\sqrt[5]{13\,534}$ (f) $\sqrt[3]{27\,000}$ (i) $\sqrt[6]{59.343}$

Extension Exercise 8.12

You need to make some decisions before you calculate the answers to these questions. It is quite acceptable for your answers to be estimates because the exact answer could depend on so many variables.

Do write down any assumptions you have made.

Note the use of $\approx$ meaning 'approximately equal to'.

You may wish to put answers in standard index form.

Example

How many apples have you eaten in your lifetime?

Assume you are 12 years and 3 months old and you have eaten about 3 apples a week since you were 2 years old.

Number of apples you have eaten in your lifetime $\approx 10.25 \times 52 \times 3$

$$\approx 10 \times 50 \times 3$$
$$\approx 1500$$
$$\approx 1.5 \times 10^3 \text{ apples}$$

1 Estimate the number of times you have blinked in your lifetime.

2 How many hours of television have you watched in your lifetime?

3 How many kilograms of chips have you eaten in your lifetime?

4 How long have you spent doing homework in your lifetime?

5 How many books have you read in total?

6 If you were to answer every single question in this book, how long would it take you?

7 How many tennis balls could you fit into your classroom?

8 How many footballs could you fit into your school hall?

9 How many litres of water have you drunk in your lifetime?

10 If you had saved all the money you have ever been given, how much would you now have in total?

11 If you were to make a pile of all the books you have ever read, how high would it be?

12 If you were to put all the teachers you have ever had on the weighing scales, what would their total mass be?

1   Write 304.983 correct to:

   (a) 1 significant figure

   (b) 3 significant figures

   (c) 2 significant figures

   (d) 4 significant figures.

2   Write 0.004 098 23 correct to:

   (a) 1 significant figure

   (b) 3 significant figures

   (c) 2 significant figures

   (d) 4 significant figures.

3   **(a)** Write ten million as a power of ten.

   (b) Write one-millionth as a power of ten.

   (c) How would you describe the number 10^9?

4   Write these numbers out in full.

   (a) 1.7×10^3

   (b) 6.025×10^6

   (c) 6.3×10^{-6}

   (d) 9.51×10^{-5}

   (e) 8.1×10^5

   (f) 5.804×10^{-3}

5   Write these numbers in standard index form.

   (a) 56 000 000

   (b) 0.004

   (c) 0.000 24

   (d) 31 205 000

   (e) 4 050 000 000

   (f) 0.000 501 23

6   What is 3.5×10^{-6} km in millimetres?

7   The first prize for a 'best pet' competition is the mass of your pet in £1 coins. My pet elephant won the competition and he weighs 5 tonnes.

   (a) How many grams is that? Give your answer in standard index form.

   (b) A £1 coin weighs about 10 g. How much money did my elephant and I win in the competition?

8   Find the answers. Give any non-exact answers correct to 2 decimal places.

   (a) $\sqrt{25.25}$ **(b)** $\sqrt{13.69}$ **(c)** $\sqrt{132}$

9   Find the answers. Give any non-exact answers correct to 3 significant figures.

   (a) $\sqrt[3]{5.75}$

   (b) $\sqrt[4]{8.95}$

   (c) $\sqrt[3]{42.875}$

   (d) $\sqrt[5]{2.48832}$

10 Estimate the number of hours that you have spent watching television in the last year. State clearly any assumptions that you have made.

Activity: Calculator games

Space invaders

You can play this with either a scientific or a non-scientific calculator.

In these two games the numbers on the calculator display are the invaders and you have to defeat them by 'firing' numbers at them. Each game has slightly different rules about which numbers you can 'fire'.

Game 1

This is basic but helps to get the idea for Game 2

Enter this number on your calculator.

1 2 3 4 . 5 6 7 8

You can only 'fire' numbers by subtracting them. The numbers that you fire can contain only one digit that is not zero, they can contain as many 0s as you like and a decimal point if you wish.

Make a table.

Fire	Display
	1 2 3 4 . 5 6 7 8

Decide what you are going to fire first, say 0.06

Enter  and press

Your display will become 1234.5078

Write these figures in your table.

Fire	Display
− 0.06	1 2 3 4 . 5 6 7 8
	1 2 3 4 . 5 0 7 8

Keep going until you have eliminated all the aliens and your calculator reads 0

Game 2

The rule this time is that you can only 'fire' single digit integers – a number in the units column. You still 'fire' by subtracting.

To move a number into the units column, you must multiply or divide all the numbers on the display; you can × 10, × 100 or × 1000, or ÷ 10, ÷ 100 or ÷ 1000

Look at the start of the game.

Fire	Display
	1 2 3 4 . 5 6 7 8
– 4	1 2 3 0 . 5 6 7 8
÷ 10	1 2 3 . 0 5 6 7 8
– 3	1 2 0 . 0 5 6 7 8
?	

Now, you continue. Remember you cannot multiply or divide by a power of ten greater than a thousand, and you must make one move only between fires. Put in some different starting displays of *aliens* and try those too.

Game 3

This is a two-player version of Game 2

Player 1 fires the first shot, then passes the calculator to player 2

Player 2 moves, then fires a shot, then passes the calculator to player 1

Player 1 moves, then fires, and so on.

The aim of the game is to get the other player into a position where he or she cannot fire, for example, 0.000 567 8 and is stuck, as × 10 000 is not allowed.

Game 4

Game 4 is a whole class version of games 2 and 3

Everyone starts with the same display.

Each player fires, then passes.

Next each player moves without firing, then passes.

Next each player moves, then fires, then passes, and so on.

If you cannot fire on your go, then you are out. Continue until only one person is left.

Perimeter and area

◯ The tangram

The tangram is an ancient Chinese puzzle. The square is divided into seven pieces and the pieces can be reassembled into other shapes.

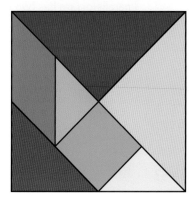

You are going to use the tangram to revise some basic geometry before moving on to the calculation of **perimeters** and areas of triangles, quadrilaterals and circles.

Exercise 9.1

Make four copies of the tangram.

1 Cut out the pieces from one copy of the tangram. Rearrange the pieces to make this shape.

   Stick your solution into your exercise book.

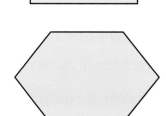

2 Cut out the pieces from the second copy of the tangram. Rearrange the pieces to make this shape.

   Stick your solution into your exercise book.

3 Cut out the pieces from the third copy of the tangram. Rearrange the pieces to make up some designs of your own. Be as creative as you can.

4 The original tangram set is arranged in a square, and one of the pieces is a square itself. Show how you can make a square, using:

   (a) two tangram pieces   **(d)** five tangram pieces

   (b) three tangram pieces   **(e)** six tangram pieces.

   (c) four tangram pieces

5 Show how you can use all seven tangram pieces to make:

   (a) a trapezium

   (b) a rectangle that is not a square

   (c) a parallelogram that is not a square

   (d) a triangle.

> Remember that a parallelogram has two pairs of opposite sides that are parallel.

Tangrams and quadrilaterals

The original set of tangram pieces was arranged as a square of side 5 cm.

The area of this **square** is therefore $5 \times 5 = 25 \, \text{cm}^2$.

What is the area of each of the shapes in questions 1–3 and question 5?

They are all $25 \, \text{cm}^2$ as well.

Although you rearranged the pieces, the total area of all the pieces did not change.

You will use this fact to discover some more area formulae.

First, here are some formulae that that you already know.

Square — b

Rectangle — h, b

Area of square $= b^2$ Area of rectangle $=$ base $\times$ height $= b \times h$

Perimeter of square $= 4b$ Perimeter of rectangle $= 2b + 2h$

The sides of a **rectangle** can be referred to as its length and width.

In this case, the formula would be:

      area of rectangle $=$ length $\times$ width   or $l \times w$

Now suppose you cut a triangle from one end of the rectangle and add it to the other end.

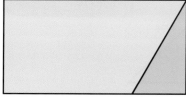

Area = base x height

Area = base x height

The shape changes from a rectangle to a **parallelogram**. Even though you have changed the shape, the area has stayed the same.

Therefore, you should see that:

area of parallelogram $= b \times h$

A rhombus is a parallelogram with four equal sides.

Using the same ideas as above:

area of rhombus $= b \times h$

perimeter of rhombus $= 4b$

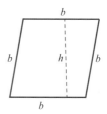

When you cut a rectangle or a parallelogram in half you get two identical triangles.

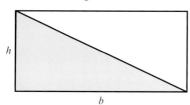

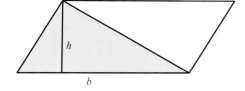

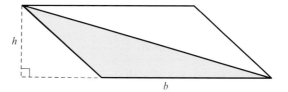

So: area of a triangle $= \frac{1}{2} b \times h$

where the base and height are equal to the base and height of the enclosing rectangle or parallelogram.

For all of these shapes remember that the height must be **perpendicular** to the base.

Perpendicular means 'at right angles to'.

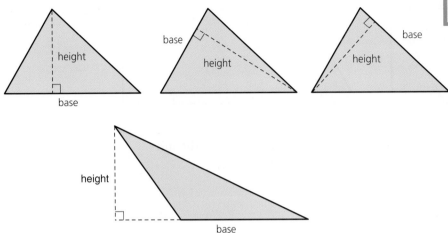

Exercise 9.2

Think again about the formula for the area of a triangle.

Work these out, given that $b = 4$ and $h = 5$

1 $\frac{1}{2}bh$

2 $\frac{b \times h}{2}$

3 $b \times h \div 2$

4 $\frac{b}{2} \times h$

5 $b \times \frac{h}{2}$

6 $\frac{1}{2}(b \times h)$

◯ Areas and perimeters of 2D shapes

You should have found that you get the same answer for the area of a triangle every time. All the formulae mean the same.

It doesn't matter which way you remember the formula but you will usually see it written as:

$$\text{area of a triangle} = \frac{1}{2}b \times h$$

To find the area or perimeter of a shape you follow the same steps as when you substitute in any other algebraic formulae.

1 Write the **formula**.

2 **Substitute**.

3 **Calculate**.

4 Write the **answer** with the correct **units**.

Example

(i) Calculate the area and perimeter of this rhombus.

Area of rhombus $= b \times h$

$\qquad = 7 \times 5.5$

$\qquad = 38.5 \, cm^2$

Perimeter of rhombus $= 4b$

$\qquad = 4 \times 7$

$\qquad = 28 \, cm$

7 cm

> Note that the units are square units because you are calculating the area.

(ii) Calculate the area of this triangle.

Area of a triangle $= \frac{1}{2} b \times h$

$\qquad = \frac{1}{2} \times 1.5 \times 1.2$

$\qquad = 0.6 \times 1.5$

$\qquad = 0.9 \, m^2$

It doesn't matter which unit you divide by 2 so choose the easier option.

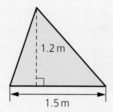

1.5 m

Exercise 9.3

1 Work out the perimeter of each shape.

(a)

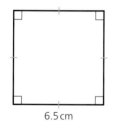

6.5 cm

(c)

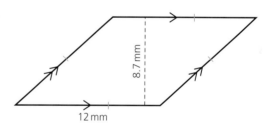

8.7 mm

12 mm

(b)

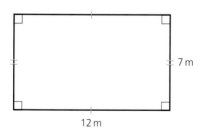

7 m

12 m

2 Calculate the areas of the shapes in question 1

3 Calculate the area of each shape.

(a)

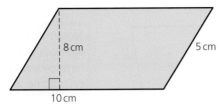

8 cm
5 cm
10 cm

(b)

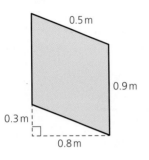

0.5 m
0.9 m
0.3 m
0.8 m

(c)

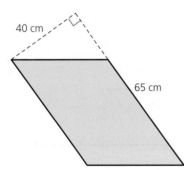

40 cm
65 cm

(d)

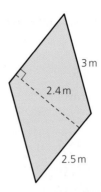

3 m
2.4 m
2.5 m

(e)

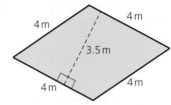

4 m
4 m
3.5 m
4 m
4 m

(f)

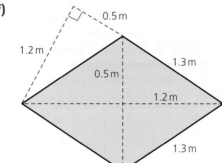

0.5 m
1.2 m
1.3 m
0.5 m
1.2 m
1.3 m

4 Calculate the area of each shape. All lengths are in centimetres.

(a)

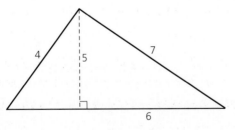

4
5
7
6

(b)

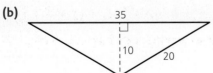

35
10
20

(c)

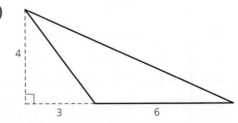

4
3
6

(d)

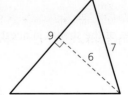

9
7
6

5 This is a cross-section through a chocolate bar.

What is the area of the cross-section of chocolate?

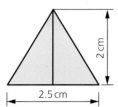

2 cm

2.5 cm

6 Our garden has some triangular flower beds. Here is a plan of the garden.

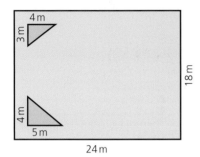

4 m

3 m

18 m

4 m

5 m

24 m

(a) Calculate the total area of the two flower beds.

(b) Calculate the area that is grassed.

7 A hexagon is made up of six triangles, all of base 2 cm and height 1.73 cm.

(a) What is the area of one triangle?

(b) What is the area of the hexagon?

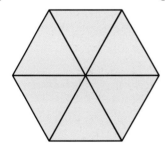

8 This square is 2 cm by 2 cm.

(a) How many triangles in total can you find in the square?

(b) What is the sum of their areas?

(c) What is the area of the square?

(d) How many times greater is your answer to (b) than your answer to (c)?

(e) Why?

Finding unknown dimensions

In the problems you have just solved, you used the base and height to find the area. However, there are times when you know the area and one of the dimensions and you need to find the missing dimension.

Example

Find the width of a rectangle of perimeter 25 cm and length 9 cm.

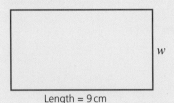

Length = 9 cm

Perimeter of rectangle $= 2l + 2w$	Formula
$25 = 2 \times 9 + 2w$	Substitute
$25 = 18 + 2w$	Calculate
$7 = 2w$ (-18)	
$(÷2)$	
$w = 3.5$ cm	
width of the rectangle is 3.5 cm	Answer with correct units

In the example above you had to **divide** by 2 to find the answer. When you are given the area of a triangle remember that you have to **multiply** by 2 first, then calculate with the given dimensions.

Example

A triangle has a base of 8 cm and area of 40 cm². What is the height?

$A = \dfrac{b \times h}{2}$

$40 = \dfrac{8 \times h}{2}$ $(\times 2)$

$80 = 8 \times h$

$(÷8)$

$10 = h$

The height of the triangle is 10 cm.

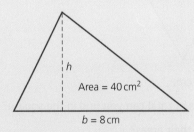

h

Area = 40 cm²

$b = 8$ cm

> It is always a good idea to draw a quick sketch if you are not given a diagram.

Exercise 9.4

1 Work out the height of each shape.

(a)

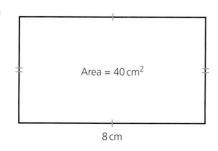

Area = 40 cm²

8 cm

(c)

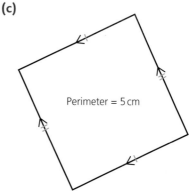

Perimeter = 5 cm

(b)

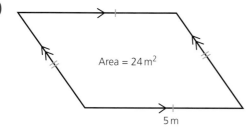

Area = 24 m²

5 m

(d)

Area = 900 mm²

2 A rectangle has perimeter of 100 cm and a height of 15 cm. What is the length of the base?

3 What is the length of the base of this triangle?

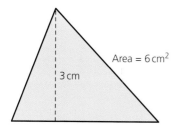

Area = 6 cm²

3 cm

4 A triangle has an area of 10 cm² and a base of 5 cm. What is its height?

5 A parallelogram has an area of 840 mm² and a height of 20 mm. What is the length of the base?

6 A square has perimeter 10 cm.

(a) What is the length of its sides?

(b) What is its area?

7 A rhombus has an area of 20 cm² and a height of 50 mm.

  (a) What is the length of the base?

  (b) What is its perimeter?

8 The area of a triangle is 6 cm² and its base is 20 mm. What is the height?

9 Triangle ADC has an area of 12 cm².

  AD = 4 cm and BD = 6 cm

  Work out:

  (a) the length of CD

  (b) the area of triangle BCD

  (c) the area of triangle ABC.

> Write both quantities in the same units.

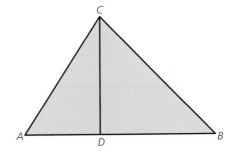

10 A triangle of height 8 cm and base length 12 cm is equal in area to a triangle with a base length of 6 cm. What is the height of this triangle?

More quadrilaterals

You can use the method of taking a formula you know and adding or subtracting areas to find the areas of some other quadrilaterals. Start by looking at the trapezium.

The trapezium

A trapezium has one pair of parallel sides of unequal lengths. You can refer to them as the top and bottom.

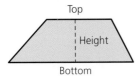

It is not easy to spot the formula for this area straight away.

Think about rotating the trapezium and joining the image to the original, like this.

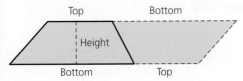

Now the two trapezia together have formed a parallelogram!

The base length of this parallelogram is equal to the sum of the top and bottom of the trapezium.

> Note that **trapezia** is the plural of trapezium.

The height of the parallelogram is the same as the height of the trapezium.

Now you can see that:

area of trapezium $= \frac{1}{2} \times$ height $\times$ (top + bottom)

$$= \frac{1}{2} h(a + b) \text{ or } \frac{h(a + b)}{2}$$

Example

Work out the area of this trapezium.

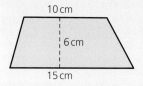

$$\text{Area} = \frac{1}{2} h(a + b) \qquad \text{Formula}$$

$$= \frac{6(10 + 15)}{2} \qquad \text{Substitute}$$

$$= \frac{^3 \cancel{6} \times 25}{_1 \cancel{2}} \qquad \text{Calculate} \qquad \text{Note that you can cancel the calculation by dividing by the common factor, 2, just as you did with fractions.}$$

$$= 3 \times 25$$

$$= 75 \text{ cm}^2 \qquad \text{Answer with correct units}$$

Exercise 9.5

Work out the area of each trapezium.

1

2
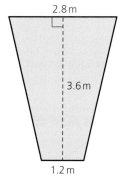

3
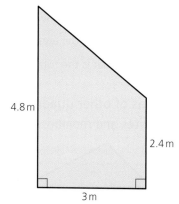

4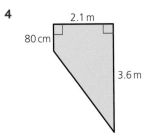

2.1 m

80 cm

3.6 m

5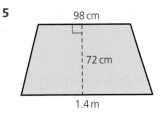

98 cm

72 cm

1.4 m

6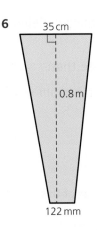

35 cm

0.8 m

122 mm

Now try some word problems.

7 This is the cross-section of a metal ingot. What is the area of the cross-section?

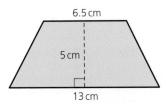

6.5 cm

5 cm

13 cm

8 This is the cross-section of a squash court.

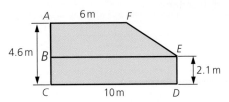

A   6 m   F

4.6 m   B   E

2.1 m

C   10 m   D

(a) What is the area of the rectangle *BCDE*?

(b) Work out the length of *AB*.

(c) What is the area of *ABEF*?

(d) What is the total cross-section area of the squash court?

Areas of other quadrilaterals

In kites and rhombuses the **diagonals** cross at right angles.

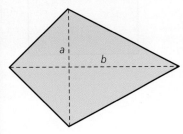

a

b

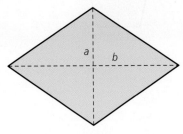

a

b

It may not be immediately obvious to see how this helps you to find the area of each of them.

Try drawing a rectangle round each shape.

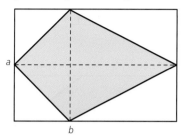 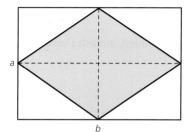

Now you can see that the kite and the rhombus each fills exactly half the rectangle that encloses it.

The area of the rectangle is base × height, which happens to be the product of the diagonals of the kite or rhombus!

Example

A rhombus has diagonals of length 8 cm and 12 cm. What is its area?

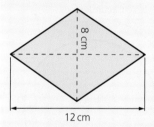 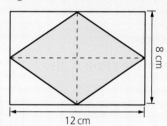

Area of the rhombus = $\frac{1}{2}$ area of rectangle

$$= \frac{1}{2} \times 8 \times 12$$

$$= 4 \times 12$$

$$= 48 \, \text{cm}^2$$

Exercise 9.6

1 Work out the area of each shape.

(a)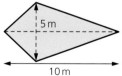

(b)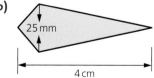

(c)

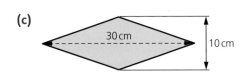

30 cm

10 cm

(d)

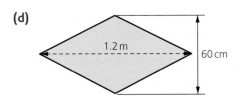

1.2 m

60 cm

2 Work out the area of the region that is shaded, in each shape.

(a)

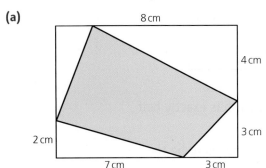

8 cm

4 cm

3 cm

2 cm

7 cm   3 cm

(b)

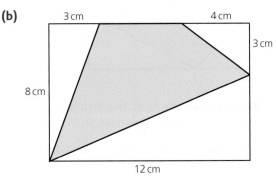

3 cm   4 cm

3 cm

8 cm

12 cm

◯ Circles

What do you know about circles?

The **circumference** is the line around the circle.

The distance all the way round the outside of the circle is also called the circumference.

All the points on the circumference are the same distance away from the **centre** of the circle.

A **radius** is a line from the centre to a point on the circumference.

The radius is also the distance from the centre to a point on the circumference.

A **diameter** is a line across the circle, from one side to the other, through the centre.

The diameter is also the distance across the circle, from one side to the other, through the centre.

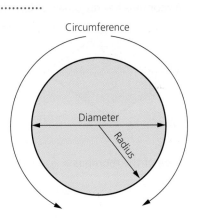

Circumference

Diameter

Radius

From this information, you can write a formula for the diameter of a circle:

diameter = 2 × radius

Use a pair of compasses to draw a circle on your page.

Use your ruler to measure the diameter and the radius.

How can you measure the circumference? Lay a piece of string carefully round the circumference of your circle.

Make a mark on the string, where it meets the point where it started.

Now measure the distance between the marks on your string against a ruler.

This is the length of the circumference.

Exercise 9.7

1 Draw three circles of different sizes in your exercise book.

2 Measure their diameters and their circumferences.

3 Record the results in a table like this.

Diameter (d)	Circumference (C)	$C \div d$

4 Now divide each circumference by the diameter. What do you notice?

Ask your friends if they get the same result. Amazing! If you all measured accurately, you should all have an answer of about 3, or even 3.1, to the calculation (circumference ÷ diameter), regardless of the sizes of your circles.

Surprising circles
Is the result you have found really so amazing?

$\dfrac{C}{d} = 3.1$ $\dfrac{C}{d} = 3.1$ $\dfrac{C}{d} = 3.1$ $\dfrac{C}{d} = 3.1$

As the diameter gets bigger, then the circumference must also get bigger. You should not be surprised that there is a link between them.

Note that the result of dividing the circumference by the diameter is not exactly 3.1 but may be close to it.

It has been calculated very precisely and is a number that has an infinite number of decimal places.

3.141 592 653 589 793 238 462 643 383 279...

This number is represented by the Greek letter π (pi).

Now you can write a formula for the circumference:

circumference = π*d*   or $C = \pi d$

As the diameter = 2 × radius you can also say:

$C = 2\pi r$

If you use the [π] button on your calculator, you will see that it gives 3.141 592 6 or 3.141 592 654 (or it may give 3.141 592 7, which tells you that the last figure has been rounded up). It depends on the type of calculator you are using. You can use this when you calculate with π.

In practice you very rarely ever need to know a number accurately to so many decimal places. You should generally use an approximation, either 3.1 or 3.14 or the fraction $\frac{22}{7}$ or $3\frac{1}{7}$

Remember that all these values are approximations.

Examples

(i) Taking π to be 3.1, find the circumference of a circle of diameter 4 cm.

π = 3.1   *d* = 4 cm

$C = \pi d$

= 3.1 × 4

= 12.4 cm

(ii) Taking π to be $\frac{22}{7}$, find the circumference of a circle with a diameter of 14 cm.

$\pi = \frac{22}{7}$ *d* = 14 cm

$C = \pi d$

$= \frac{22}{\overset{1}{7}} \times 14^{2}$

= 22 × 2

= 44 cm

(iii) Using the π button on your calculator, find the circumference of a circle with a diameter of 14 cm. Give your answer to 1 decimal place.

d = 14 cm

$C = \pi d$

= π × 14

= 43.982 297...

= 44.0 cm (to 1 d.p.)

Write out most of the digits on the calculator, followed by three dots, before you round the result.

Exercise 9.8

1 Taking π = 3.1 and without using a calculator, find the circumference of each circle.

(a)
8 cm

(b)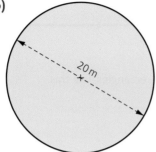
20 m

(c)
5 cm

(d) diameter of 4 m   **(e)** radius of 6 cm   **(f)** diameter of 50 cm

2 Taking π = $\frac{22}{7}$ and without using a calculator, find the circumference of each circle.

(a)
7 cm

(b)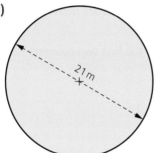
21 m

(c) 28 mm

(d) radius of 14 m   **(e)** diameter of 49 cm   **(f)** radius of 1.4 m

3 Using the π button on your calculator, find the circumference of each circle. Give your answers correct to 3 significant figures.

(a)
3.2 cm

(b)
9.4 m

(c) 15.4 mm

> Remember that you must write down all your working even though you are using a calculator this time.

(d) diameter of 0.45 m

(e) diameter of 1.4 km

(f) radius of 75 cm

Area of a circle

If it was difficult to measure the circumference of a circle, it is even harder to measure the area. As a start, you can try drawing circles on squared paper and counting squares.

Exercise 9.9

1 Draw three circles of different radii on graph paper.

2 Inside each of your circles, drawing a square and four rectangles, like this.

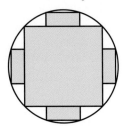

Calculate the total area of the square and rectangles, then count the remaining squares. Remember to include any part squares that are more than half inside the circle and ignore any that are less than half.

3 Record your radius and area results from question 2 in the first two columns of a table like this.

Radius (r)	Area (A)	$A \div r^2$

4 Now divide each area by the radius squared ($A \div r^2$) and put the results in the third column of your table. What do you notice?

π again

Look at your results for $A \div r^2$. What have you found? If you have been accurate, you should find that, again, the answer is close to 3.1, otherwise known as π

Now you can work out the formula for calculating the area of a circle.

As $\frac{A}{r^2} = \pi$ then $A = \pi r^2$

> Area is measured in square units, cm², m² or km², not in cm, m or km. This means that when you divide the area by the radius squared (simply written as $\frac{A}{r^2}$) the answer is just a number, with no units.

Example

(i) Find the area of a circle of diameter 14 cm. Take $\pi = \frac{22}{7}$

The diameter $d = 14$ cm so the radius $r = 7$ cm

$A = \pi r^2$

$= \frac{22}{7} \times \overset{1}{7} \times 7$

$= 22 \times 1 \times 7$

$= 154 \text{ cm}^2$

Remember you are calculating area, which is measured in square units.

> For the circumference, you have a choice of working with the diameter or the radius. For the area, you must always use the radius.

(ii) Using the $\boxed{\pi}$ button on your calculator, find the area of a circle of diameter 14 cm. Give your answer correct to 1 decimal place.

The diameter $d = 14$ cm so the radius $r = 7$ cm

$A = \pi r^2$

$= \pi \times 7 \times 7$

$= 153.938...$

Write out most of the digits on the calculator, followed by three dots, before you round the result.

$= 154.0 \text{ cm}^2$ (to 1 d.p.)

Exercise 9.10

1 Using $\pi = \frac{22}{7}$, work out the area of each circle.

(a) 28 cm

(b)
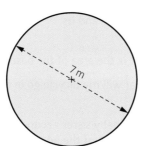
7 m

(c)

1.4 cm

2 Using $\pi = 3.1$, work out the area of each circle.

(a) 10 cm

(b)
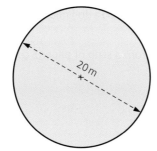
20 m

(c)
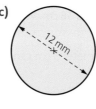
12 mm

3 Using the π button on your calculator, work out the area of each circle. Give your answers correct to 3 significant figures.

(a)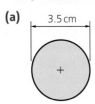
3.5 cm

(b)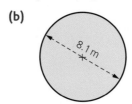
8.1 m

(c) 18.4 mm

(d) radius 15 cm

(e) diameter 45 m

(f) diameter 15 cm

Exercise 9.11

Use the π button on your calculator to answer these questions. Give your answers correct to 3 significant figures.

1 Given that the diameter of the Earth is 12 756 km, calculate the length of the equator.

2 I am making a circular table cloth with a diameter of 2.8 m. What length of ribbon must I buy in order to trim the edge of my tablecloth?

3 I have made a model tank out of a cotton reel, a matchstick, a drawing pin and a rubber band. The cotton reel has a radius of 3 cm. How far will my tank go in one full turn of the cotton reel?

4 I cut a slice of orange. The slice has a diameter of 8 cm. Work out the area of one side of my slice.

5 A table mat has a diameter of 12 cm. Calculate its area and its circumference.

6 I have a glass with a base diameter of 7 cm. What is the area of the base?

7 My bicycle has wheels of diameter 84 cm. How far will my bicycle go in one turn of the wheels?

8 (a) My mother has just cut a wooden lid to fit my baby sister's round sand pit. The lid has a radius of 1.5 m. Calculate the area of the lid.

(b) The lid needs a length of wooden trim round the circumference. What length of wooden trim does my mother need?

9 I have a round hat of radius 18 cm. What length of ribbon do I need to fit all the way round it?

10 How many circles of diameter 5 cm can be cut from a strip of paper 5 cm wide and 1 m long?

11 Work out the area of the shaded region in the diagram.

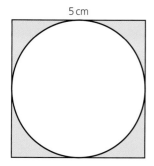

5 cm

12 Work out the area of the shaded region in the diagram.

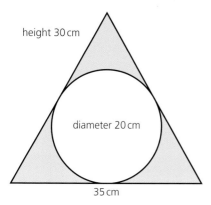

height 30 cm

diameter 20 cm

35 cm

Units of area

In each of the calculations you have done so far, you have used only one unit of area, for example, mm^2, cm^2, m^2 or km^2

Sometimes you will need to change from one unit of area to another. This is more complicated than it looks.

Look at these two squares.

$$area = 1 \times 1 = 1\,m^2$$

1 m

1 m

$$area = 100 \times 100 = 10\,000\,cm^2$$

100 cm

100 cm

You know that $1\,m = 100\,cm$

Therefore $1\,m^2 = 10\,000\,cm^2$

This is very important. Just remember that there are **not** $100\,cm^2$ in $1\,m^2$. If you can remember this, it will stop you making mistakes.

Extension Exercise 9.12

1 Draw squares like the two shown on the previous page to find how many:

   (a) square millimetres there are in a square centimetre

   (b) square millimetres there are in a square metre

   (c) square metres there are in a square kilometre

   (d) square metres there are in a square centimetre

   (e) square metres there are in a square millimetre

   (f) square kilometres there are in a square metre.

These are not easy to remember. If you need to write the answer in different units from those that you are given in the question, it is much easier to change the units first. If you cannot do that, always draw a square and make sure that you have the correct conversion.

2 A square is 4 m by 4 m. Give its area in:

   (a) square centimetres

   (b) square kilometres.

3 A triangle has base 5 m and height 3 m. Give its area in:

   (a) square millimetres

   (b) square centimetres.

4 A rectangle has a base of 30 cm and a height of 4 m. Give the area of the rectangle in:

   (a) square centimetres

   (b) square metres.

5 A rectangle has an area of 2 m^2 and a width of 20 cm. What is its length?

6 A triangle has an area of 1 m^2 and a height of 20 mm. What is its base?

7 A square has an area of 4 km^2. What is the length of a side, in metres?

8 A triangle of base 40 cm has an area of 10 000 mm^2. What is its height?

A **hectare** is a measure used for larger areas.

1 hectare (ha) = 10 000 m^2

100 hectares = 1 km^2

9 (a) How many square metres are there in 3.6 hectares?

   (b) How many hectares are there in 5.7 km^2?

   (c) What is the area, in hectares, of a parallelogram with base 1.2 km and height 800 m?

10 Bill and Ben are having an argument. Bill has a field in the shape of a kite. The diagonals of the kite are 1.8 km and 600 m. Ben has a field in the shape of a trapezium. The parallel sides are 400 m and 500 m long, and the perpendicular distance between them is 1.2 km. Bill and Ben each think his field is the larger. Who is right?

Extension: Parts of a circle

If you look at a slice of a circular cake you can see that it is a fraction of a whole circle.

In mathematical terms the slice of a cake is called a **sector**.

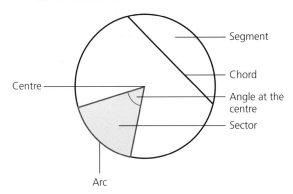

A **chord** is a line that joins two points on the circumference but does not pass through the centre.

If you cut a piece off the cake, along a chord, so that the knife did not go through the centre, you would have a **segment**.

When you cut a circle with a chord you form two **segments**. The small one is the minor segment and the large one is the major segment.

An **arc** is a section of the circumference of a full circle. Its length is determined by the angle formed between the two radii that run from the ends of the arc. This is the angle at the centre.

A **sector** is formed by an arc and the two radii that run to the centre from the ends of the arc.

There are two special sectors.

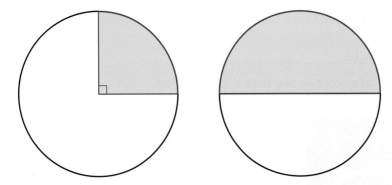

When the angle at the centre is 90° it forms a quarter circle known as a **quadrant**.

When the angle at the centre is 180° it forms a half circle known as a **semicircle**.

With this information you can find the area and perimeter of a sector.

Examples

(i) Find the area and perimeter of a semicircle of diameter 12 cm. Use the π button on your calculator and give your answer correct to 1 d.p.

$d = 12\,\text{cm}$ $\qquad r = 6\,\text{cm}$

Area of semicircle $= \frac{1}{2}\pi r^2$

$\qquad\qquad\quad = \frac{1}{2} \times \pi \times 6 \times 6$

$\qquad\qquad\quad = 56.548...$

$\qquad\qquad\quad = 56.5\,\text{cm}^2$ (to 1 d.p.)

Perimeter of semicircle $= \frac{1}{2}\pi d + d$ $\qquad$ To find the perimeter you need to add the length of the arc to the diameter.

$\qquad\qquad\quad = \frac{1}{2} \times \pi \times 12 + 12$

$\qquad\qquad\quad = 18.849... + 12$

$\qquad\qquad\quad = 30.849...$

$\qquad\qquad\quad = 30.8\,\text{cm}$ (to 1 d.p.)

(ii) Find the area and perimeter of this sector of a circle. Use the $\boxed{\pi}$ button on your calculator and give your answer correct to 1 d.p.

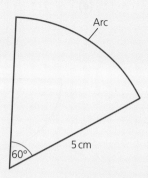

Arc

5 cm

60°

> 60° is $\frac{1}{6}$ of the angle at the centre of the circle.

$d = 10\,\text{cm}$ $r = 5\,\text{cm}$

Area of sector $= \frac{1}{6}\pi r^2$

$\phantom{\text{Area of sector }} = \frac{1}{6} \times \pi \times 5 \times 5$

$\phantom{\text{Area of sector }} = 13.089\ldots$

$\phantom{\text{Area of sector }} = 13.1\,\text{cm}^2$ (to 1 d.p.)

Perimeter of sector $= \frac{1}{6}\pi d + 2r$

> To find the perimeter you need to add the length of the arc to the two radii.

$\phantom{\text{Perimeter of sector }} = \frac{1}{6} \times 2 \times \pi \times 5 + 2 \times 5$

$\phantom{\text{Perimeter of sector }} = 5.235\ldots + 10$

$\phantom{\text{Perimeter of sector }} = 15.235\ldots$

$\phantom{\text{Perimeter of sector }} = 15.2\,\text{cm}$ (to 1 d.p.)

Extension Exercise 9.13

For this exercise, use the $\boxed{\pi}$ button on your calculator and give your answers correct to 1 d.p.

1 Find the area of a semicircle of:

   (a) diameter 20 cm   **(b)** radius 25 mm   **(c)** radius 3.5 m.

2 Find the perimeter of each of the semicircles in question 1

3 Find the area of a quadrant of:

   (a) radius 15 cm   **(b)** radius 2 m   **(c)** radius 35 m.

4 Find the perimeter of each of the quadrants in question 3

5 Find the area and perimeter of each sector.

(a)

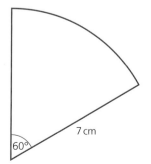

7 cm

60°

(b)

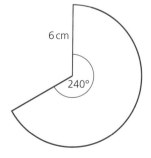

6 cm

240°

(c)

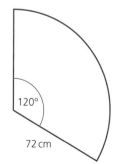

120°

72 cm

(d)

25 mm

30°

(e)

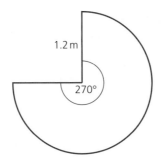

1.2 m

270°

(f)

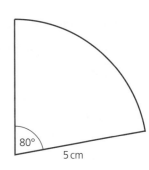

80°

5 cm

Summary Exercise 9.14

1 Write down the formula for:

(a) the area of a parallelogram

(b) the perimeter of a rhombus

(c) the area of a trapezium

(d) the area of a kite

(e) the circumference of a circle

(f) the area of a circle.

2 Calculate the area of each shape.

(a)

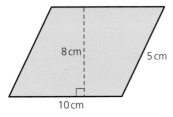

8 cm

5 cm

10 cm

(b)

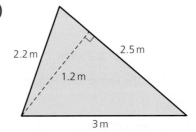

2.2 m

2.5 m

1.2 m

3 m

3 Find the height of a triangle of area 72 cm² and base 12 cm.

4 This is the cross-section of a stand at a sports stadium.

CD, BE and AF are parallel and AB = BC = DE

(a) Calculate the area of:

(i) BCDE

(ii) ABEF

(b) Hence find the area of the cross-section.

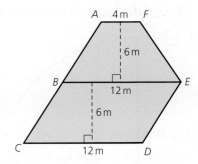

A   4 m   F

6 m

B   E
     12 m

6 m

C   12 m   D

5 Taking $\pi = \frac{22}{7}$, work out the circumference of a circle of diameter 63 cm.

6 Taking $\pi = 3.1$, work out the area of a circle of radius 5 cm.

7 Using the π button on your calculator, calculate:

   (a) the circumference of a circle of radius 5 cm, giving your answer correct to 3 significant figures

   (b) the area of a circle of diameter 17 cm, giving your answer correct to 3 significant figures.

8 Use the π button on your calculator and give non-exact answers correct to 1 decimal place for this question.

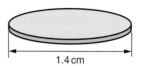

1.4 cm

   (a) This disc is a token for a game machine. What is the area of the token?

   (b) The tokens are cut from a sheet measuring 1 m by 1 m. How many tokens can be cut from one sheet?

Activity: Drawing spirals

You will need graph paper for this activity.

The spiral of a snail's shell is just one example of a geometrical shape occurring in nature. Nature knows that a thin shell is much stronger when it is curved, and the progressive curves of a spiral give additional strength as well as additional protection. Architects, in conjunction with structural engineers, have used this theory to produce the stunning curves of the Sydney Opera House and the gentle spiral of the Guggenheim Art Gallery.

A spiral may look simple but how exactly do you draw one?

The Fibonacci series, 1, 1, 2, 3, 5, 8, 13, ... is formed by adding the two previous numbers together to get the next number. If you illustrate this with each number in the series being the side of a square, you get a spiral of squares.

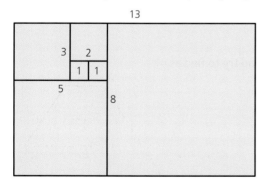
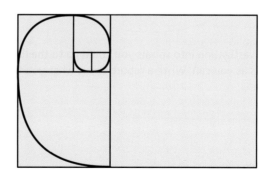

If you then draw a quarter circle in each square, you can produce a spiral.

Copy the pattern of squares and extend it as far as your piece of paper will allow. Then draw the spiral.

You can make a device for drawing a spiral like this.

Step 1: Cut a circle with a radius of 3 cm from a piece of thick card and glue it firmly to the centre of a piece of paper.

Step 2: Cut another circle, but this time with a radius of 3.5 cm. Cut a small slit in the edge of this circle. Glue this circle firmly on top and in the centre of the first slightly smaller circle.

Step 3: Then get a piece of thick thread 70 cm long and tie a knot in one end. Slip the thread through the slit you cut and pull it until the knot stops it pulling through any further. It should now be securely attached. At the other end of the thread make a small loop, large enough to get a pencil through. Then wind the thread round the circle (under the rim of the larger circle) until only the loop is showing.

Step 4: Put a pencil in the loop. Then, keeping the thread taught, put the tip of the pencil on the paper and move it so that you start to unwind the thread. As you do this you will see that you are drawing a spiral.

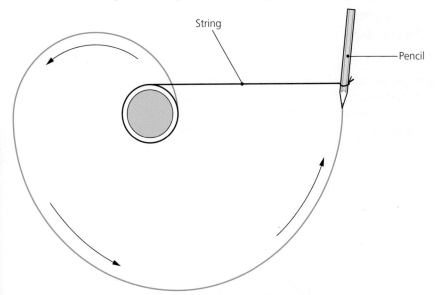

As a final investigation into spirals you could go to the library and try to find as many spirals as you can. Write a report about what you find.

10 Percentages

What do you think of when you hear the word 'percentage'? It is used in many contexts, varying from price reductions offered by shops during special sales, through discussions about the nation's economy to the results you achieve in exams. But what makes percentages so important?

The word 'percentage' means 'out of a hundred', which gives you a big clue about what a percentage is. Any fraction written out of 100 can also be written as a percentage.

Fractions, decimals and percentages

The simple fraction families have corresponding decimal and percentage families that you should know.

$25\% = \frac{1}{4} = 0.25$ $75\% = \frac{3}{4} = 0.75$

$10\% = \frac{1}{10} = 0.1$ $30\% = \frac{3}{10} = 0.3$ $70\% = \frac{7}{10} = 0.7$ $90\% = \frac{9}{10} = 0.9$

$20\% = \frac{1}{5} = 0.2$ $40\% = \frac{2}{5} = 0.4$ $60\% = \frac{3}{5} = 0.6$ $80\% = \frac{4}{5} = 0.8$

For other fractions, decimals and percentages you need to know how to convert from one to another.

Rules of conversion

Fractions to decimals

Divide the top number (numerator) by the bottom number (denominator).

Example

Change $\frac{3}{8}$ to a decimal.

$\frac{3}{8} = 3 \div 8$

$\quad = 0.375$

Decimals to percentages

Multiply by 100

> ### Example
> Change 0.125 to a percentage.
>
> $0.125 = 0.125 \times 100\%$
>
> $\qquad = 12.5\%$
>
> $\qquad = 12\frac{1}{2}\%$

Percentages to decimals

Divide by 100

> ### Example
> Change 85% to a decimal.
>
> $85\% = 85 \div 100$
>
> $\qquad = 0.85$

Percentages to fractions

Write as a fraction with 100 as the denominator and simplify if possible.

> ### Example
> Change 72% to a fraction.
>
> $72\% = \frac{72}{100}$
>
> $\qquad = \frac{18}{25}$

Decimals to fractions

Write a fraction with the correct denominator (10, 100, 1000,...) and simplify if possible.

> ### Example
> Change 0.625 to a fraction.
>
> $0.625 = \frac{625}{1000}$
>
> $\qquad = \frac{25}{40}$
>
> $\qquad = \frac{5}{8}$

Fractions greater than one

Look at the number $1\frac{2}{5}$

As a decimal this is 1.4

As a percentage this is 140%

It is important to remember that, just as you can have mixed numbers, you can also have percentages greater than 100%

Exercise 10.1

1 Write each number as: **(i)** a decimal **(ii)** a percentage.

   (a) $\frac{7}{10}$

   (b) $1\frac{2}{5}$

   (c) $1\frac{2}{3}$

   (d) $\frac{7}{8}$

2 Write each decimal as: **(i)** a percentage **(ii)** a fraction.

   (a) 0.27

   (b) 0.7

   (c) 0.65

   (d) 0.6

3 Write each percentage as: **(i)** a decimal **(ii)** a fraction.

   (a) 40%

   (b) 55%

   (c) 84%

   (d) 24%

4 Write each number as: **(i)** a decimal **(ii)** a percentage.

   (a) $\frac{4}{25}$

   (b) $\frac{9}{20}$

   (c) $\frac{37}{40}$

   (d) $1\frac{1}{5}$

5 Write each decimal as: **(i)** a percentage **(ii)** a fraction.

   (a) 1.19

   (b) 0.325

   (c) 2.6

   (d) 0.77

6 Write each percentage as: **(i)** a decimal **(ii)** a fraction.

   (a) 43%

   (b) $66\frac{2}{3}$ %

   (c) $37\frac{1}{2}$ %

   (d) $112\frac{1}{2}$ %

Finding a percentage of an amount

When you are finding a percentage of an amount, the first thing to do is convert the percentage to either a fraction or a decimal. If you do not have a calculator, then using a fraction may be the better method. If you do have a calculator then convert to a decimal.

Example

Find 25% of £36

$$25\% \text{ of } £36 = \frac{1}{4} \times 36$$
$$= £9$$

Sometimes the fraction is not so simple and you will need to use a calculator. Most calculators have %️ buttons but it is just as easy, and good practice, to turn the percentage into a decimal and use the calculator to do the straight calculation.

Example

Work out 37% of £6.35

$$37\% \text{ of } £6.35 = 0.37 \times 6.35$$
$$= 2.3495$$
$$= £2.35 \text{ (to 2 d.p.)}$$

> If you are calculating with money you should always give your answer to the nearest penny, which is 2 d.p.

Exercise 10.2

Work out these amounts. Do not use a calculator.

1 25% of 80 cm

2 40% of £200

3 35% of 500 g

4 60% of £1000

5 80% of 4 m

6 64% of £5

7 28% of 5 kg

8 35% of 8 km

9 85% of £300

10 12% of 20 m

Use a calculator to work out these amounts. If the answers are not exact give them correct to 2 decimal places.

11 27% of 250 cm

12 18% of £22

13 7% of 250 g

14 63% of £150

15 41% of 5 m

16 78% of £6.50

17 124% of 6.2 kg

18 3% of 8.7 km

19 89% of £324

20 $12\frac{1}{2}$% of 6 m

Fractional percentages

As you have seen, some percentages include fractions. Some of these are in the common fraction families, but some are not.

For example: $12\frac{1}{2}\% = 0.125 = \frac{1}{8}$ but consider $36\frac{1}{2}\%$

If you are not using a calculator, then turn the percentage into a fraction by:

- first making it a top-heavy fraction

- then dividing by 100

So: $36\frac{1}{2}\% = \frac{73}{2}\% = \frac{73}{200}$

> Remember that to turn a percentage into a fraction you divide by 100, which is the same as multiplying by $\frac{1}{100}$

Example

Work out $17\frac{1}{2}\%$ of 80 cm.

$17\frac{1}{2}\%$ of 80 cm $= \dfrac{\cancel{35}^{7}}{\cancel{2}_{1}} \times \dfrac{1}{\cancel{100}_{5/1}} \times \cancel{80}^{40^{2}}$

   Simplify by cancelling by common
   factors: 2, 20 and 5

$= 7 \times 2$

$= 14$ cm

Exercise 10.3

Calculate these amounts.

1 $12\frac{1}{2}\%$ of 120 g

2 $37\frac{1}{2}\%$ of £200

3 $30\frac{1}{3}\%$ of 66 m

4 $66\frac{2}{3}$ of 144 litres

5 $87\frac{1}{2}\%$ of 240 grams

6 $16\frac{2}{3}\%$ of £30

7 $83\frac{1}{3}\%$ of £6

8 $12\frac{1}{2}\%$ of 2 km

9 $44\frac{1}{9}\%$ of 18 g

10 $16\frac{2}{3}\%$ of 3 litres

Finding a percentage

When Justin gets 45 marks out of 60 for a test, he writes this:

$$\frac{45}{60}$$

to express his marks as a fraction. He can change the fraction to a percentage by multiplying by 100

Example

What is 45 out of 60 as a percentage?

$$\frac{45}{60} = \frac{\overset{3}{\cancel{45}}}{\underset{4}{\cancel{60}}} \times 100\%$$

$$= 75\%$$

> In the fraction, the denominator (bottom number) is important because it shows what the mark is out of.

Example

In my class of 24 there are 15 boys. What percentage of the class are girls?

$$\text{Percentage} = \frac{9}{24} \times 100$$

$$= 9 \div 24 \times 100$$

$$= 37.5\%$$

Problem solving with percentages

In percentage questions, always take care to check what the question is actually asking for.

Example

45% of Year 8 boys do Latin. If there are 20 boys in Year 8 how many do not do Latin?

$$45\% \text{ of } 20 = \frac{45}{\underset{5}{\cancel{100}}} \times \overset{1}{\cancel{20}}$$

$$= \frac{45}{5}$$

$$= 9$$

9 boys do Latin and therefore 11 boys do not do Latin.

> If the question is a sentence, you should make sure you write your answer as a phrase or sentence that relates to the original question.

It would be very easy to think that, having worked out that 9 boys do Latin, you have answered the question, but the question asks how many boys do **not** do Latin.

Exercise 10.4

1 In my school there are 240 pupils. 144 of these are girls. What percentage of the pupils are boys?

2 I am growing a bean plant. Last week it was 1.6 m tall and this week it is 2 m tall. What is its growth as a percentage of its previous height?

3 I have £4 pocket money each week, and I put £1.50 into my money box. What percentage of my pocket money do I not put in my money box?

4 48% of the pupils in our school are boys. If there are 300 pupils in the school, how many are boys and how many are girls?

5 There are 30 trees in our road and 40% of them are now in blossom. How many trees are in blossom?

Use a calculator for questions 6–10; give any non-exact answers correct to one decimal place.

6 What is 45 marks out of 65 as a percentage?

7 £4 service is added to our bill of £32. What percentage charge is this?

8 Trainers normally cost £39.99 but in the sale they cost £29.99. What percentage saving is this?

9 A 3-kg cake contains 210 g of dried fruit. What percentage of the cake is this?

10 A service charge of 12% is added to our bill. What is the value of the service charge on a bill of £48?

Use whichever method you prefer to answer questions 11–15

11 For my exams I got 60 out of 75 for French, 52 out of 70 for maths, 80 out of 110 for English, 45 out of 65 for history and 63 out of 80 for geography. If I add all my marks up, what percentage of the total possible marks did I get?

12 In my maths exam I scored 60 marks out of a possible 75. How many more marks would I have had to get to have scored over 90%?

13 In a recent leaflet from our local council we were told that 40% of the people in our borough were in employment. If there are 240 000 people in the borough, how many are unemployed?

14 When we bought a litre of cleaning fluid, we were told to leave the top on or as much as 15% of the liquid could evaporate overnight. My mother forgot and the next morning there were only 850 cubic centimetres of fluid left in the bottle. How accurate was the manufacturer's claim?

15 For a maths project we decided to test an advertiser's claim that over 65% of people had eaten a McJimmy's hamburger. Between us we interviewed 300 people and 124 of them had not eaten a McJimmiburger. Does that mean that the advertising claim was correct or not?

◯ Percentage change

So far, you have been working out percentages and finding pecentages of amounts. Another use of percentages is to show a **change**, such as an increase in population.

When you are working with percentage change, you need to consider an original value and a new value.

For a percentage increase:

original value + increase = new value

Example

In 2000 the population of Littlehampton was 350 000. It increased by 8% from 2000 to 2010. What was the population of Littlehampton in 2010?

8% of 350 000 $= 0.08 \times 350\,000$

$\qquad\qquad\qquad = 28\,000$

New population $= 378\,000$

For a percentage decrease:

original value − decrease = new value

Example

Last year there were 440 pupils in the school. This year there are 418 pupils. What is the percentage decrease?

Decrease $= 440 - 418$

$\qquad\quad = 22$

Percentage decrease $= \frac{22}{440} \times 100$

$\qquad\qquad\qquad\quad = 5\%$

> When calculating the percentage increase or decrease you are comparing the change to the original amount.

Exercise 10.5

1 The population of our village has risen by 10% in the last ten years. If the population was 120 000 ten years ago, what is it now?

2 A cake rises in the oven by 25%. If its original height was 15 cm, what is the final height of the cake?

3 The population of a holiday resort drops by 25% in the winter. If the population is 350 000 in the holiday season, what is it in the winter?

4 A hotel had 120 guests in August and 90 guests in September. What was the percentage decrease in the number of guests between August and September?

5 A restaurant served 240 meals on Thursday and 320 meals on Friday. What is the percentage increase in the number of meals from Thursday to Friday?

10 Percentages

6 A school had 125 pupils last year but increased the number of pupils by 12%. How many pupils in there in the school this year?

7 My monthly allowance has increased by 15%. It was £20. What is it now?

8 My sister's monthly allowance of £25 was decreased by 20% as she now cycles to school and does not pay a bus fare. What is her new monthly allowance?

9 Mrs Brown has had a 5% pay rise. If she used to earn £26 000, what is her new salary?

10 Mr Black has decided to work part time and is earning £80 less each week. If he used to earn £400 a week, what is the percentage decrease in his earnings?

Percentages and money

The last four questions in Exercise 10.5 concerned money. Percentages are often used as a way of comparing prices and earnings.

Profit and loss

When people buy and sell goods, they want to make money.

- A trader who can sell goods for more than they cost to buy or make will gain a **profit**.
- A trader who has to sell goods for less than they cost to buy or make will sustain a **loss**.

When manufacturers, wholesalers and shopkeepers work out the price at which to sell their goods, they usually work in percentages.

The manufacturer adds a percentage on to the cost of making the goods and sells to the wholesaler.

The wholesaler adds a percentage on to the total purchase and transport costs and sells to the shopkeeper.

The shopkeeper adds a percentage on to the costs, and then has to add on VAT before fixing a price to sell to the public.

The profit or loss is the difference between the selling price and the buying or cost price.

- If selling price > cost price the trader makes a profit.
- If selling price < cost price the trader makes a loss.

The **percentage profit** is the **profit** expressed as a percentage of the buying price.

The **percentage loss** is the **loss** expressed as a percentage of the buying price.

> VAT is a tax imposed by the government and is applied to most goods and services, with a few exceptions such as food, books and children's clothing.

> When writing the calculation, make sure that you put the percentage sign in the right place to make your mathematical statements correct.

Example

A shopkeeper buys pencils at £7.50 per 100 and sells them for 12p each.
What is his percentage profit?

Cost price: £7.50   Selling price: £12.00

Profit = £12.00 − £7.50

$\qquad$ = £4.50

> Always start by identifying the total cost price and the total selling price.

Percentage profit = $\frac{\text{profit}}{\text{cost price}} \times 100\%$

> Write the rule or formula first.

$$= \frac{\overset{15}{\cancel{450}}}{\underset{3}{\cancel{750}}} \times \cancel{100}^{\,4}\%$$

$$= 15 \times 4\%$$

$$= 60\%$$

The shopkeeper's percentage profit is 60%

Use the smallest unit, such as pence, for your calculations so that you can cancel common factors without worrying about decimals.

If the selling price is less than 100% of the cost price, then the shopkeeper makes a loss.

Example

A shopkeeper buys 10 jumpers for £150 and then sells them for £12.50 each.
What is his percentage profit or loss?

Total cost price = £150   Total selling price = 12.5 × 10 = £125

$\qquad$ Loss = £25

Percentage loss = $\frac{\text{loss}}{\text{cost price}} \times 100\%$

> If you are using a calculator, do not just write down the full display. Always check if your answer is a simple fraction.

$$= \frac{25}{150} \times 100\%$$

$$= 16.666...\%$$

$$= 16\frac{2}{3}\%$$

Exercise 10.6

1 Work out the percentage profit for each of these transactions.

(a) Trainers were bought for £18 and sold for £24

(b) A loaf of bread was sold for £2.40 when manufacturing costs are 84p

(c) A cake made with ingredients costing £1.20 was sold at the fete for £6.00

> First find the profit then calculate the percentage.

(d) A book bought for £3.20 was then sold for £4.00

2   Work out the percentage loss for each of these transactions.

   (a) A book bought for £5 was sold for £3

   (b) Potatoes bought from the farm for £5 for 10 kg were sold for £2.40 for 5 kg.

   (c) Black bin liners bought from the factory at £4 for 100 were sold in the market at 60p for 20

   (d) A DVD was bought for £8 and sold for £6

> First find the loss, then calculate the percentage.

3   Find the selling price for each of these transactions.

   (a) A shopkeeper adds 20% VAT to his own price of £10.00

   (b) A manufacturer adds 15% profit to his costs of £8.00

   (c) A shop is having a sale with all prices marked down 25%. A jacket normally costs £40

   (d) A wholesaler adds 12.5% to his own costs of £20

> First find the profit or loss then add it to or subtract it from the original value.

4   A manufacturer works out that his total costs for 100 DVDs are £150. If he sells boxes of 100 DVDs at £175, what is his percentage profit? Is this the same if you calculate it for one DVD or for 100 DVDs?

5   A shopkeeper has to add VAT at 20% to his price of £60. How much is the VAT?

6   A wholesaler sells trainers for £12 a pair. He paid £15 for each pair. What is his percentage loss?

7   A market trader buys in potatoes at £50 for 200 kg and sells them in 5 kg bags for £2. What percentage profit does he make?

8   I make 2.4% per year by investing my money in a National Savings account.

   (a) If I started with £125, how much will I have earned in one year?

   (b) How much money will I then have?

9   A jacket was being sold for £44.50 but has been marked down by 40% in a sale. What price can I buy it for now?

10   A manufacturer's total costs on 1000 print cartridges are £5000. At what price should he sell a box of 5 cartridges in order to make a 20% profit?

11   A car devalues by 20% of its original price in its first year, and from then on it devalues each year at 12% of its price at the beginning of that year. If a car cost £9000 in January 2012:

   (a) What was its value in January 2013?

   (b) What was its value in January 2014?

   (c) What is the total percentage devaluation of the car from January 2012 to January 2014?

12 A salesman claims that if you let him invest your money it will appreciate (grow) by at least 5% per annum. You invest £2000 with his fund. At the end of the year you have lost 8%.

(a) How much money would you have made if his claims were true?

(b) How much money have you lost?

(c) If you had invested the money elsewhere it would have made the 5% growth, so what is your actual percentage loss from investing with the salesman?

Extension Exercise 10.7

Write each of these fractions as a percentage.

1 $\frac{5}{9}$

2 $\frac{4}{7}$

3 $\frac{5}{11}$

4 $\frac{9}{22}$

5 $\frac{11}{19}$

6 $\frac{17}{24}$

7 $\frac{7}{15}$

8 $\frac{7}{18}$

9 $\frac{12}{17}$

10 $\frac{17}{33}$

Use a calculator to work these out. Give any non-exact answers correct to 2 decimal places.

11 $65\frac{1}{2}$ % of £3.20

12 $16\frac{3}{4}$ % of 450 m

13 $25\frac{1}{5}$ % of 5 kg

14 $42\frac{3}{8}$ % of £1725

15 $33\frac{1}{3}$ % of 4.7 km

16 $17\frac{4}{15}$ % of £35

17 $68\frac{3}{11}$ % of £6.40

18 $24\frac{2}{7}$ % of 65 tonnes

19 $65\frac{5}{9}$ % of 12 kg

20 $2\frac{4}{17}$ % of 35 litres

Summary Exercise 10.8

Do not use a calculator for questions 1–6

1 Write each of these as a fraction.

(a) 0.35   **(b)** 0.12   **(c)** 42%   **(d)** $12\frac{1}{2}$ %

2 Write each of these as a decimal.

(a) 82%   **(b)** $\frac{3}{8}$ **(c)** $87\frac{1}{2}$ %   **(d)** $\frac{7}{25}$

3 Write each of these as a percentage.

(a) 1.5   **(b)** 0.125   **(c)** $\frac{1}{3}$ **(d)** $\frac{17}{20}$

4 Work out these amounts.

(a) 25% of £14

(b) 14% of 500 g

(c) 80% of 1200 people

(d) 45% of 500 km

(e) $87\frac{1}{2}$ % of £400

(f) $66\frac{2}{3}$ % of 900 miles

5 There are 240 pupils in the school and 5% of them have chicken pox. How many pupils is that?

6 I scored 42 out 60 in my French test. What is that as a percentage?

You may use a calculator for the remaining questions, if you wish, but remember to write down your working.

7 Of the 24 people in my class, $37\frac{1}{2}$% are going on the school ski trip. How many of us are not going in the school trip?

8 Last year, which was not a leap year, there were 146 days when it rained for more than one hour. For what percentage of the year did it rain for more than one hour a day?

9 I wanted a new game for my computer but last week it cost £39. In the sale today it is marked down by 25%. What could I buy it for now?

10 In my school tuck shop we buy boxes of 50 packets of potato crisps for £6.00 and we sell the crisps for 30p per packet. What is our percentage profit?

11 An old wives' tale says that the height you are on your second birthday is exactly half the height you will be when fully grown. My mother's baby book says that a baby will grow by 40% of its height at birth in its first year, while in its second year it will grow by to 20% of its height at the beginning of the year. The height of my new baby sister is 50 cm. How tall will she be:

(a) on her first birthday

(b) on her second birthday

(c) as an adult?

12 A market trader bought some bunches of daffodils. He paid £15 for every hundred daffodils and hoped to make a fortune on Mother's Day. Unfortunately it rained that day and he ended up selling his flowers at 50p per bunch of 10. What percentage profit or loss did he make?

Activity: Tormenting tessellations

The word tessellation comes from *tessella,* the Latin for 'little tile'.

Bathroom walls or kitchen floors are often covered in tiles. These tiles are generally square. This is because a square is the easiest shape to use, to cover a whole area, without leaving any gaps.

Use the 'nibble' technique described here to design your own tessellations. These instructions are given for using paper and card, but if you have an appropriate computer graphics program then you can use it to make some fantastic patterns. However, try this method first.

Step 1: Draw a square with sides of 3 cm.

Step 2: Start at the top corner and draw an outline of the piece you are going to cut out or 'nibble'.

Step 3: Cut out the nibbled piece and stick it back on either the opposite side, as in the example, or on an adjacent side if you prefer.

Step 4: Do the same thing again but, this time, go from top to bottom or bottom to top or a different pair of adjacent sides.

Step 5: Decorate your shape. Stick it on to card and draw round it carefully. Cut it out. This is now your tessellating template.

Step 6: Position the card on the worksheet. Line up the corners very carefully. Trace round it. Now reposition your template so that it notches into the first figure. Trace round it again. Keep going!

When you have finished, decorate the whole design.

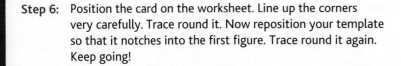

Ratio and enlargement

Have you ever made yourself a drink by adding water to concentrated fruit cordial? Think about the instructions on the bottle, which usually tell you to: 'Mix one part cordial with 4 parts water.'

Mathematically, this is the same as saying that the ratio of cordial to water is 1 : 4

Ratio

A **ratio** is method for comparing numbers. The numbers in the ratio are generally separated by a **colon** (:)

Think back to what you learnt about ratio in *Mathematics for Common Entrance Book One.*

- You must put the quantities the right way round. For example, if you mixed your fruit cordial in the ratio 4 : 1 it would be far too strong.

- A ratio should be expressed in its **lowest terms**. You can simplify a ratio by dividing both parts by a **common factor**.

Examples
(i) Simplify the ratio 3 : 6

  3 : 6 = 1 : 2   Divide both 3 and 6 by 3

(ii) Simplify the ratio 20 : 30

  20 : 30 = 2 : 3   Divide both 20 and 30 by 10

(iii) Simplify the ratio 4 : 8 : 16

  4 : 8 : 16 = 1 : 2 : 4   Divide 4, 8 and 16 by 4

> You need to divide each part of the ratio by the highest common factor of all the parts.

- If you are comparing quantities, you must make sure that they are in the same units and leave the units out of any ratio.

Examples

(i) Simplify the ratio 60 cm to 1.2 m.

$$60 \text{ cm to } 1.2 \text{ m} = 60 \text{ cm} : 120 \text{ cm}$$
$$= 6 : 12$$
$$= 1 : 2$$

(ii) Simplify the ratio 40p : £1.20 : £3

$$40\text{p} : £1.20 : £3 = 40\text{p} : 120\text{p} : 300\text{p}$$
$$= 2 : 6 : 15$$

Exercise 11.1

1 Simplify these ratios.

   (a) 8 : 2   (b) 2 : 8   (c) 5 : 10   (d) 10 : 5

2 Simplify these ratios.

   (a) 15 : 25   (b) 20 : 8   (c) 50 : 35   (d) 10 : 55

3 Simplify these ratios.

   (a) 70p : £1.20   (c) 5 km : 1.4 km : 600 m

   (b) 350 g : 1.25 kg

4 Copy and complete these statements, replacing the stars to make the ratios equivalent.

   (a) 2 : 3 = * : 60   (c) 25 : 80 : 120 = 5 : * : *

   (b) 21 : 7 = * : 1

5 Look at this pattern.

   (a) What is the ratio of black squares to grey squares?

   (b) What is the ratio of white squares to grey squares?

   (c) What is the ratio of black squares to the total number of squares?

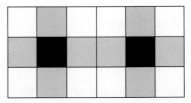

6 There are 240 boys and 360 girls in my school. What is the ratio of boys to girls?

7 I earn £120 per week and my sister earns £30 more than I do. What is the ratio of my sister's earnings to mine?

8 To make a blackcurrant fruit drink, cordial needs to be mixed with water in the ratio one part cordial to five parts water.

   (a) Write the mix as the ratio of cordial to water.

   (b) Write the mix as the ratio of water to cordial.

   (c) I carefully measure 100 ml of cordial. How much water will I need?

(d) I carefully measure 100 ml of cordial. How many millilitres of blackcurrant fruit drink will I have?

(e) I pour a litre of water into a jug. How much cordial do I need to add?

9 I mix 50 ml blackcurrant concentrate with 200 ml of water to make blackcurrant squash.

(a) What is the ratio of concentrate to water?

(b) What is the ratio of concentrate to diluted squash?

10 To make a MacTavish special drink, mix 50 litres of GlenTav with 350 litres of GlenVish.

(a) What is the ratio of GlenTav to GlenVish?

(b) What is the ratio of GlenTav in the blended MacTavish drink?

Ratios as fractions

Suppose you are working with the ratio of 8 to 12

You can write this as 8 : 12 or as a fraction $\frac{8}{12}$

You would say that the ratio is 'eight to twelve'.

This simplifies to 2 : 3 or $\frac{2}{3}$

> You can write a ratio without the colon, as a fraction.
>
> $1 : 2 \rightarrow \frac{1}{2}$

Exercise 11.2

1 Copy and complete each statement, replacing the star to make the ratios equivalent.

(a) $\frac{14}{8} = \frac{*}{4}$

(b) $\frac{16}{12} = \frac{4}{*}$

(c) $\frac{15}{45} = \frac{*}{9}$

2 Copy and complete each statement, replacing the star to make the ratios equivalent.

(a) $\frac{14}{*} = \frac{1}{4}$

(b) $\frac{*}{72} = \frac{2}{9}$

(c) $\frac{*}{144} = \frac{5}{9}$

3 The ratio of tin to zinc in 100 g of solder is 60 : 40

(a) What is the ratio of tin to zinc, in its lowest terms?

(b) What is the ratio of zinc to tin?

(c) What fraction of the mix is zinc?

(d) What fraction of the mix is tin?

4 A recipe for fruit cake requires 200 g of raisins, 150 g of currants and 100 g of sultanas.

(a) What is the ratio of currants to raisins?

(b) What fraction of the dried fruit is sultanas?

(c) What is the ratio of sultanas to raisins?

(d) What is the ratio of raisins : currants : sultanas?

(e) Why can you not write the ratio in (d) as a fraction?

◯ Ratio as parts of a whole

Sometimes you need to divide an amount up into several parts. Look at these lines.

The line *AC* is divided into five parts.

AB is one part and *BC* is four parts.

AB : *BC* = 1 : 4 and *AB* : *AC* = 1 : 5

The line *DF* is divided into five parts.

DE is two parts and *EF* is three parts.

So *DE* : *EF* = 2 : 3 and *DE* : *DF* = 2 : 5

Both these lines have been divided into five parts but the first has been divided in the ratio 1 : 4, and the second in the ratio 2 : 3

Now consider the rod *AD*, five units long. It can be divided into three parts, in different ways.

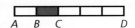  

AB : *BC* : *CD* = 1 : 1 : 3   *AB* : *BC* : *CD* = 1 : 2 : 2   *AB* : *BC* : *CD* = 1 : 3 : 1

You can also take the full length of the rod into account.

AB : *BC* : *AD* = 1 : 1 : 5   *AB* : *BC* : *AD* = 1 : 2 : 5   *AB* : *BC* : *AD* = 1 : 3 : 5

Always read the question carefully and make sure that you use the correct letters to describe each part. This is very important when you are solving ratio problems in geometry.

Exercise 11.3

In questions 1–6, *B* is a point on the line *AC*. Draw a line *ABC* and then answer the question.

1 Draw a line *AC* 6 cm long. Mark a point *B* such that *AB* : *BC* = 1 : 2

2 Draw a line *AC* 10 cm long. Mark a point *B* such that *AB* : *BC* = 2 : 3

3 Draw a line *AC* 8 cm long. Mark a point *B* such that *AB* : *BC* = 1 : 3

4 Draw a line *AC* 12 cm long. Mark a point *B* such that *AC* : *AB* = 6 : 1

5 Draw a line *AD* 12 cm long. Mark points *B* and *C* such that *AB* : *BC* : *CD* = 3 : 2 : 1

6 Draw a line *AD* 12 cm long. Mark points *B* and *C* such that *AB* : *BC* : *AD* = 4 : 2 : 6

Answer these questions without drawing the lines.

7 *AB* = 20 cm, *BC* = 40 cm. Write down each ratio.

   (a) *AB* : *BC*   **(b)** *BC* : *AB*   **(c)** *AB* : *AC*   **(d)** *BC* : *AC*

8 *AB* = 40 cm and *BC* = 1.2 m. Write down each ratio.

   (a) *AB* : *BC*   **(b)** *BC* : *AB*   **(c)** *AB* : *AC*   **(d)** *BC* : *AC*

9 I have to draw a line *AC* and mark a point *B* such that *AB* : *BC* = 2 : 5. If the length of *AB* is 4 cm, how long are *AC* and *BC*?

10 The points *X*, *Y* and *Z* on a straight line are such that *XY* : *YZ* = 4 : 7 and *XZ* is 22 cm long. How long is:

   (a) *XY*   **(b)** *YZ*?

◯ Solving problems with ratio

These are the steps you should follow, when you need to solve problems with ratio.

1 Write out the ratio, making sure you have the parts the right way round.

2 Work out the total number of parts.

3 Find the value of one part.

4 Identify what you are trying to find.

5 Answer the question.

> **Example**
>
> My uncle gives my brother and me £50 to be divided in the ratio of our ages. My brother is 9 and I am 11. How much do we each receive?
>
> Ratio of brother's age : my age = 9 : 11
>
>   Total number of parts = 9 + 11 = 20
>
>   One part = £50 ÷ 20
>
>   = £2.50
>
> My brother has 9 parts. This is 9 × 2.50 = £22.50
>
> I have 11 parts. This is 11 × 2.50 = £27.50

1   Two sisters share £100 in the ratio of their ages. The elder sister is 13 years old and the younger is 7 years old. How much money does each sister receive?

2   I need to make 140 kg of mortar. The ratio of cement to sand is 1 : 6. How much cement and how much sand will I need?

3   In a chemistry lesson I mix 75 ml of chemical A with 120 ml of chemical B. What is the ratio of chemical A to chemical B?

4   I make an orange drink by mixing orange juice concentrate and water in the ratio 3 : 7. If I want to make 5 litres of orange drink, how many litres of orange juice concentrate will I need?

5   Garden fertiliser is made from a mixture of the chemical concentrate and water in the ratio 2 : 25. If I need 1 litre of water, how much concentrate must I add?

6   My brother mixes his fruit drink with cordial and water in the ratio 2 : 5

   (a) If he puts in 50 ml of cordial, how much water does he need?

   (b) How many millilitres is his drink in total?

   (c) Yesterday I made a mistake and mixed his drink in the ratio 2 : 5 but with 50 ml of water. How many millilitres was this drink?

7   I am making some rectangular invitation cards. The ratio of width to height is 3 : 5. If the width is 9 cm what is the area of the card?

8   I am painting my bedroom green. To make just the right shade I have to mix yellow and blue paint in the ratio 2 : 7. If I have 6 litres of yellow paint, how many litres of blue will I need? How many litres of green paint will I make?

9   I am going to paint another room pale yellow and I must mix lily white and buttercup in the ratio 2 : 5. If I need 28 litres of paint altogether, how many litres each of lily white and buttercup will I need?

10 I am making a tropical cocktail by mixing lime juice, coconut milk and pineapple juice in the ratio 1 : 3 : 6. If I want to make 5 litres of cocktail, how much will I need of each ingredient?

11 The angles in a triangle are in the ratio 1 : 2 : 3
    What are the angles and what type of triangle is it?

12 The angles of a triangle are in the ratio 1 : 2 : 2
    What are the angles and what special type of triangle is it?

○ Proportional division: The unitary method

In the unitary method, you work out the value of one unit (unit equals one) and then use this to work out the answer to the question.

Example

If a distance of 8 km is equivalent to 5 miles, what distance, in miles, is equivalent to 320 km?

A distance of 8 km is the same as 5 miles.

$$(\div 8)$$

Then a distance of 1 km is the same as $\frac{5}{8}$ miles.

$$(\times 320)$$

So a distance of 320 km is the same as $\frac{5}{\cancel{8}_1} \times \cancel{320}^{40} = 200$ miles.

Exercise 11.5

Use the unitary method to solve these problems but, be warned, some questions may not be quite as they seem! Leave your answer as a fraction when necessary.

1 If my car travels 84 miles on 14 litres of petrol, how far will it travel on 21 litres of petrol?

2 If I can buy 12 bars of Candynut for 80p, how much will it cost me to buy 9 bars?

3 If a bricklayer, on average, lays 84 bricks in 2 hours, how many bricks could he lay in five hours?

4 My cat eats 18 tins of cat food in two weeks. How many tins of cat food would she eat in three weeks?

5 Two of my class took 40 minutes to complete the school cross-country course. How long will it take 18 of my class to complete the same course?

6 An electric golf caddie can travel two miles in 50 minutes. How long would it take to travel three miles?

7 In four weeks my bean plant has grown 1.2 m. How high might it grow in 7 weeks?

8 A car travels 122 miles on 4 gallons of petrol. How many miles will it travel on 9 gallons of petrol?

9 Mrs Smith can type 12 pages in 45 minutes. If she keeps typing at the same rate, how long will it take her to type 20 similar pages?

10 I read three books in five days. How many books will I read in nine days?

If you check your answers to questions 5, 7 and 10, you will notice something interesting. The time it takes one person to run a race is generally different from the time that it takes anyone else. Bean plants do not grow at a steady rate. Books can be different lengths.

You can only use ratio methods when the amounts are proportional. This means that they increase or decrease at the same rate.

11 A capacity of 91 litres is equivalent to 20 gallons. How many gallons are there in 70 litres?

12 Water can be added to five tins of concentrated soup to make 2.2 litres of diluted soup. How many tins of concentrated soup will I need to make 3.5 litres of diluted soup?

13 Five bags of cement together weigh 280 lb. How much will three bags of the same cement weigh?

14 If three men can, on average, shift 90 bags of cement in one hour, how many men would I need to shift 150 similar bags of cement in one hour?

15 This is a recipe for making 16 Scotch pancakes.

250 g self-raising flour

250 ml water

4 tablespoons of milk

1 egg

Rewrite the recipe so that you could make 24 Scotch pancakes.

Ratio and enlargement

Look at this line.   *A*   *B*   *C*

Measure the length of *AB*, *BC* and *AC*

You should find that the ratio of *AB* : *BC* = 1 : 3

Then you can also say that *AB* : *AC* = 1 : 4

Therefore *AC* is 4 times as long as *AB*

You could say that *AC* is an enlargement of *AB*

This is an enlargement in one dimension.

Now think about enlarging a 4 × 2 rectangle.

Suppose you want to enlarge it in the ratio:

new : original = 2 : 1

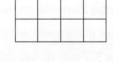

The 4 × 2 rectangle becomes an 8 × 4 rectangle.

The original rectangle's dimensions have been multiplied by 2

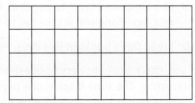

When you enlarge by the ratio 2 : 1, the length of the enlargement is twice the length of the original, so you can say that the enlargement has **scale factor** 2

Any enlargement always has to be defined by a scale factor. Each length in the object is multiplied by the scale factor to give the corresponding length in the image.

Exercise 11.6

1 Draw a line that is 2 cm long.

   Draw the enlargement of that line by scale factor 3

2 Draw a line that is 2 cm long.

   Draw an enlargement of that line by scale factor 2

3 Draw a line that is 4 cm long.

   Draw an enlargement of that line by scale factor 1.5

4 Copy these rectangles on squared paper.

   (a)   **(b)**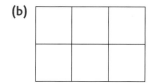

   (i) Draw their enlargements by scale factor 2

   (ii) Write down the ratio

        area of original : area of enlargement.

5 Copy this shape on squared paper. Label it A.

   Draw the enlargement of A:

   (a) with scale factor 2 and label the enlargement B

   (b) with scale factor 3 and label the enlargement C

   (c) in the ratio 3 : 2 and label the enlargement D.

6 Calculate the areas of the shapes A, B, C and D that you drew in question 5

   Then write down these ratios.

   (a) area A : area B

   (b) area A : area C

   (c) area A : area D.

   What do you notice about the relationships between the areas?

Enlargement on a grid

To draw an enlargement on a **co-ordinate grid**, you need to identify a centre of enlargement as well as a scale factor.

This example will lead you through the steps you need to follow.

Example

Triangle *ABC* has vertices *A*(2, 3), *B*(2, 4) and *C*(4, 3). Draw *DEF*, the enlargement of *ABC* by scale factor 3 with centre of enlargement (1, 1)

Step 1: Draw the object *ABC*

Step 2: Mark the centre of enlargement *X*

Step 3: Draw lines from *X* passing through *A*, *B*, *C* and beyond them.

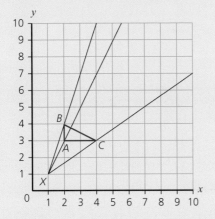

Step 4: Mark points *D*, *E* and *F* on your extended lines *XA*, *XB*, *XC* respectively, such that the length of *XD* is the length of *XA* multiplied by the scale factor of the enlargement, and so on.

Step 5: Join up the new points to produce the enlarged image *DEF*

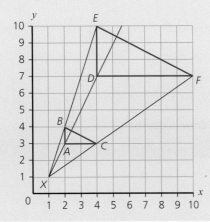

Finding the centre of enlargement

Sometimes you may be given the object and its image after an enlargement.

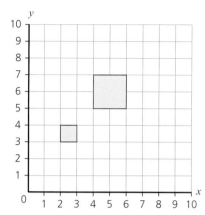 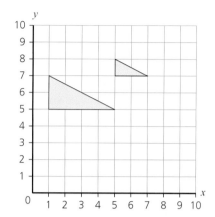

To find the **centre of enlargement**, first look carefully at the diagram and work out its approximate position.

Then draw lines through the corresponding points, extending each line so it goes past the approximate position of the centre of enlargement. Extend the lines back until they meet.

The point where they meet is the exact centre of enlargement.

Example:

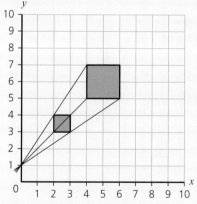 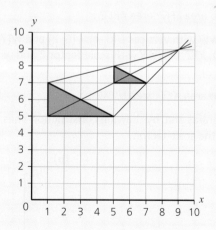

Centre of enlargement is (0, 1)

Scale factor 2

Centre of enlargement is (9, 9)

Scale factor 2

For each question in this exercise, start by drawing a set of co-ordinate axes, with each **axis** labelled from 0 to 10, as in question 1

1 **(a)** Copy the co-ordinate grid below. Draw on it the triangle and the construction lines.

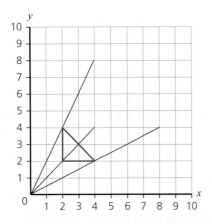

(b) Draw the image of the triangle after an enlargement with scale factor 2 and centre of enlargement the origin (0, 0)

2 **(a)** Draw triangle *ABC* with vertices *A*(1, 2), *B*(2, 1) and *C*(3, 2). Then draw the enlargement, *EFG*, of *ABC* with scale factor 3 and centre of enlargement (0, 0)

(b) What is the ratio area *EFG* : area *ABC*?

3 **(a)** Draw triangle *UVW* with vertices *U*(6, 4), *V*(6, 2) and *W*(7, 2). Draw the enlargement, *XYZ*, of *UVW* with scale factor 2 and with centre of enlargement (9, 2)

(b) What is the ratio area *XYZ* : area *UVW*?

4 Copy these four diagrams and, by drawing construction lines, find the centre of enlargement and the scale factor.

(a)

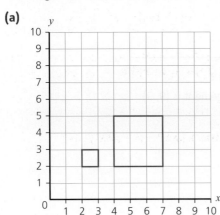

(b)

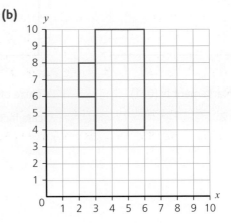

(c)

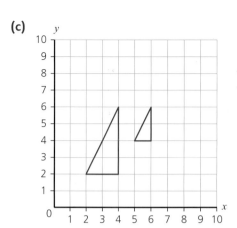

(d)

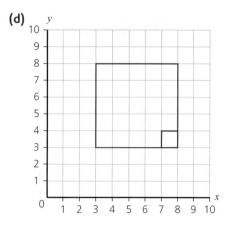

5 (a) Draw triangle *ABC* with vertices *A*(3, 4), *B*(5, 4) and *C* (4, 5). Draw triangle *DEF* with vertices *D*(2, 7), *E*(6, 7) and *F*(4, 9)

(b) Find the centre of enlargement and the scale factor for the enlargement that maps triangle *ABC* to triangle *DEF*.

6 (a) Draw triangle *GHI* with vertices *G*(3, 5), *H*(3, 4) and *I*(4, 4). Draw triangle *JKL* with vertices *J*(5, 9), *K*(5, 6) and *L*(8, 6)

(b) Find the centre of enlargement and the scale factor for the enlargement that maps triangle *GHI* to triangle *JKL*.

7 (a) Draw rectangle *ABCD* with vertices *A*(2, 7), *B*(2, 6), *C*(3, 6) and *D*(3, 7). Draw the enlargement, *EFGH*, of *ABCD* with scale factor 3 and centre of enlargement (1, 8)

(b) What is the ratio area *EFGH* : area *ABCD*?

8 (a) Draw rectangle *PQRS* with vertices *P*(3, 4), *Q*(3, 2), *R*(5, 2) and *S*(5, 4). Draw the enlargement, *JKLM*, of *PQRS* with scale factor 2 and centre of enlargement (3, 1)

(b) What is the ratio area *JKLM* : area *PQRS*?

9 (a) Draw a square *PQRS* with vertices *P*(4, 3), *Q*(4, 2), *R*(5, 2) and *S*(5, 3). Draw a square *WXYZ* with vertices *W*(5, 8), *X*(5, 5), *Y*(8, 5) and *Z*(8, 8)

(b) Find the centre of enlargement and the scale factor for the enlargement that maps *PQRS* to *WXYZ*.

10 (a) Draw the shape *ABCD* with vertices *A*(3, 2), *B*(5, 2), *C*(5, 4) and *D*(3, 4). Draw the enlargement, *AFGH*, of *ABCD* with scale factor 2 and centre of enlargement (3, 2)

(b) What is the ratio area *AFGH* : area *ABCD*?

11 Write a rule about the ratio of the areas when you know the scale factor.

These questions are similar to those you have met before, but a little harder. As always, make sure you read the questions carefully and show all your working.

1   I have to make a bar of an alloy. I do this by mixing copper and zinc in the ratio 3 : 8. If my finished bar has to have a mass of 187 kg, how many kilograms each of copper and zinc will I require?

2   James and Jane mixed up jugs of orange squash for sports day. Each jug contained 2 litres. The orange concentrate and water were supposed to be mixed in the ratio 1 : 7. Jane mixed her squash correctly but James did not read the instructions and mixed his in the ratio 1 : 4. If the concentrate came in bottles of 1.5 litres, how many more jugs did Jane make from one bottle of concentrate than James did?

3   My bicycle is geared in the ratio 2 : 3, so two turns of the pedals turns the wheel three times. If the circumference of the wheel is 1.2 m, how many turns of the pedals will I need to go one kilometre?

4   The angles of a quadrilateral are in the ratio 1 : 2 : 3 : 4 What are the angles?

5   The angles of a quadrilateral are in the ratio 2 : 3 : 3 : 4
    What are the angles and what special quadrilateral could this be? (Could it be any other quadrilateral?)

6   Colonel Mustard likes his cranberry juice and tonic in the ratio 2 : 3 of cranberry juice to tonic. His wife, Mrs Mustard, likes hers in the ratio 1 : 5. If they both have 200 ml of drink, how much cranberry juice do they each have?

7   My uncle has given £100 to be shared between my brothers and me in the ratio of our ages. Tom gets twice as much as Tim and I get half the amount of Tom and Tim together.

    (a) I am 12 years old. How old are Tom and Tim?

    (b) The amount of money does not share exactly. If we all get a whole number of pounds, how much do we each get and how much is left over?

8   In a class the ratio of boys to girls is 2 : 3. Two boys joins the class and the ratio of boys to girls becomes 4 : 5. If a class size cannot be more than 30, how many pupils are there in the class now?

9   I have some black squares and some white squares. I make 10 identical patterns in which the ratio of black squares to white squares is 1 : 3. My dog comes to help and eats 30 black squares. I can now make 9 identical patterns with a ratio of black squares to white squares of 1 : 4. How many white squares do I have?

10 A quadrilateral ABCD has been enlarged by a scale factor of 2.5 to its image, WXYZ.

    (a) If side AB = 4 cm, what is the length of side WX?

    (b) If side XY is 12.5 cm long, what is the length of side BC?

    (c) If the area of WXYZ is 125 cm², what is the area of ABCD?

Summary Exercise 11.9

1 I have four tins of white paint and seven tins of red paint.

   (a) What is the ratio of white paint to red paint?

   (b) What is the ratio of red paint to white paint?

   (c) What is the ratio of red paint to the total number of tins of paint?

2 Simplify each of these ratios.

   (a) 12 : 24   (b) 32 : 144   (c) 108 : 45

3 I mix 12 g of chemical A to 14 g of chemical B to make a new compound C.

   (a) What is the ratio of chemical A to chemical B?

   (b) I want to make 130 g of Compound C. How much Chemical B will I need?

4 Draw a line AC 5 cm long.

   Mark a point B so that AB : BC = 2 : 3

5 Draw a line AC 12 cm long.

   Mark a point B so that AB : BC = 1 : 2

6 Replace the x in these ratios, to make them true.

   (a) 34 : x = 2 : 1   (b) 24 : 8 = 6 : x (c) 2 : 7 = 34 : x

7 A piece of string 1.2 m long is cut into two pieces in the ratio 3 : 5

   How long is each of the two pieces?

8 I need 12 litres of fertiliser to treat 30 m² of lawn. How many litres will I need to treat a lawn that measures 8 m by 6 m?

9 In two hours 2.3 cm of rain fell. If it keeps falling at the same rate, how many centimetres of rain would fall in 3 hours?

10 Draw a co-ordinate grid with both axes numbered from 1 to 10. Draw triangle A with vertices at (2, 3), (3, 3) and (3, 5). Draw triangle B, which is the enlargement of A with scale factor 3 and centre of enlargement at (1, 4)

Activity: Christmas lunch investigation

It is Christmas Day in Acacia Avenue and here, at number 12, Mum is trying to draw up the table plan. Freddy, Sally, Vinnie and I are coming for lunch as well as Mum, Dad, Granny and Grandpa, Aunt Ethel and Uncle Bert, and cousins Cynthia and Sonnie.

How many different ways of arranging the Christmas lunch table are there?

After spending several hours on this, Dad suggests that we make it easier by trying to find the answer for tables of fewer people. If we can find a pattern then we might be able to use that to solve the problem.

At number 1 Acacia Avenue lives Stan. He will have Christmas lunch on his own, so there is only one way to arrange his table.

At number 2 Acacia Avenue live Dot and Doris. The two of them always eat together. Of course, Dot sits next to Doris and Doris next to Dot, so there is only one way their table can be arranged.

At number 3 Acacia Avenue live Mr and Mrs Blott and their son, Inky Blott. Whichever way their table is arranged, Inky sits between his Mum and Dad, and his Mum sits between Inky and Mr Blott and his Dad sits between Inky and Mrs Blott, only one arrangement again! How easy life must be in the Blott household!

At number 4 Acacia Avenue live the Whites. There is Chalky White and his sisters, Pearl and Ivory, and their dog, Snowy. Snowy always sits down for Christmas lunch too. These are the different arrangements for the table at number 4.

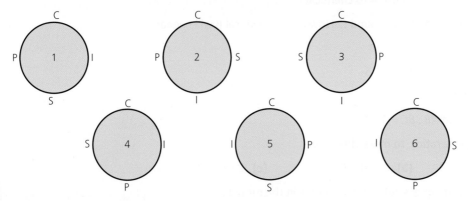

This looks like six arrangements, but if you look carefully you will see that arrangement 1 is the same as 5, 2 is the same as 3 and that 4 is the same as 6, so there are only three different arrangements.

You can see from number 4 Acacia Avenue that we think of a table arrangement by considering who sits next to whom. Although arrangement 1 looked different from arrangement 5, Chalky was still opposite Snowy and next to Pearl and Ivory. Remember this definition when you work out the next few answers.

At number 5 Acacia Avenue live Mr and Mrs Cake and their children, Pan, Fairy and Sponge. Can you work out the 12 different ways in which they can arrange their table?

At number 6 Acacia Avenue live the Gone family. As well as Mum and Dad there are the twins, Octa and Nona, and Uncle Penta and Aunt Polly. How many ways can their table be arranged?

Working out the arrangements for the seven people at number 7 might be quite hard. First copy and complete this table, and then see if you can spot a pattern.

Check your pattern is correct by drawing all the arrangements for the family of seven at number 7.

Now can you work out how many arrangements there are for our family of 12 at number 12? You need to remember that Dad refuses to sit next to Aunt Ethel, no two boys can sit next to each other, as they fight, nor two girls, as they argue.

House number	Arrangements
1	1
2	1
3	1
4	3
5	12
6	

 Algebra 2: Equations and brackets

A greengrocer sells baskets containing 5 pieces of fruit.
A basket contains three apples and two bananas.

I buy two of these baskets:

Altogether I have twice the number of apples and twice the number of bananas that are in one basket. I have 6 apples and 4 bananas; that is 10 pieces of fruit in total.

You could write a statement about the numbers of pieces of fruit, using brackets:

$(3 + 2) + (3 + 2) = 2(3 + 2)$ $2(3 + 2)$ means two lots of $3 + 2$

$2(3 + 2) = 2 \times 5$

$= 10$

When a calculation includes brackets, you normally do the calculation inside the brackets first.

Here is another example:

$2(7 + 2) = 2 \times 9$

$= 18$

You do, however, get the same answer if you multiply out the brackets like this:

$2(7 + 2) = 2 \times 7 + 2 \times 2$

$= 14 + 4$

$= 18$

Multiplying out brackets

If there is an algebraic expression with two or more unlike terms inside the brackets, you cannot simplify it but you can expand it by multiplying out the brackets like this.

$3(x + 2) = 3 \times x + 3 \times 2$

$= 3x + 6$

> Remember that when you use x as an algebraic variable, you write it as a curly x so that you do not mistake it for the $\times$ that is a multiplication sign.

Multiply out the brackets.

1	$3(x + 1)$	**6**	$3(2b + 1)$
2	$2(x + 3)$	**7**	$2(4x + 3)$
3	$2(x - 3)$	**8**	$2(5 + 2a)$
4	$4(3 + x)$	**9**	$5(2y + 3)$
5	$2(5 - a)$	**10**	$3(7 - 3a)$
11	$4(6 + 3a)$	**16**	$3(7 - 2x)$
12	$2(2x - 3y)$	**17**	$2(6a - 3b)$
13	$3(4a - b)$	**18**	$6(4 - 3x)$
14	$5(2x + 1)$	**19**	$8(2n - 4m)$
15	$3(b - 5a)$	**20**	$5(3p - q)$

Collecting like terms

When a term with brackets is part of an expression, you may need to expand the brackets and then check, to see if you can collect like terms.

Example

$3x + 4(2x + 3) = 3x + 8x + 12$ Expand the brackets.

$= 11x + 12$ Collect like terms, $3x + 8x = 11x$

An expression may include two sets of brackets.

Example

$2(3x - 1) + 3(x + 4) = 6x - 2 + 3x + 12$ Expand the brackets.

$= 9x + 10$ Collect like terms.

Multiply out the brackets and then simplify each expression.

1	$2 + 3(x + 2)$	**7**	$2 + 3(4 - 2x)$
2	$4x + 2(x - 1)$	**8**	$4(3x - 4) - 12x$
3	$2x + 5(x - 3)$	**9**	$4 + 4(2x - 1)$
4	$x + 2(2x + 5)$	**10**	$3x + 5(2 + 3x)$
5	$3(x + 2) - 3$	**11**	$2(4x + 3) + 3(2x - 4)$
6	$3(4 - 2x) + 3x$	**12**	$3(x + 2) + 2(2x + 1)$

13 $4(3 + x) + 3(5 - 2x)$

14 $2(1 + 2x) + 3(x + 2)$

15 $3(2x + 4) + (5x + 3)$

16 $2(4x - 3) + 3(5 - x)$

17 $5(2 + 3x) + (5x + 6)$

18 $4(5 - 3x) + 2(4 - 6x)$

19 $3(7 + 3x) + 2(5 - x)$

20 $2(6 - x) + (3 - 2x)$

Brackets and minus signs

So far the number outside the bracket has been positive but this will not always be the case. If there is a negative number, or a minus sign, before the brackets, you must multiply whatever is inside the brackets by a negative number rather than a positive number. So, if there is a minus sign before the brackets, you must apply it to whatever is inside the brackets.

Examples

(i) $6x - 2(2x + 1) = 6x - 4x - 2$
$$= 2x - 2$$

(ii) $5 - 3(x - 2) = 5 - 3x + 6$
$$= 11 - 3x$$

> Remember that
> negative × positive is negative
> but
> negative × negative is positive

Take care when there is a minus sign but no number in front of the brackets. This means 'multiply by ⁻1' so you must change the sign of each term inside the brackets as you multiply through.

Examples

(i) $5x - (3 + 2x) = 5x - 3 - 2x$
$$= 3x - 3$$

(ii) $5 - (3x - 1) = 5 - 3x + 1$
$$= 6 - 3x$$

(ii) $2(3x - 3) - 3(x + 4) = 6x - 6 - 3x - 12$
$$= 3x - 18$$

Exercise 12.3

Multiply out the brackets and simplify each expression.

1 $4 - 2(x + 1)$

2 $3x - 2(2 + x)$

3 $5x - 2(5 + 2x)$

4 $8 - 3(3x + 2)$

5 $3 - (2x + 1)$

6 $8x - (4 + 5x)$

7 $10x - 3(2 + 3x)$

8 $8 - 4(3x + 2)$

9 $12 - (2 + x)$

10 $3x - 2(5x - 1)$

Take care, these expressions have two sets of brackets.

11 $2(4x + 3) - 3(x - 1)$ **16** $2(x + 3) - 3(3x - 4)$

12 $3(x + 2) - 2(2x + 1)$ **17** $5(2 + x) - (5x + 1)$

13 $4(2 + 2x) - 3(4 - 2x)$ **18** $4(3 - 2x) - 2(6 - 6x)$

14 $2(1 + 3x) - 3(x + 1)$ **19** $4(5 + 3x) - 2(5 + 6x)$

15 $3(2x + 2) - (3x + 3)$ **20** $2(3 - x) - (6 - 2x)$

What happens when your answer looks like one of these?

- $^-6x + 7$

- $^-2x - 12$

It is always best to avoid starting an expression with a negative number, because it is easy to miss.

In the first of these examples, it would be better to write the expression as $7 - 6x$

There is nothing you can do about the answer for $^-2x - 12$, so you have to leave it as it is.

Remember this when you do the next exercise.

Exercise 12.4

Multiply out the brackets and then simplify each expression.

> Remember to take care with any minus signs and deal with them correctly. Do not let them catch you out!

1 $8 + 3(2x - 4)$ **6** $12 - (2x - 4)$

2 $10 - 2(2x + 1)$ **7** $5(2 + 3x) - 8x$

3 $3(3 + x) - 2(5 - 2x)$ **8** $3(3 - 4x) + 2(6x - 1)$

4 $2(1 + x) + 3(x + 2)$ **9** $3(6 + 3x) - 2(9 - x)$

5 $3(3x + 4) - (5x + 4)$ **10** $2(7 + x) - (3 + 5x)$

11 $2(4x + 3) - 6$ **16** $2(4x + 6) + 3(2x - 4)$

12 $4x - 2(2x + 1)$ **17** $6(2 + 3x) - 3(5x + 6)$

13 $4(3 + 6x) - 3(5 - 8x)$ **18** $12x - 2(4 - 6x)$

14 $4(1 + 2x) - 2(x + 2)$ **19** $3(7 + 3x) - 21$

15 $15x - 5(5x + 3)$ **20** $4(6 - 3x) - 3(8 - 4x)$

Factorising

Sometimes an expression may have the same numbers or letters in both terms, for example, as in $2 + 2x$

In this case, 2 is a **common factor** in the same way that 2 is a common factor of 4 and 6

$$2 + 2x = 2(1 + x)$$

If you find a common factor and take it outside the brackets, you have **factorised** the expression. You can always check that your factorising is correct by multiplying out the brackets.

Examples

(i) Factorise: $2x + 8$

$$2x + 8 = 2 \times x + 2 \times 2 \times 2$$
$$= 2(x + 4)$$

Check: $2(x + 4) = 2x + 8$

> Think of each part of the expression as a product of its prime factors.

(ii) Factorise: $2a + 6b$

$$2a + 6b = 2 \times a + 2 \times 3 \times b$$
$$= 2(a + 3b)$$

Check: $2(a + 3b) = 2a + 6b$

Exercise 12.5

1 Copy and complete these. The common factor has already been taken out for you.

(a) $2x + 6 = 2(x + *)$

(b) $3x + 12 = 3(x + *)$

(c) $4x - 8 = 4(* - 2)$

(d) $3x + 6 = 3(x + *)$

2 Copy and complete these. You need to write down the common factor in each case.

(a) $3x + 12 = *(x + 4)$

(b) $6x - 3 = *(2x - 1)$

(c) $4x + 2y - 6 = *(2x + y - 3)$

(d) $15 - 3x + 6y = *(5 - x + 2y)$

3 This time the common factors have been taken out and you have to fill in the brackets.

(a) $4x + 6 = 2(* + *)$

(b) $3x - 15 = 3(* - *)$

(c) $6x + 9y - 12 = 3(* + * - *)$

(d) $12 + 9x - 3y = 3(* + * - *)$

4 Factorise these expressions.

(a) $4x + 8$

(b) $3y - 6$

(c) $12 + 18y$

193

5 Factorise these expressions. Note that you may need to write the number 1 as a term inside the brackets.

(a) $15y + 5$ (b) $16x - 20xy + 4$ (c) $8x + 4y - 12xy$

6 Factorise these expressions, if possible.

(a) $2x + 8$ (g) $18c + 6ab - 12$

(b) $12a + 5$ (h) $8 - 16a + 24c$

(c) $15 - 21x$ (i) $18 + 16a$

(d) $18a + 16b$ (j) $4x + 16y - xy$

(e) $9a + 16b$ (k) $7 + 14p - 21q$

(f) $8a + 16b - 24ab$ (l) $8ab + 16$

◯ Equations

You already know how to solve simple equations. You will recall that an equation is like a balance. In order to keep it balanced, you must do the same thing to both sides. When you have completed a solution, it is good practice to check your answer by substituting the value you found into the original equation.

Example

(i) Solve the equation: $x + 3 = 9$

$$x + 3 - 3 = 9 - 3$$

(-3) (-3) Subtract 3 from both sides

$$x = 6$$

                                 Check: $6 + 3 = 9$ ✓

(ii) Solve the equation: $3x = 6$

$$3x \div 3 = 6 \div 3$$

$(\div 3)$ $(\div 3)$ Divide both sides by 3

$$x = 2$$

                                 Check: $3 \times 2 = 6$ ✓

Sometimes you need to go through two or more stages. As you become more confident, you can leave out some of the working.

> Note that the equals signs align in a column and the operations in brackets described on either side show what you have done to both sides of the equation. You must write these down clearly so that, as your equations get more complicated, it is clear how you have solved them – and it makes it easier for you to check your working. Once you have become confident you can write the operations in brackets on the right-hand side only, to show what you have done to both sides of the equation.

Examples

(i) Solve the equation: $2x - 3 = 9$

$2x - 3 = 9$

$\qquad\qquad (+ 3)$ Add 3 to both sides

$2x = 12$

$\qquad\qquad (\div 2)$ Divide both sides by 2

$x = 6$

$\qquad\qquad$ Check: $2 \times 6 + 3 = 15$ ✓

(ii) Solve the equation: $7 - 3x = 6$

$7 - 3x = 6$

$\qquad\qquad (+ 3x)$ Add $3x$ to both sides

$7 = 6 + 3x$

$\qquad\qquad (- 6)$ Subtract 6 from both sides

$1 = 3x$

$\qquad\qquad (\div 3)$ Divide both sides by 3

$x = \frac{1}{3}$

$\qquad\qquad$ Check: $7 - 3 \times \frac{1}{3} = 6$ ✓

Exercise 12.6

Solve these equations. Remember to check your answers in your head.

1   $x + 4 = 6$

2   $a - 6 = 3$

3   $4b = 8$

4   $2c = 10$

5   $p + 8 = 4$

6   $4x = 12$

7   $m - 4 = 7$

8   $3d = 12$

9   $7 + x = 6$

10   $7 = 5 + m$

11   $2a + 4 = 8$

12   $3m - 1 = 5$

13   $5 = 13 + 4p$

14   $1 + 3n = 13$

15   $2x + 14 = 9$

16   $3s + 7 = 16$

17   $2t - 4 = 10$

18   $7 = 13 + 3q$

19   $6x + 1 = 7$

20   $9 = 1 + 4n$

21   $5 + 3b = 8$

22   $6 = 2 + 3x$

23   $11 = 2 - 3b$

24   $1 + 4b = 6$

25   $5 - 2c = 8$

26   $5 = 2 - 3n$

27   $7 = 8 - 2b$

28   $9 = 1 + 2x$

29   $7 = 2 - 5c$

30   $3 = 8 + 5a$

> If the unknown term is negative, add it to both sides. This way it appears on the other side of the equals sign, but becomes positive. It is important to keep the unknown term positive.

Squares and square roots

Powers and roots can be used in algebra too.

If x^2 is the square of x, then x is the square root of x^2

1 is the square of 1 and also of $^-1$ 1 and $^-1$ are the square roots of 1

4 is the square of 2 and of $^-2$ 2 and $^-2$ are the square roots of 4

9 is the square of 3 and of $^-3$ 3 and $^-3$ are the square roots of 9

16 is the square of 4 and of $^-4$ 4 and $^-4$ are the square roots of 16

The symbol for 'square root' looks like this: $\sqrt{}$

You can write the square root of 4 as $\sqrt{4}$ $\sqrt{4} = 2$ or $^-2$

You can write '2 or $^-2$' as $^\pm 2$, which you say as 'positive or negative two'.

Exercise 12.7

Write down these squares and square roots.

1 $\sqrt{16}$ **6** $\sqrt{0.25}$

2 $\sqrt{25}$ **7** $\sqrt{144}$

3 $\sqrt{10\,000}$ **8** 100^2

4 0.4^2 **9** 0.1^2

5 1.2^2 **10** $\sqrt{121}$

Square roots

You know that $3 \times 3 = 9$ and also that $^-3 \times {}^-3 = {}^+9$

Therefore equations that include a term such as x^2 can have two solutions.

Example

Solve the equation: $x^2 = 9$

$x^2 = 9$

$(\sqrt{})$

$x = 3$ or $x = {}^-3$

Exercise 12.8

Solve these equations.

1 $x^2 = 1$ **4** $c^2 = 81$

2 $a^2 = 100$ **5** $y^2 = 4$

3 $b^2 = 49$ **6** $a^2 = 64$

7 $x^2 = 0.09$

9 $b^2 = 0.16$

8 $c^2 = 1600$

10 $y^2 = 400$

Write an equation and solve it to find the answer to each of these questions.

11 The area of a square is $144\,\text{m}^2$. What is the length of one of its sides?

12 The area of a square is $1.44\,\text{m}^2$. What is the length of one of its sides?

13 The area of a square is $0.64\,\text{cm}^2$. What is the length of one of its sides?

14 The area of a square is $0.04\,\text{cm}^2$. What is its perimeter?

Equations with brackets

As you have seen, you sometimes need brackets in an expression.

Example

Two of my friends are having birthdays. I have £10 to spend. Birthday cards cost £2

Assuming I spend the same amount on each friend, how much can I spend on each present?

You could write the puzzle like this where the cost (in pounds) of one present is represented by 🎁

$(🎁 + 2) + (🎁 + 2) = 10$

But it is more mathematical to say: 'Let the present cost £x,' and then form an equation in x, which you can solve.

$2(x + 2) = 10$

               (B) expand the brackets

$2x + 4 = 10$

               $(- 4)$

$2x = 6$

               $(\div 2)$

$x = 3$

The presents each cost £3

        Check: $2(3 + 2) = 2 \times 5 = 10$ ✓

> Note that you leave the units, £ in this case, out of the equation, then solve it. You give the answer to the question, including the units, after the calculation.

Exercise 12.9

Solve these equations. Remember to multiply out the brackets first and to write down what you are doing at each stage. Check your answers in your head. Remember that an answer may be a negative number or a fraction.

1 $3(x + 1) = 12$

6 $15 = 3(2x + 3)$

2 $2(x - 3) = 10$

7 $2(2x + 3) = 8$

3 $4(3 + x) = 16$

8 $2(2x - 3) = 8$

4 $3(2 + x) = 15$

9 $16 = 3(4 + 2x)$

5 $2(2x - 1) = 18$

10 $4(2x + 5) = 3$

11 $5(x - 4) = 5$

12 $2(5 + 3x) = 1$

13 $2(x - 1) = 8$

14 $12 = 4(x + 2)$

15 $2(4 + 3x) = 2$

16 $4 = 3(2 + 2x)$

17 $4(3x - 2) = 16$

18 $2(2 + 3x) = 22$

19 $3(2x - 1) = 9$

20 $4(x + 3) = 8$

Fractions and equations

If an equation involves a fraction, start by multiplying the whole equation by the denominator (the bottom number) of the fraction.

Examples

(i) Solve the equation: $\frac{x}{3} = 4$

$$\frac{x}{3} = 4$$

$$\qquad (\times 3)$$

$$x = 12$$

Check: $(12 \div 3) = 4$ ✓

(ii) Solve the equation: $\frac{x - 4}{3} = 2$

$$\frac{x - 4}{3} = 2$$

$$\qquad (\times 3)$$

$$x - 4 = 6$$

$$\qquad (+ 4)$$

$$x = 10$$

Check: $(10 - 4) \div 3 = 2$ ✓

> Make sure you include the short notation to explain the steps.

You can see that, in both examples, by multiplying by 3 first you can get rid of the fraction. The equation then becomes simpler to solve.

Exercise 12.10

Solve these equations.

1 $\frac{x}{5} = 2$

2 $\frac{a}{2} = 7$

3 $9 = \frac{m}{3}$

4 $\frac{b}{4} = 5$

5 $\frac{3a}{2} = 9$

6 $\frac{4a}{3} = 12$

7 $\frac{3n}{4} = 1$

8 $\frac{x + 5}{5} = 3$

9 $\frac{a - 4}{3} = 5$

10 $\frac{2x + 4}{5} = 2$

◯ Writing story puzzles with brackets

When you are trying to solve a story or word problem, you need to decide whether to use brackets. In the example about buying presents for friends, there were two 'presents' of the same size.

(🎁 + 2) and (🎁 + 2)

The brackets indicate that 2 was added to the unknown quantity 🎁, in each case.

Then the whole expression, (🎁 + 2), was multiplied by 2 because there were two presents to be bought.

It is a good idea to use brackets round amounts that are added or subtracted, even if you are not sure if they are really necessary.

Example

If you double the age that I will be in five years' time, you will get my mother's age now.

My mother is 38. How old am I?

Let my age be x years.

In five years' time I will be $(x + 5)$ years old.

My mother's age is 38

$2(x + 5) = 38$ Double $(x + 5)$ is my mother's age.
            (B)
$2x + 10 = 38$
            (− 10)
$2x = 28$
            (÷ 2)
$x = 14$

I am 14 years old.

> Remember to write out the answer with the correct units.

Exercise 12.11

Write an equation for each story puzzle and then solve it to find the solution to the puzzle.

1 I think of a number, add 5, double the result and I get 30. What was my number?

2 I think of a number, double it, add 5 and I get 25. What was my number?

3 I think of a number, subtract 3, double the result and I get 14. What was my number?

4 I think of a number, double it, subtract 3 and I get 17. What was my number?

5 If you double the age that I will be in 4 years' time, you will get 40. How old am I now?

6 If you treble the age that I was 4 years ago, you will get 36. How old am I now?

7 If you subtract 5 from Mum's age and then double it you will get 70 (Grandpa's age.) How old is Mum?

Some of the answers to the rest of the exercise will be expressions in terms of x.

8 I am 5 years younger than my sister. My brother is twice as old as I am.

   (a) If my sister is x years old, how old am I?

   (b) How old is my brother?

   (c) Write an expression in x for the sum of our ages.

   (d) The sum of our ages is 33. Form an equation in x and solve it. How old is my sister?

   (e) How old am I? How old is my brother?

9 My sister is three years younger than I am and my brother is three times as old as my sister.

   (a) If I am x years old, how old is my sister?

   (b) How old is my brother?

   (c) Write an expression in x for the sum of our ages.

   (d) The sum of our ages is 28. Write an equation in x and solve it to find my age.

   (e) How old is my brother?

10 Tom, Sally and I divide up a packet of sweets. Tom has the green ones, Sally has the orange ones and I have the rest. I have twice as many as Tom and 5 more sweets than Sally.

   (a) If Tom has x sweets, how many do I have?

   (b) How many does Sally have?

   (c) Write an expression in x for the total number of sweets.

   (d) There were 15 sweets in total. Write an equation in x and solve it to find how many sweets we each had.

Writing story puzzles with brackets

Extension Exercise 12.12

Here are some more complicated equations. In these questions you have to multiply out the brackets first and then simplify before solving the equation.

Example

Solve this equation: $2(3x - 1) + 4x = 10$

$$2(3x - 1) + 4x = 10$$

(B)

$$6x - 2 + 4x = 10$$

(S)

$$10x - 2 = 10$$

(+ 2)

$$10x = 12$$

(÷ 10)

$$x = \frac{12}{10}$$

(C)

$$= \frac{6}{5}$$

$$= 1\frac{1}{5}$$ Convert the improper fraction to a mixed number.

Now solve these equations.

1 $3(2x - 2) + 4 = 8$

2 $2(3 + 2x) - 1 = 12$

3 $5 + 2(x - 2) = 7$

4 $3(1 + 2x) + 5 = 8$

5 $3 - 2(x + 4) = 6$

6 $4 - 3(2x + 1) = 7$

7 $12 = 3 - 4(2 + x)$

8 $9 = 4 - 2(3x + 1)$

9 $2(4x - 1) - 3x = 8$

10 $6 - (2x + 5) = 7$

11 $3x + 4(2x - 3) = 21$

12 $4x - 3(2 + 3x) = 36$

13 $3(x + 3) + 2(x + 4) = 22$

14 $3(3 - 2x) - 4(4 + 3x) = 6$

15 $2(x - 1) + 3(x - 4) = 1$

16 $4(2 + 3x) - 4(3 + 2x) = 11$

17 $3(2 + x) - (4x + 1) = 8$

18 $3(x + 3) - 2(x + 4) = 12$

19 $2(3x + 2) + 5(3x - 3) = 22$

20 $2(x + 2) - (x - 1) = 4$

1 Multiply out the brackets.

    (a) $2(x + 1)$ **(c)** $4(5 + 3x)$

    (b) $3(2x - 4)$

2 Multiply out the brackets and then simplify the expressions.

    (a) $2(x + 1) + 3x$ **(c)** $4x - 5(2x + 1)$

    (b) $3 + 2(2x - 1)$ **(d)** $6(3x + 4) - 20x$

3 Factorise these expressions, if possible.

    (a) $2a + 4$ **(e)** $24a + 15b - 21c$

    (b) $3b - 18c$ **(f)** $10y - 5x$

    (c) $8x + 4$ **(g)** $3ab + 7b + 12a$

    (d) $4a + 5c$ **(h)** $8a + 16ab - 24$

4 Solve these equations.

    (a) $3x = 12$ **(c)** $m - 6 = 11$

    (b) $a + 4 = 7$ **(d)** $4s = 3$

5 Solve these equations. Show each stage of your working.

    (a) $4x - 7 = 9$ **(c)** $3 - 2m = 11$

    (b) $2a + 3 = 7$ **(d)** $4 = 3 + 5t$

6 Solve these equations.

    (a) $\frac{x}{5} = 4$ **(b)** $\frac{2x - 1}{3} = 2$

7 Solve these equations.

    (a) $2(x + 3) = 5$ **(c)** $8x + 3(4 - 2x) = 7$

    (b) $3 + 2(3x - 2) = 5$

8 I think of a number, double it, add 7 and get the result 15. What was my number?

9 Freddy, Henry and Casper are going on a sponsored walk. Henry walks 10 miles further than Casper, and 6 miles fewer than Freddy.

    (a) If Henry walks x miles, how far does Freddy walk?

    (b) How far does Casper walk?

    (c) Write an expression in x for the total distance the three boys walk.

    (d) They walk a total of 41 miles. Write an equation in x and solve it to find how far each one walks.

13 Angles and polygons

The study of angles and shapes is called **geometry**. You already know a great deal about geometry. Here is a summary of some of the terms that you should recognise.

◯ Angles

An **angle** is formed when two straight lines meet at a point.

Acute angle
Less than 90°

Right angle
90°

Obtuse angle
Between 90 and 180°

Reflex angle
More than 180°

What else do you already know about angles?

Angles in a circle (at a point) add up to 360°

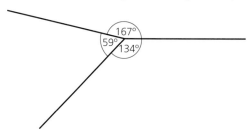

Angles on a straight line add up to 180°

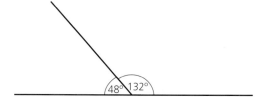

Angles in a triangle add up to 180°

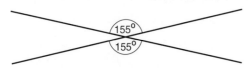

Vertically opposite angles are equal.

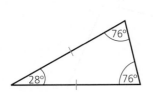

Base angles of an isosceles triangle are equal.

Angles in an equilateral triangle are all equal to 60°

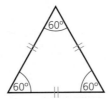

> Remember to give reasons for your answers so that other people can follow your working.

Even if you only know some of the angles in a given diagram you can often use these facts to calculate others.

Example

Calculate the values of x, y and z in this diagram.

$x = 48°$ Vertically opposite angles

$y = 180° - 48°$ Angles on a straight line

   $= 132°$

$z = 180° - (48° + 54°)$ Angles in a triangle

   $= 180° - 102°$

   $= 78°$

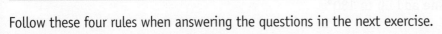

Follow these four rules when answering the questions in the next exercise.

1 Draw the diagram.

2 Write down each angle fact, giving the reason that you know the fact.

3 Work down the page, aligning the equals signs vertically.

4 Show all your calculations, however simple.

Exercise 13.1

Find the value of the unknown angles (marked by letters) in each question.
Remember to follow the rules.

1

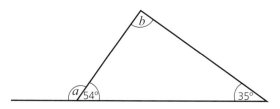

6

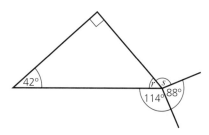

2

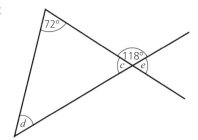

7

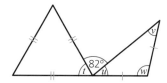

3

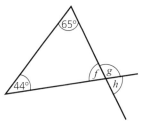

8

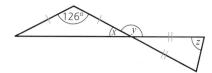

4

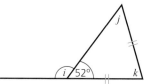

9

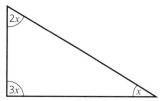

5

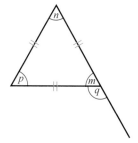

10

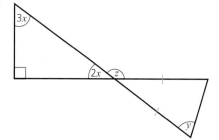

Parallel lines and angles

Two lines are **parallel** if, however far you extend them, they will never meet and they remain the same distance apart.

These two lines are parallel.

If you draw a **transversal** across parallel lines, you produce some angles. Some of these angles are equal.

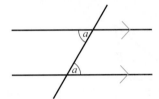   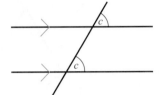

Alternate angles are equal.   **Corresponding angles** are equal.

The angles are either **acute** or **obtuse**. The four obtuse angles are all equal and the four acute angles are all equal. Because the obtuse angle and the acute angle are adjacent angles on a straight line, they must add up to 180°. This leads to a third pair of angles special to parallel lines.

Co-interior angles add up to 180°

$i + j = 180°$

These angles are sometimes called **supplementary angles**, which actually means that they add up to 180°, and they are sometimes called **allied angles**.

The most commonly used names now are interior or co-interior angles. In this book, they are called co-interior angles, to distinguish them from the interior angles of **polygons**.

Exercise 13.2

1 State whether these pairs of angles are alternate, corresponding, co-interior, or none of these.

(a)

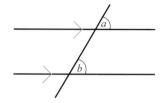

(d)

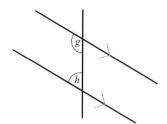

(b)

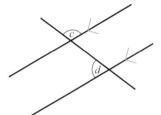

(e)

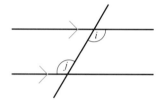

(c)

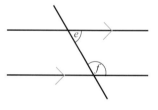

(f)

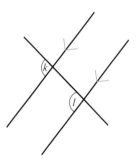

2 Find the size of the angle represented by a letter in each of these diagrams and say whether it is alternate to, corresponding to or co-interior with the other angle given.

(a)

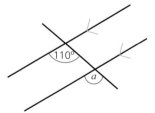

(c)

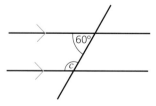

(b)

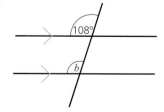

(d)

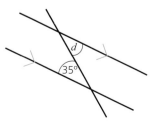

(e)

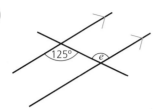

(f)

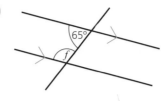

3 Look at this diagram. Find as many pairs of equal angles as you can. For each pair, give a reason why they are equal, for example, corresponding angles or alternate angles.

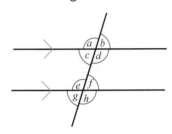

4 Refer again to the diagram in question 3. This time, find as many pairs of angles as you can that add up to 180°. For each pair give the angle reason for their relationship, for example, angles on a straight line or co-interior angles.

5 Find the size of each angle represented by a letter in this diagram. Write your answers in the order that you calculate the angles, which will not necessarily be in the order *a*, *b*, *c*, … Give your reason for each answer. (You may need vertically opposite angles and angles on a straight line, in addition to the three special cases for parallel lines.)

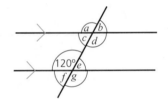

6 Now do the same as in question 5 for the angles in this diagram.

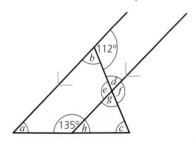

Naming angles

So far, unknown angles in diagrams have been marked by small, italic letters. In more complicated diagrams it is customary to mark the corners or **vertices** and the **intersections** of lines with capital letters. Then you can describe the angles in terms of the two lines that join at the point.

This is the angle *ABC*. It is the angle formed at point *B*, where *AB* meets *BC*

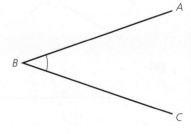

Look at this triangle, in which three angles meet at point *A*

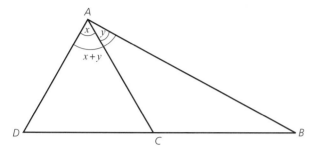

Run your finger over the diagram to make sure that you understand that:

Angle *BAC* is marked y

Angle *DAC* is marked x

Angle *BAD* is $x + y$

Exercise 13.3

1 Copy the diagram above.

   (a) Colour angle *ACD* red.

   (b) Colour angle *BCA* blue.

   (c) Colour angle *CBA* yellow.

2 Copy this diagram.

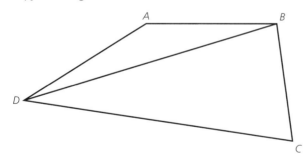

   (a) Colour angle *ABD* red.

   (b) Colour angle *CBD* blue.

   (c) Colour angle *ADC* yellow.

In Exercise 13.1 you saw that if you know the size of only one or two angles in a diagram you actually know enough about angles to find the size of most, or even all, of the other angles. Now, with what you know about parallel lines, you can find the sizes of even more angles.

In mathematics you have to be able to justify your statements. In your answers to any angle questions, you must give the reasons for your answers.

Example

Find the size of:

(i) angle *ABE*

(ii) angle *EBD*

(iii) angle *DBC*

Give reasons for your answers.

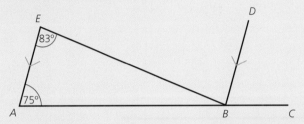

(i) angle *ABE* $= 180° - (75° + 83°)$ Angles in a triangle add up to 180°

   $= 180° - 158°$

   $= 22°$

(ii) angle *EBD* $= 83°$ Alternate angles

(iii) angle *DBC* $= 75°$ Corresponding angles

Exercise 13.4

1 In this diagram *AB* is parallel to *CE* and angle *ABD* $= 72°$

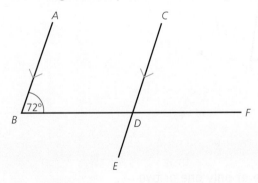

Find, giving reasons, the size of:

(a) angle *CDF*   **(b)** angle *CDB*   **(c)** angle *FDE*

2 In this diagram *AB* is parallel to *CD*, *AD* = *CD* and angle *BAD* = 32°

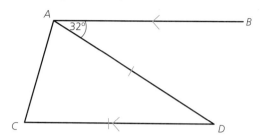

Find, giving reasons, the size of:

(a) angle *ADC*   **(b)** angle *DCA*

3 In this diagram *AD* is parallel to *EH*, angle *DCG* = 65° and angle *BFH* = 80°

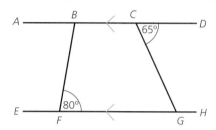

Find, giving reasons, the size of:

(a) angle *ABF*   **(c)** angle *CGH*

(b) angle *CBF*   **(d)** angle *CGF*

4 In this diagram *AB* is parallel to *DE*, angle *BAC* = 44° and angle *EDC* = 87°

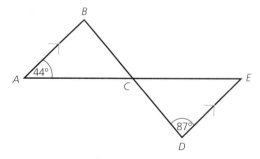

Find, giving reasons, the size of:

(a) angle *CED*   **(c)** angle *ACB*

(b) angle *ECD*   **(d)** angle *ABC*

5 In this diagram *ABC* is an equilateral triangle and *AB* is parallel to *DC*.

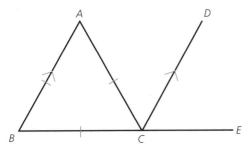

Find, giving reasons, the size of:

(a) angle *BCA*   **(c)** angle *DCE*

(b) angle *ACD*

6 In this diagram *AB* is parallel to *CD* and *BC* is parallel to *AD*, angle *DAB* = 32°
and angle *ABD* = 48°

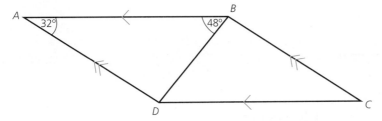

Find, giving reasons, the size of:

(a) angle *BDA*   **(c)** angle *DBC*

(b) angle *BDC*   **(d)** angle *BCD*

7 In this diagram *CD* is parallel to *AB*, angle *ECD* = 72° and angle *DBA* = 47°

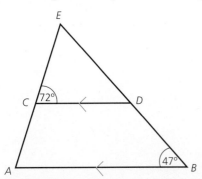

Find the size of angle *CED*. Show your working clearly and state any other
angles that you have had to find first. Give reasons for all your calculations.

8 In this diagram *AE* is parallel to *FK*, angle *BGI* = 74° and angle *DJK* = 105°

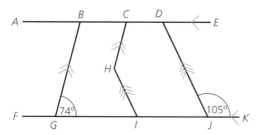

Find, giving reasons, and stating any other angles that you may have to find first, the size of:

(a) angle *GBC*

(b) angle *CDJ*

(c) angle *BCH*

(d) obtuse angle *CHI*

Polygons

Polygons are multi-sided shapes. The name comes from the Greek *poly* meaning 'many' and *gonia* meaning 'angles'. You frequently meet the prefix *poly* in words such as polyglot (a person who speaks many languages), polychrome (having several colours) and of course polygon (a shape with many angles and sides).

Polygons can be either **regular** or **irregular**. In regular polygons all the sides are the same length and all the interior angles are equal.

Regular	Irregular	Regular
3 sides: triangle		7 sides: heptagon
4 sides: quadrilateral		8 sides: octagon
5 sides: pentagon		9 sides: nonagon
6 sides: hexagon		10 sides: decagon

There are three angles that are of particular interest in a polygon.

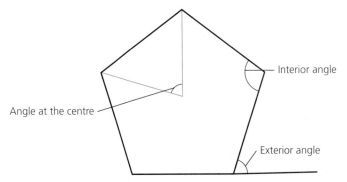

In *Maths for Common Entrance Book One*, you investigated the sums of the interior angles of polygons. Work through the next exercise, to review your earlier work and to find out more about the exterior angles of polygons.

Exercise 13.5

1 In your exercise book, draw a pentagon. It does not have to be regular. Divide it into triangles, like this.

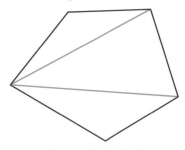

2 Now draw a hexagon, a heptagon, an octagon, a nonagon and a decagon. Divide them into triangles in the same way.

3 Copy and complete this table. When you come to the last column, think how you can calculate the interior angle of a regular polygon.

Polygon	Number of sides	Number of triangles	Angle sum	Interior angle of regular polygon
Triangle	3	1	180°	60°
Quadrilateral	4	2	360°	90°
Pentagon	5	3		
Hexagon	6			
	7			
	8			
	9			
	10			

4 The last row of the table is blank. Use this row to write the formulae for a polygon with n sides.

  (a) How many triangles will there be in a polygon with n sides?

  (b) What is the angle sum of a polygon with n sides?

  (c) What is the interior angle for a regular polygon with n sides?

  (d) Fill in the last row of the table.

Formula	n	$n - 2$		

5 Now look at the exterior angles. On each of the polygons that you have drawn, extend the sides so they look like Catherine wheels.

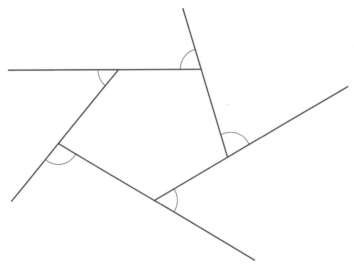

For each polygon, measure all the exterior angles and add them up.

6 Now draw a triangle, a quadrilateral, a hexagon, a heptagon, an octagon, a nonagon and a decagon. Draw and measure their exterior angles and calculate the sum for each shape.

7 Copy and complete this table. When you come to the last column, think how you can calculate the exterior angle of a regular polygon.

Polygon	Number of sides	Sum of exterior angles	Exterior angle of regular polygon
Triangle	3		
Quadrilateral	4		
Pentagon	5		
Hexagon	6		
	7		
	8		
	9		
	10		

8 The last row of the table is blank. Use this row to write the formulae for a polygon with n sides.

    (a) What is the sum of the exterior angles for a polygon with n sides?

    (b) What is the exterior angle for a regular polygon with n sides?

    (c) Fill in the last row of the table.

Formula	n		

9 Compare the interior and exterior angles for each regular polygon. What do you notice? Can you explain?

Polygon formulae

From the above exercise you have discovered three formulae.

- Angle sum of a polygon is $180°(n-2)$
- Interior angle of a regular polygon is $\dfrac{180°(n-2)}{n}$
- Exterior angle of a regular polygon is $\dfrac{360°}{n}$

You also know that:

- interior angle + exterior angle is $180°$

You can use these formulae to calculate angles in any regular polygon.

> ## Example
>
> Work out the interior angle of a regular nonagon.
>
> $$n = 9$$
>
> $$\text{Interior angle} = \frac{180(n-2)}{n}$$
>
> $$= \frac{\cancel{180}^{20}(9-2)}{\cancel{9}_{1}}$$
>
> $$= 20° \times 7$$
>
> $$= 140°$$

If you are given the exterior angle of a regular polygon, you can rearrange the formula to find the number of sides.

As exterior angle $x = \dfrac{360°}{n}$

then it follows that $n = \dfrac{360°}{x}$

where x is the exterior angle and n is the number of sides in the regular polygon.

Example

The exterior angle of a regular polygon is 72°. How many sides does the polygon have?

$$n = \frac{360}{x}$$

$$= \frac{360}{72}$$

$$= 5$$

It is a pentagon.

> If you know the interior angle of a regular polygon, first calculate the exterior angle and then calculate the number of sides.

Exercise 13.6

1 Use the correct formula to calculate the size of an exterior angle for a regular:

   (a) dodecagon (12 sides)   (c) triacontagon (30 sides)

   (b) octadecagon (18 sides)

2 Find the number of sides in a regular polygon if the exterior angle is:

   (a) 24°   (b) 10°   (c) 15°

3 Why can a regular polygon not have an exterior angle of 65°?

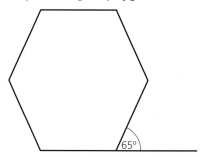

4 Can the exterior angle of a regular polygon be an obtuse angle?

Exterior angle

5 Use the formula to calculate the sum of the interior angles of:

   (a) a dodecagon   (c) an icosagon (20 sides)

   (b) an octadecagon

6 Use the formula to calculate the interior angle of a regular:

   (a) dodecagon   (c) pentadecagon (15 sides)

   (b) hexadecagon (16 sides)

7 Work out the number of sides of a regular polygon in which the interior angle is:

   (a) 90°   (b) 140°   (c) 162°

8 Work out the number of sides of a regular polygon if:

   (a) the interior angle is twice the exterior angle

   (b) the interior angle is three times the exterior angle

   (c) the interior angle is four times the exterior angle

   (d) the interior angle is seven times the exterior angle.

9 The angles at the centre of a regular polygon are equal. Because they are angles at a point they must add up to 360°. Work out the size of an angle at the centre of a regular:

   (a) octagon   (b) pentagon   (c) icosagon.

10 This diagram shows part of a regular polygon.

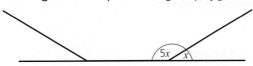

   (a) The interior angle is five times as large as the exterior angle. How many sides does the polygon have?

   (b) If the interior angle were 11 times the size of the exterior angle, how many sides would the polygon have?

Calculating angles in polygons

You can use what you know about polygons to solve even more angle problems. As all the sides of a regular polygon are equal, it is likely that you will find isosceles triangles inside regular polygons.

Remember:

- the sum of the interior angles of any polygon is $180°(n - 2)$
- the sum of the exterior angles of any polygon is $360°$

where n is the number of sides of the polygon.

For a regular polygon, you also know that:

- the exterior angle $= \dfrac{360°}{n}$

- the interior angle $= \dfrac{180°(n-2)}{n}$ or $180° -$ exterior angle

- the number of sides $(n) = \dfrac{360°}{\text{exterior angle}}$

- the angle at the centre $= \dfrac{360°}{n}$

Note also that some regular polygons have some diagonals that are parallel to their sides.

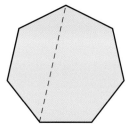

Regular heptagon

This one is parallel.

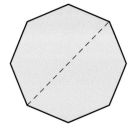

Regular octagon

This one is not parallel.

Example

ABCDEFGH is a regular octagon.

Find the size of:

(a) angle *GFE*

(b) angle *FGE*

(c) angle *GHA*

(d) angle *HGB*

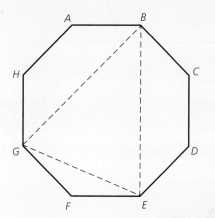

Exterior angle $= \dfrac{360°}{n}$

$\qquad\qquad\quad = \dfrac{360°}{8}$

$\qquad\qquad\quad = 45°$

(a) angle $GFE = 180° - 45°$ Interior angle of a regular polygon

$\qquad\qquad\quad\ = 135°$

(b) angle $FGE = \dfrac{180° - 135°}{2}$ Base angle of an isosceles triangle

$\qquad\qquad\quad\ = 22.5°$

(c) angle $GHA = 135°$ Interior angle of a regular polygon (octagon)

(d) angle $HGB = 180° - 135°$ Co-interior angles, *HA* parallel to *BG*

$\qquad\qquad\quad\ = 45°$

> It is a good idea always to start by finding the exterior and interior angles.

> Read through the working in the example carefully. This is how you should set out your answers.

With all this information, you are ready to tackle the next exercise. The calculations are not difficult but it is important to recognise which formula to use and to follow the steps. This is why you should write down each step carefully.

These questions are about polygons. Find the sizes of the angles, giving reasons for all your calculations.

1 *ABCDE* is a regular pentagon.

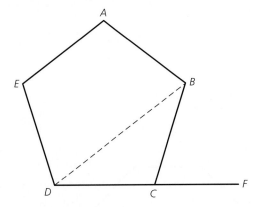

Find the size of:

(a) angle *BCE*

(b) angle *BCD*

(c) angle *CBD*

(d) angle *ABD*

2 *BCDEFG* is a regular hexagon.

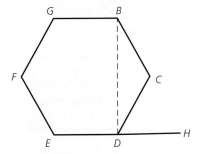

Work out the size of:

(a) angle *CDH*

(b) angle *BCD*

(c) angle *CDB*

(d) angle *BDE*

3 *ABCDEF* is a regular hexagon, with centre *O*.

Work out the size of:

(a) angle *EOD*

(b) angle *ODE*

(c) angle *ABC*

(d) angle *CDO*

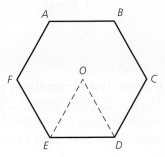

4 *ABCDEFGH* is a regular octagon with centre *O*.

Find the size of:

(a) angle *COD*

(b) angle *FEA*

(c) angle *ABC*

(d) angle *BCO*

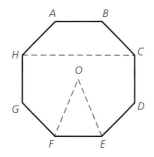

5 *ABCDE* is a regular pentagon with centre *O*.

Find the size of:

(a) angle *AEF*

(b) angle *BCD*

(c) angle *CBD*

(d) angle *ABD*

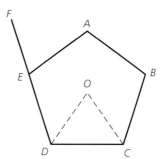

Extension Exercise 13.8

Maths from stars: Calculating angles

You started to look at tessellations at the end of Chapter 10. Now that you know how to calculate interior and exterior angles of regular polygons, you can investigate whether polygons tessellate.

1 What is the interior angle of a regular hexagon?

2 Look at the middle of this pattern.

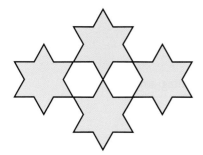

Calculate the size of the acute angle inside the six-pointed star.

3 The six-pointed star is an irregular dodecagon. What is the sum of the interior angles of a dodecagon?

4 Calculate the size of the reflex angle inside the six-pointed star.

5 Draw a six-pointed star on triangular spotted paper and check that your answers are correct.

This is a regular pentagon with all its diagonals shown. This design is known as a pentagram and has been linked with magic for centuries.

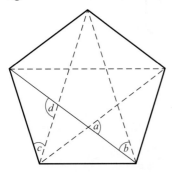

> The word *magi* in the New Testament refers to wise men and has the same origin as the word magic. Sometimes mathematical patterns are so amazing that they seem magical.

This is a pentagram from *Transendental Magic* by Eliphas Levi (1810–1875)

The Pentagram from Eliphas Levi's (1810–1875)
'*Transcendental Magic*'

6 What is the interior angle of a regular pentagon?

7 Now calculate the sizes of the angles labelled *a*, *b*, *c* and *d* in the pentagram in question 5

This eight-pointed star is an important part of Islamic tiling patterns. It is made from two squares and in its centre is a regular octagon.

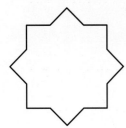

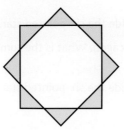

8 What is the interior angle of a regular octagon?

9 Look at the eight-pointed star pattern in question 7. Calculate all the angles in one of the coloured isosceles triangles.

10 The eight-pointed star is an irregular 16-sided figure. What is the sum of the interior angles of a 16-sided figure?

11 Calculate the size of the reflex angle in the eight-pointed star.

Eight-pointed stars can be put together to make a pattern of tiles. This is a part of a tiling pattern from the Alhambra Palace in Spain.

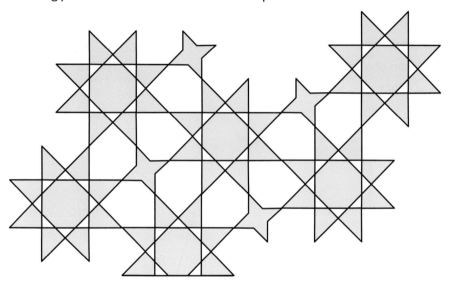

12 The new eight-pointed star has eight kites forming its eight points. Calculate the angles in the kites.

13 Between the four eight-pointed stars there are four irregular hexagons that meet and form an irregular octagon. Calculate all the angles in the hexagon and the octagon.

Summary Exercise 13.9

1 Copy this diagram three times.

   Mark a pair of alternate angles on the first diagram, a pair of corresponding angles on the second and a pair of co-interior angles on the third.

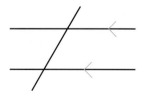

2 Find the sizes of the angles marked by the letters in this diagram and give reasons for your answers.

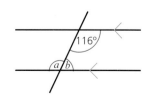

116°

a b

3 In this diagram AB is parallel to CD and BCE is a straight line. You are also told that angle $BAC = 44°$ and angle $DCE = 118°$

Find the size of:

(a) angle DCB

(b) angle ABC

(c) angle ACB

(d) angle ACE

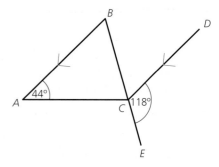

4 (a) What is the exterior angle of a regular 9-sided polygon?

(b) What is the interior angle of regular 15-sided polygon?

5 Write down the number of sides of a regular polygon with:

(a) an exterior angle equal to $36°$

(b) an interior angle equal to $160°$

6 What is the sum of the interior angles of a 13-sided polygon?

7 $ABCDE$ is a regular pentagon.

Work out the size of:

(a) angle CDF

(b) angle BCD

(c) angle ADE

(d) angle CDA

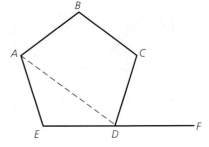

8 In this diagram AE is parallel to BD, $AB = EB$, angle $EBD = 54°$ and angle $DCB = 37°$

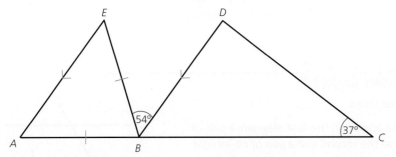

Find, giving reasons, and stating any other angles that you have had to find first, the size of:

(a) angle BEA

(b) angle DBC

(c) angle ABE

(d) angle BDC

9 In this diagram *AC* is parallel to *DH*, angle *BEF* = 54°, angle *BFG* = 73° and *BF* = *FG*

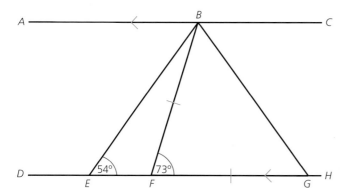

Find, giving reasons and showing any other angles that you have to find, the size of:

(a) angle *ABE* **(b)** angle *FBE* **(c)** angle *GBC*

10 *ABCDE* is part of a regular polygon with centre *O*. Angle *COD* = 30°

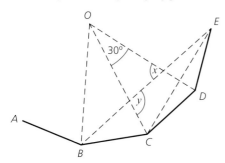

(a) Calculate the number of sides of the polygon.

(b) Calculate the size of:

    (i) angle *ODC* **(ii)** angle *CDE* **(iii)** angle *ECD*

(c) Calculate the size of the angle marked:

    (i) *x* **(ii)** *y*

Activity: Hexagon investigation

Hexagons are fascinating because they tessellate. The cells of the honeycomb built by honey bees are hexagonal.

A regular hexagon can be cut into six equilateral triangles. Look at these patterns of hexagons.

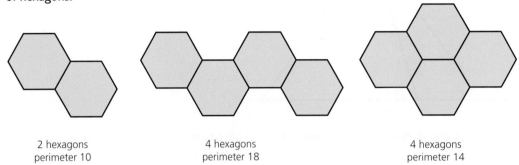

| 2 hexagons perimeter 10 | 4 hexagons perimeter 18 | 4 hexagons perimeter 14 |

There should be a connection between the number of hexagons and the perimeter of the whole shape. However, the patterns with four hexagons have different perimeters. What else is different about them?

In the shape with the larger perimeter, the hexagons are in a row.

In the shape with the smaller perimeter the hexagons are in a block with two points completely enclosed in the shape.

Now look at these patterns.

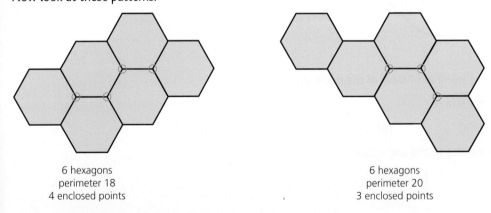

| 6 hexagons perimeter 18 4 enclosed points | 6 hexagons perimeter 20 3 enclosed points |

1   On triangular spotted paper, draw as many groups of four hexagons as you can. Which has the shortest perimeter?

2   Now draw as many different combinations of five hexagons as you can. Which has the shortest perimeter?

3   Draw some more hexagon combinations. Work out the perimeter and count the enclosed points for each.

4   Put your results in a table.

5   Let n be the number of hexagons, and d the number of enclosed points. Try to write a formula for the perimeter, in terms of n and d.

14 Scale drawings and constructions

Architects and engineers use drawings to show their designs. These need to be constructed very carefully. Many drawings are not full size. Can you think of a reason for this? They may be scaled down to make them smaller or scaled up to make them larger. When working with scale you will need to use some of the methods that you learnt in Chapter 11: Ratio.

◯ Scale drawings

When you want to represent an object, diagram or plan, it is rarely possible to draw it at its full size but you can draw it to **scale**.

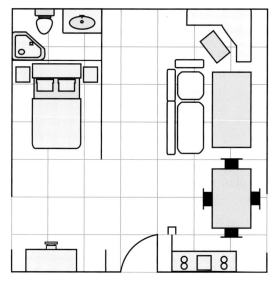

This plan of an apartment is 7 cm wide but the real apartment is 14 metres wide.

So each centimetre on the plan represents two metres on the floor.

The scale is 1 cm to 2 m.

You can write this as a ratio by expressing both parts in the same units and then writing it in its lowest terms.

Example

Convert the scale of 1 cm to 2 m to a ratio in its lowest terms.

Scale 1 cm to 2 m = 1 cm : 200 cm

= 1 : 200

Exercise 14.1

1 A map is drawn so that 1 cm represents 1 km. What is the scale as a ratio?

2 A plan is drawn so that 1 cm represents 1 m. What is the scale as a ratio?

3 A map is drawn so that 1 cm represents 500 m. What is the scale as a ratio?

4 A diagram is drawn so that 2 cm represents 10 cm. What is the scale as a ratio?

5 A plan is drawn so that 1 cm represents 5 m. What is the scale as a ratio?

6 A map is drawn so that 1 cm represents 5 km. What is the scale as a ratio?

7 A diagram is drawn so that 2 cm represents 1 m. What is the scale as a ratio?

8 A map is drawn so that 4 cm represents 1 km. What is the scale as a ratio?

Using scale

Look back at the plan of the apartment.

The scale is 1 : 200 so 1 cm represents 200 cm (2 m).

Therefore: If the bedroom is 5 m wide, the width on the plan will be 2.5 cm.

If the bathroom on the plan is 2.2 cm wide, then the actual bathroom will be 4.4 m wide.

But, remember, there are some things that don't change. For example, if the plan has four chairs, then the apartment will also have four chairs!

When you are working with scale, start by finding out what 1 cm represents. Make sure you set out your working carefully, as shown in the next example.

Examples

I am drawing a plan of my classroom to a scale of 1 : 50

(i)   My classroom is 5 m wide. How wide will it be on the plan?

(ii) On the plan, I have a teacher's desk that is 4 cm long. How long is the real desk?

(i)   Scale is 1 : 50

1 cm represents 50 cm   First find out what 1 cm represents.

The width of the classroom is 5 m (500 cm).

The scaled length of the classroom is

$$500 \div 50 = 10 \text{ cm}$$ The scaled length is smaller so divide.

(ii) The scaled length of the desk is 4 cm.

The length of the real desk $= 4 \times 50$ cm   The scaled length is larger so multiply.

$$= 200 \text{ cm}$$

$$= 2 \text{ m}$$

Exercise 14.2

1 I have drawn a plan of my bedroom to a scale of 1 : 50

   (a) What does 1 cm on my plan represent?

   (b) My bed is 2 m long. What length is it on my plan?

   (c) On my plan, my desk is 1.2 cm wide. How wide is it really?

   (d) My plan is 10 cm by 14 cm. What are the actual measurements of my bedroom?

   (e) I have two chairs in my bedroom. How many chairs should there be on my plan?

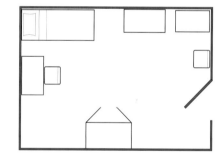

2 A model train has been built to a scale of 1 : 100

   (a) What is the length of a real carriage, if a model carriage is 12 cm long?

   (b) What is the length of the real goods van, if the model is 20 cm long?

   (c) What is the length of the model engine, if the real engine is 15 m long?

   (d) What is the diameter of a model wheel, if the real wheels are 1 m in diameter?

   (e) If the model has four carriages, how many carriages does the real train have?

3 This seed is drawn to a scale of 5 : 1

Measure the diameter of the drawing and find the diameter of the real seed.

4 This is the image of a hair from an insect's body, enlarged by a scale of 20 : 1
Measure the length of the drawing of the hair then calculate the real length
of the hair, in millimetres.

5 A map is drawn to a scale of 1 : 10 000

(a) What does 1 cm on the map represent?

(b) What distance in the map represents a real distance of 4 km?

(c) On the map, the distance from the church to the post office is 3.2 cm.
What is this distance on the ground?

(d) On Monday we walked 2.4 km. What distance is this on the map?

(e) There are two churches on the map. How many are there in reality?

6 I want to draw a map of a field that is 600 m by 1.4 km on a piece of paper
that is 20 cm by 30 cm. What scale should I use? (You may need to try a few
scales before you get your answer!)

7 I am building a model boat to a scale of 1 : 20

(a) What does 1 cm on the model represent?

(b) What length on the model represents 1 metre on the real boat?

(c) The masts are 6 m and 7.5 m tall. How long are they on my model?

(d) There are two masts on the model. How many are there on the real boat?

8 I want to make a scale model of another boat that was built a long time ago
and was therefore measured in imperial units. I find that a scale of 1 : 24
makes more sense because there are 12 inches in a foot.

(a) What does 1 inch on the model represent?

(b) If the boat was 20 feet long, what length is my model?

(c) If the model is 4 inches wide, how wide is the actual boat?

(d) One mast was 15 feet high. How tall will the model's mast be?

Constructions

You have already learnt how to use a **protractor** and a pair of
compasses to draw triangles, and how to use a pair of compasses to
bisect an angle. Here is a quick review of what you know.

In mathematics, an accurate representation of a geometric figure is
called a **construction**.

To **bisect** is to divide something exactly in two.

Bisecting an angle

Copy the diagram and work through the steps to bisect the angle *ABC*.

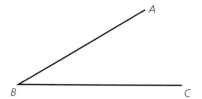

Step 1: Open your compasses to a radius of about 4 cm. Place the point on *B* and draw two arcs, one on *AB* and one on *BC*.

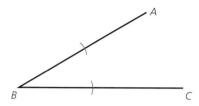

Step 2: Without changing the setting of your compasses, place the point on the place where the arc cuts *AB* and draw another arc, then put the point on the place where the arc cuts *BC* and draw an arc to cut the first.

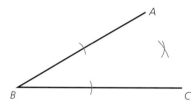

Step 3: Draw a line from *B* through the point of intersection of the arcs and label it *BD*.

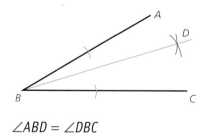

$$\angle ABD = \angle DBC$$

Why does the construction work?

Label the points where the arcs cut the lines *AB* and *BC* as *P* and *Q*

Join *DP* and *DQ*

As *BP* = *BQ* = *DP* = *DQ* the quadrilateral *BPDQ* is a rhombus.

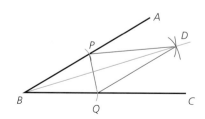

Do you remember the properties of the diagonals of a rhombus?

- The diagonals bisect each other.
- The diagonals are perpendicular to each other.
- The diagonals bisect the angles.

Therefore, since the construction makes the sides of the angle into the sides of a rhombus, the diagonal must be the angle bisector.

Bisecting a line

Look at this rhombus. It is positioned so that the diagonal *PQ* is horizontal.

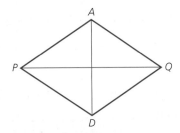

Therefore the diagonal *AD* bisects the diagonal *PQ* and is perpendicular to it.

> Remember:
> **perpendicular** means 'at right angles to'.

Then *AD* is the **perpendicular bisector** of *PQ*.

To construct a perpendicular bisector of any line, you make the line into the diagonal of a rhombus.

Copy the diagram of the line *PQ* and work through the steps to bisect it.

Step 1: Open your compasses to a radius that is a little greater than half the length of *PQ*. Put the compass point on point *P* and draw an arc above the line and below the line.

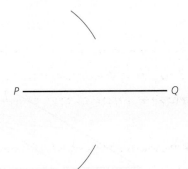

Step 2: Without changing the setting of your compasses, put the compass point on point Q and draw two more arcs to cross the first two. Label the points where they cross X and Y.

Step 3: Join X and Y. XY is the perpendicular bisector of AB.

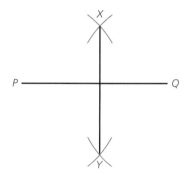

> If you were to join the points to draw the quadrilateral PXQY it would be a rhombus, but you do not need to draw it.

Dropping a perpendicular from a point to a line

Now you are going to draw a line from a point X to meet line AB at right angles.

Copy the diagram of the line AB and the point X above it. Then work through the steps to draw the perpendicular from X to AB.

A ———————— B

Step 1: Open your compasses to a radius that is a little greater than the distance from *X* to *AB*. Place the compass point on *X* and draw two arcs to cross *AB*.

Step 2: Close your compasses slightly, to a radius that is just over half the distance between the two arcs. Put the compass point at the point where one arc crosses *AB* and draw a new arc below the line. Now put the compass point on the point where the other arc crosses *AB* and draw an arc to cross the first one. Label this point *Y*.

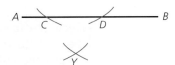

Step 3: Join *XY* and label the point where *XY* crosses *AB* as *P*. *XP* is perpendicular to *AB*.

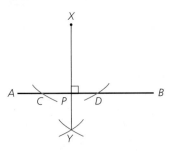

Why does this work? If you join the places where your first arcs cut *AB* to *X* and *Y* you have this quadrilateral.

You should see that it is a kite.

Do you remember the properties of the diagonals of a kite?

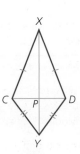

- The diagonals cross at right angles
- One diagonal bisects the other.

You have constructed a kite with the horizontal diagonal along *AB* and the top point at *X*. You could have constructed a rhombus, as in the previous construction, but this would take up more space on the page.

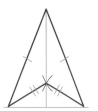

If you are very short of space you could make the two arcs with smaller radius cross above *AB*.

This makes an isosceles arrowhead. Its diagonals have the same properties as those of a kite.

Exercise 14.3

1 **(a)** Draw an acute angle in your book. Construct the bisector of your angle. Check your accuracy by measuring the angles with a protractor.

  (b) Draw a line *PQ* halfway across your exercise book. Construct its perpendicular bisector. Check your accuracy by measuring the angle with a protractor and the line with a ruler.

  (c) Draw another line *AB* on your exercise book. Mark a point *X* above it. Construct a line perpendicular to *AB* from *X*. Check your accuracy by measuring the angle with a protractor.

2 Repeat question 1 but draw a different angle, a different line *PQ* and a different line *AB* and point *X*.

3 Draw an obtuse angle *ABC* of 130°. Construct the angle bisector.

4 Draw a line *XY* 8 cm long. Construct its perpendicular bisector.

5 Draw a line *AB* 10 cm long. Mark a point *P* 5 cm above it. Construct a line perpendicular to *AB* from point *P*.

6 **(a)** Construct an equilateral triangle *ABC* with sides of 8 cm. Construct all the angle bisectors.

  (b) What do you notice? Explain what you have found.

  (c) Measure the distance from where the angle bisectors meet to the sides *AB*, *BC* and *AC*. What do you notice? Draw a circle that just touches *AB*, *BC* and *AC*.

7 **(a)** Construct an equilateral triangle *PQR* with sides of 10 cm. Construct the perpendicular bisectors of all the sides.

  (b) What do you notice? Explain what you have found.

  (c) Measure the distance from where the perpendicular bisectors meet to sides *PQ*, *PR* and *RP*. What do you notice? Draw a circle that passes through *P*, *Q* and *R*.

8 Construct triangle *ABC* in which *AB* = 8 cm, *BC* = 9 cm and ∠*ABC* = 65° Construct all the angle bisectors. Draw a circle that just touches *AB*, *BC* and *AC*.

9   Construct triangle *DEF* with *DE* = 7 cm, *EF* = 5.5 cm and *DF* = 6 cm. Construct the perpendicular bisectors of all the sides. Draw a circle that passes through *D*, *E* and *F*.

10 Construct triangle *PQR* in which *PQ* = 7.2 cm, ∠*PQR* = 55° and ∠*QPR* = 42° Draw a circle that passes through *P*, *Q* and *R*.

Three-figure bearings

Think back to what you know about angles. In day-to-day life, you will see angles in many situations. One example is in **navigation**. The captain of a boat or an aeroplane relies on navigation all the time.

The most useful tool in navigation is a simple instrument called a **magnetic compass** – this is quite different from the pair of compasses you used in the last exercise. Compasses come in many styles, but you will probably be most familiar with these.

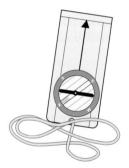

Inside the compass there is a magnetic pointer that is free to turn about its centre. The end with the arrow always points to **magnetic north**. Around the rim of the compass there is a **scale**, from 0 to 360, similar to that on a circular protractor. To use the compass on the right, above, you hold it horizontally so that the arrow on the rectangular base plate points to a landmark such as a spire. Then you rotate the case of the compass until the needle pointer is over the zero on the scale. The angle shown on the compass is the **bearing** of the landmark from the point where you are standing, measured clockwise from north.

Once you know how to use a compass, you can use it to work out the bearing of any object from your own position. It can tell you the direction to take when you are walking or sailing. You can also use a map or chart with a compass and a bearing to identify where you are. For example, if you see that there is a lighthouse on a bearing of 045° from you, you can construct a diagram to show its position, relative to your own.

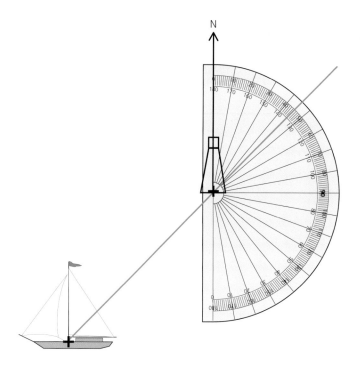

Note that, as your own position is not marked on the map, you cannot draw the north line from where you are, so you draw it at the lighthouse. Mark the angle at the lighthouse and draw the line along the bearing. You know that you must be on the line somewhere.

If you can do the same with another two landmarks, you can identify your own position uniquely.

Remember that you can use a **set square** to draw north lines, and use your ruler as a straight edge, so that you can slide the set square along it and keep north lines parallel.

> When you are using bearings, angles such as 45° are identified by three figures, 045° (zero-four-five degrees) in this case.

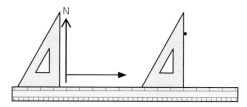

Line the set square up on the ruler, against the north line, then slide the set square along the ruler.

1 The diagram represents a map showing a yacht in the middle of a bay. Around it are another boat, a tanker, a lighthouse and a hilltop. Find the bearing of each one from the yacht's position.

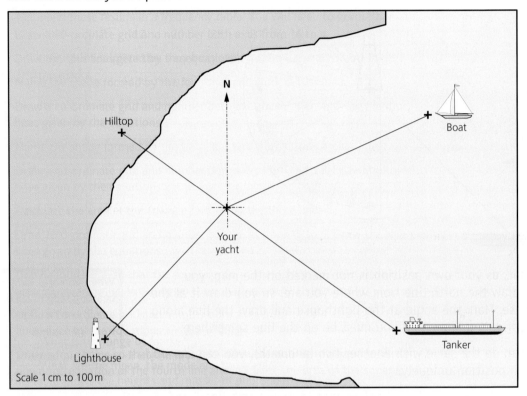

For the lighthouse and the hilltop you will have to put the protractor the other way round and add 180° to the reading.

If you have a 360° protractor then you only have to line up north carefully with 000° and then you can read all four bearings without changing the position of the protractor.

2 Look at this chart of the Yantlet channel.

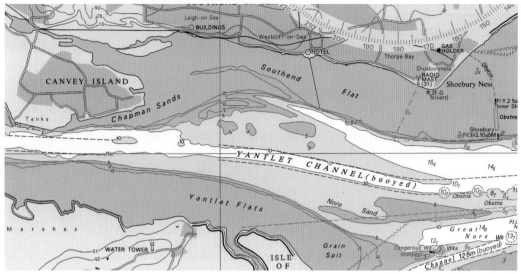

Not to be used for navigation

Trace over the outline of the land on the chart (the line between the yellow and the green).

3 On your tracing, mark the hotel and the radio mast on the north shore and the water tower on the south bank.

4 A man on the yacht measures the bearing of the radio mast as 052° Construct the line along which the yacht will lie.

5 A woman on the yacht measures the bearing of the water tower as 245° Construct the line along which the yacht will lie.

6 The man on the yacht measures the bearing of the hotel as 345°. Mark the position of the yacht.

7 Compare the tracing to the chart. Is the yacht in the main channel?

Using scale diagrams

You can use bearings to draw scale diagrams representing positions and journeys.

Example

Draw point *A*, which is 35 metres from point *B* on a bearing of 110° on a scale of 1 cm to 10 m.

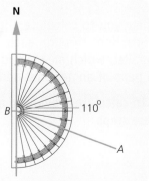

Draw diagrams to show these points. Use the scales stated.

1 Draw a point *P* that is 7 m from point *Q* on a bearing of 045°, using a scale of 1 cm to 1 m.

2 Draw a point *A* that is 800 m from point *B* on a bearing of 127°, using a scale of 1 cm to 100 m.

3 Draw a point *X* that is 120 m from point *Y* on a bearing of 175°, using a scale of 1 cm to 10 m.

4 Draw a point *M* that is 60 m from point *N* on a bearing of 200°, using a scale of 1 cm to 10 m.

5 Draw a point *A* that is 750 m from point *B* on a bearing of 312°, using a scale of 1 : 10 000

6 Draw a point *R* that is 6.5 m from point *S* on a bearing of 163°, using a scale of 1 : 100

7 Draw a point *V* that is 72 m from point *W* on a bearing of 035°, using a scale of 1:1000

8 Draw a point *P* that is 8.6 km from point *Q* on a bearing of 287° using a scale of 1 cm to 1 km.

9 In question 1 and question 8 measure the bearings of *Q* from *P* and in question 2 and question 5 measure the bearings of *B* from *A*.

Calculating bearings

When you learned about angles formed by transversals and parallel lines you discovered you could find pairs of equal angles and pairs of angles that add up to 180°

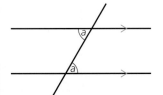
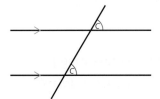
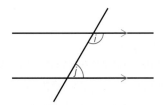

You can use this fact to help you to calculate angles and bearings. You do this by drawing north lines through each of the points. These two north lines will be parallel, which means you can use them to find pairs of equal angles and pairs of angles that add up to 180°

You can use this method to calculate previously unknown angles and bearings by following these steps.

1 Draw a sketch showing given points and the north lines.

2 Mark the given angle and the one you are trying to find.

3 Use letters to mark any other angles that you may need to calculate.

4 Give your answer as a three-figure bearing.

Example

If the bearing of A from B is 140°, what is the bearing of B from A?

Draw a sketch showing A and B and the north lines.

Let the angle between AB and the north line at A be x

Then $x = 180° - 140°$ Co-interior angles add
        $= 40°$ up to 180°

The bearing of B from A $= 360° - 40°$ Angles at a point
                         $= 320°$ add up to 360°

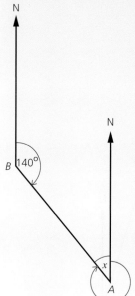

Exercise 14.6

1 If the bearing of A from B is 120°, what is the bearing of B from A?

2 If the bearing of P from Q is 072°, what is the bearing of Q from P?

3 If the bearing of X from Y is 213°, what is the bearing of Y from X?

4 If the bearing of M from N is 298°, what is the bearing of N from M?

5 A yacht race is in the shape of an isosceles triangle, with base angles equal to 63°, starting from point P.

The first mark, Q is on a bearing of 055° from P. Calculate the bearing of:

(a) R from Q

(b) P from R

(c) R from P.

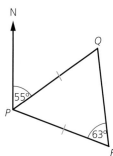

6 I have to run a square course starting from point *A*.

The first corner, *B*, is on a bearing of 200° from *A*.

(a) Calculate the bearing of:

    (i) *C* from *B*

    (ii) *D* from *C*

    (iii) *A* from *D*.

(b) I sprain my ankle when I get to *C* and hobble back to *A*. What is the bearing of *A* from *C*?

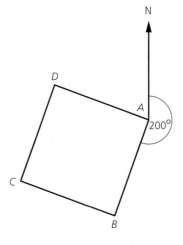

7 Look at this plot of a ship's course. *PQ* is equal to *QR*.

(a) Calculate the bearing of:

    (i) *P* from *Q*

    (ii) *Q* from *R*.

The ship is in trouble when it reaches *R* and an emergency helicopter is sent out from *P*.

(b) What is the bearing of *R* from *P*?

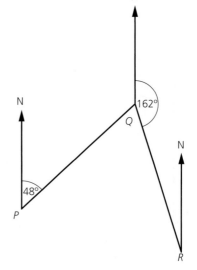

8 A ship sails from Ayport on a course of 127° to a point *B*, then turns 90° anticlockwise. What is its new bearing?

9 An aircraft flies WSW and then changes course to head NNW. Through how many degrees did it turn and in what direction?

10 I am on an expedition and set off from base on a bearing of 037°. I walk for 6 km, then turn 120° clockwise, walk another 6 km and turn 120° clockwise. What are my bearing and distance from the base camp now?

◯ Scale drawing and bearings

When you are answering a question about scale drawing or bearings, always start with a sketch. That will help you to position your drawing on the page sensibly and also make sure that you have the correct angles and distances in the right places.

Example

I start from a point *A* and walk 100 m on a bearing of 110° to *B*.

I then walk 75 m on a bearing of 040° to *C*.

Draw my journey, using a scale of 1 cm to 10 m.

From your drawing, measure the distance and bearing of *A* from *C*.

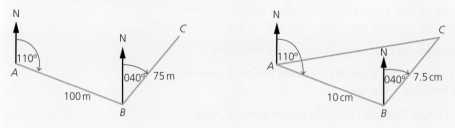

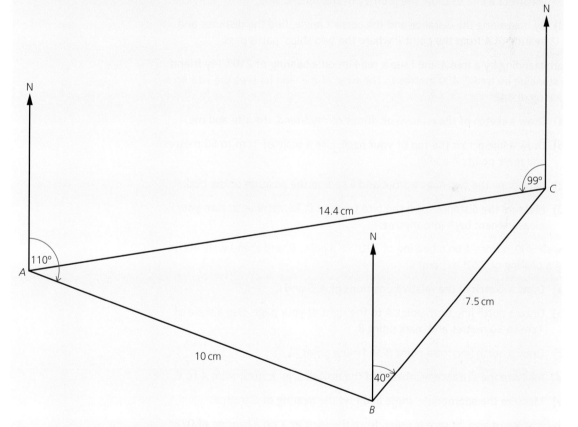

AC = 14.4 cm, which represents 144 m

Angle measured at *C* is 99°

To find the bearing subtract this angle from 360°   360° − 99° = 261°

Distance *AC* = 144 m

The bearing of *A* from *C* is 261°

Make a scale drawing for each question. Draw a sketch first. Mark your scale drawing with the given information and do not forget to answer the question.

1 Look again at the last example. Draw the sketch, and make the scale drawing for yourself. Check that your measurements agree.

2 A ship sails on a bearing of 125° from a port A. Another ship starts from port B, 15 km due south of A, at the same time, and sails at a bearing of 070°

(a) Draw a sketch to show the relative positions of the two ships.

(b) Draw a line to the left of your page. Mark point A and then construct a line to show the first ship's journey.

(c) Using a scale of 1 cm to 1 km, plot point B on your drawing. Now construct a line to show the journey of the second ship.

(d) By measuring the distance and the correct angle, find the distance and bearing of A from the point P where the two ships' paths pass.

3 I am standing by a tree A and I see a red kite on a bearing of 210°. My friend is standing by tree B, 400 metres to the west of me, and he sees the kite on a bearing of 142°

(a) Draw a sketch of the relative positions of my friend, the kite and me.

(b) Draw a line across the top of your page. Use a scale of 1 cm to 50 metres and mark points A and B.

(c) Now draw the two lines from A and B to find the position of the bird.

(d) Measure the distance from the bird to point B. Remember to turn your measurement back into metres.

4 I walk 300 m from A on a bearing of 310° to a point B, and then I walk 400 m on a bearing of 220° to point C.

(a) Draw a sketch of the relative positions of A, B and C.

(b) Draw a north line from point A to the right of your page. Use a scale of 1 cm to 50 metres and mark point B.

(c) Draw a north line from point B and mark point C.

(d) Measure the distance AC then find the distance, in metres, from A to C.

(e) Measure the appropriate angle and find the bearing of C from A.

5 The first leg of a yacht race is sailed from the start at X on a bearing of 072° for 4.5 km to a buoy Y. The next leg of the course is to a buoy at Z, a distance of 6.3 km from X on a bearing of 164°. Draw a plan of the course to a scale of 1 cm to 0.5 km. What is the length of the second leg and what is the bearing of Z from Y?

6 **(a)** I am lost. I can see a road running from a farm to a white house. My map says they are 4 km apart and the farm lies on a bearing of 102° from the white house. If the farm is on a bearing of 124° from me, and the white house on a bearing of 238° from me, draw an accurate scale drawing showing our relative positions. Choose a suitable scale.

> Draw the relative positions of the farm and the white house first and then draw in my position.

(b) Work out my shortest distance to the road by constructing a line from my position that is perpendicular to the road from the farm to the white house.

7 A yacht leaves Ayport and sails for 8 km on a bearing of 102°. It then changes direction and sails for 5 km on a bearing of 138°. Here it runs into difficulties. Beeport is 10 km due south of Ayport. A lifeboat leaves Beeport and heads for the yacht. How far does the lifeboat have to go and on what bearing should it travel?

The previous exercises all involved angles. Sometimes we have angle problems that are best solved using algebra. First identify the unknown quantity with a letter and use known facts to write an equation. Solve the equation to solve the problem.

Extension Exercise 14.8

1 The hands of a 12-hour clock move at different speeds. In one hour the minute hand will have gone a full circle, turning through 360°, but the hour hand will have gone through one twelfth of a full circle, turning through 30°. At what times will the angle between the hands of the clock be exactly 90°?

2 The time is m minutes past four.

(a) How many degrees round from 12 is the minute hand of the clock, in terms of m?

(b) How many degrees round from 12 is the hour hand of the clock, in terms of m?

(c) At m minutes past four, the hour and minute hand are in exactly the same place. Form an equation in m and solve it.

(d) Give the time to the nearest minute.

(e) What is the angle between the hands 15 minutes later?

3 **(a)** The bearing of point X from point Y is $b°$, and b is greater than 0 and less than 90. What is the bearing of Y from X in terms of b?

(b) Is your answer the same if b lies between 090 and 180? Explain your answer carefully.

(c) What is the bearing of Y from X if b lies between 180 and 270?

(d) What is the bearing of Y from X if b lies between 270 and 360?

4 The bearing of A from B is $x°$ and the bearing of C from B is $y°$. Both x and y lie between 0 and 180 and y is greater than x. AB is equal to BC.

Find the bearing of C from A in terms of x and y.

5 ABD is an isosceles triangle with base angles equal to $y°$.

BCD is an isosceles triangle with the angle at the apex equal to $x°$.

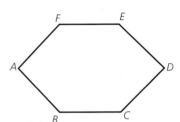

(a) Write angle CBD in terms of x.

(b) Write angle ADB in terms of y.

(c) Given that AB is parallel to CD write a simple formula for y in terms of x.

(d) Suppose AD is parallel to BC write a formula for x in terms of y.

(e) Suppose AD is parallel to BC write a formula for z in terms of x.

6 ABCDEF is a semi-regular hexagon. The sides are equal but the angles are not.

(a) Given that angle FAB is 80° find the size of:

(i) angle ABF   (ii) angle ABC   (iii) angle ABD.

(b) Given that angle FAB is 100° find the size of:

(i) angle ABF   (ii) angle ABC   (iii) angle ABD.

(c) Given that angle FAB is $x°$ find the size of:

(i) angle ABC   (ii) angle ABF   (iii) angle ABD.

Summary Exercise 14.9

1 (a) A map is drawn so that 1 cm represents 200 m. What is the scale as a ratio?

(b) A map is drawn to a ratio of 1 : 50 000. What does 1 cm on the map represent?

2 A plan is drawn to a scale of 1 : 50

(a) A room is drawn 10 cm by 8 cm. What are its true dimensions?

(b) A single bed is 2 m by 1 m. What will its dimensions be on the plan?

(c) There are two windows drawn on the plan, how many windows are there in the actual room?

3 (a) Construct a triangle ABC such that AB = 10 cm, AC = 6 cm and BC = 8 cm.

(b) Construct the bisector of ∠ACB.

(c) Construct the perpendicular bisector of AB.

(d) Construct another copy of triangle ABC and construct the line CP that meets AB at P and is perpendicular to AB.

4 (a) Using a scale of 1 cm to 1 km, draw point Q, 7.5 km from point P on a bearing of 127°

(b) Measure the bearing of P from Q.

5 Given that the bearing of *A* from *B* is 217°, what is the bearing of *B* from *A*?

6 *ABC* is an equilateral triangle, and the bearing of *B* from *A* is 110°

Give the bearing of:

(a) *C* from *A*

(b) *B* from *C*.

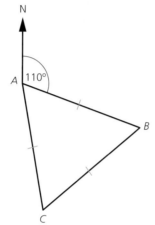

7 On a geography field trip, we walked for 4.5 km on a bearing of 129° from the base camp. Simon wrote down the directions incorrectly. He walked for 5.4 km on a bearing of 192°

(a) Draw a sketch to show the relative positions of the base camp, *B*, my group, *G*, and Simon, *S*.

(b) Using a scale of 2 cm to 1 km, make an accurate scale drawing to show the positions of *B*, *G* and *S*.

(c) Simon has to come and find us. From your drawing, measure *GS* and find out how far he has to walk.

(d) Measure the bearing of *G* from *S* to find the direction that Simon has to walk.

8 Reaton lies 2 km from Toytown on a bearing of 235°. A track runs between them. A boy scout has got lost. He works out that, from his position, the bearing of Toytown is 105° and the bearing of Reaton is 192°

(a) Draw a sketch to show the relative positions of Toytown, *T*, Reaton, *R*, and the scout, *S*.

(b) Using a scale of 5 cm to 1 km, draw an accurate scale drawing to show the positions of *R*, *T* and *S*.

(c) By constructing a line from *S* and perpendicular to *RT*, calculate the shortest distance the scout has to walk to join the track.

Activity: Black-eyed Jack's treasure

Imagine that you are the pirate, Black-eyed Jack. You are going to bury your ill-gotten treasure on a desert island.

First draw a map of the island. Put in lots of detail.

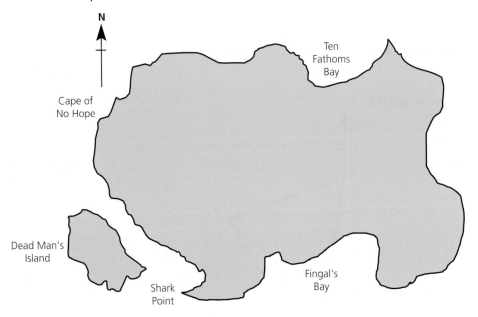

Now decide where your treasure is to be buried.

The next thing you have to do is to write some instructions so that Lucky Jim can discover the treasure. The instructions must not be too easy, and should use both bearings and compass directions. To follow the instructions, the map will need a scale. This could be in kilometres, leagues or even paces.

For example:

- Start at the stricken pine tree.
- Take forty paces on a bearing of 045°
- From there turn due east and take twenty paces.
- Walk fifteen paces on a bearing of 312°
- Walk north until you meet the coast.
- Turn south-west and take five paces.
- There lies the treasure!

Once you are happy with your set of instructions, give them, with your map, to a friend. Can they find the treasure? Or were your instructions not clear enough?

 # Straight-line graphs

A **graph** is a diagram showing the relationship between certain quantities plotted on a grid, with reference to a set of **axes**.

○ Parts of a graph

The axes are very important. When drawing, or looking at, a graph, you should always start with the axes. You must label the axes carefully to show what each one represents.

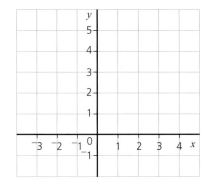

This is a co-ordinate grid of y against x.

The x-axis is numbered from ⁻3 to 4

and the y-axis is numbered from ⁻1 to 5

The grid is drawn on squared paper and, on each axis, one unit is represented by the side of one square.

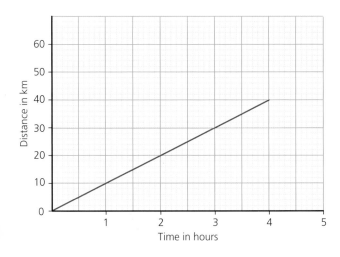

Now look at this graph. The word graph is often used to describe the illustration on the left. This consists of a grid with axes and the red line. The red line is also known as a graph.

This is drawn on graph paper, which has darker and lighter lines.

The horizontal axis shows time in hours, with 1 unit made up of of ten small squares representing 1 hour.

The vertical axis represents distance with 1 unit made up of of five small squares representing 10 kilometres.

The red line is a graph of distance against time. It shows a journey of 40 km taking 4 hours.

Any point on a graph has two **co-ordinates**.

The co-ordinates are written as a pair of numbers, in brackets. The horizontal co-ordinate always comes first.

To remember this, think of how you wake up horizontal — then you stand up to become vertical.

The *x* and *y*-axes

Look at this grid. Any point on the grid can be identified exactly and uniquely by a pair of co-ordinates.

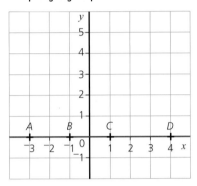 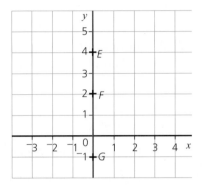

These points are on the *x*-axis:

$A(^-3, 0)$ $B(^-1, 0)$

$C(1, 0)$ $D(4, 0)$

All the points on the *x*-axis have a *y*-co-ordinate of 0

These points are on the *y*-axis:

$E(0, 4)$ $F(0, 2)$

$G(0, ^-1)$

All the points on the *y*-axis have an *x*-co-ordinate of 0

Therefore the *x*-axis is the line $y = 0$ and the *y*-axis is the line $x = 0$

Exercise 15.1

Copy this co-ordinate grid into your exercise book.

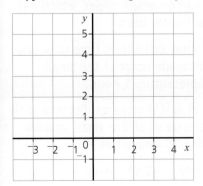

1 Plot these points.

  A (3, 1)   B (3, 0)   C (0, 3)

  D (2, 0)   E (0, 2)   F (2, ⁻1)

  G (⁻1, 0)   H (⁻1, 4)   I (0, ⁻1)

2 List the points that lie on the x-axis.

3 List the points that lie on the y-axis.

Graphs parallel to the axes

In this next exercise we are going to look at graphs parallel to the
x-axis and y-axis and find the rule or equation for each one of them.

Example

Write down the co-ordinates of
each of the lettered points. From
these, write down the equation of
that line.

A (⁻2, 3) B (0, 3) C (2, 3) D (4, 3)

All the y-co-ordinates are 3

Therefore the equation of the line
is $y = 3$

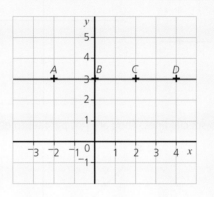

Exercise 15.2

On each grid there is a straight-line graph. Some points on the line are marked
by letters.

Write down the co-ordinates of the lettered points. From these, write down the
equation of the line.

1
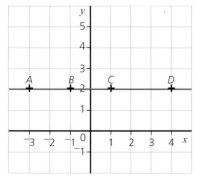

2
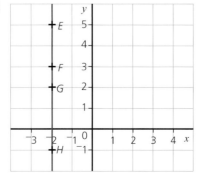

3

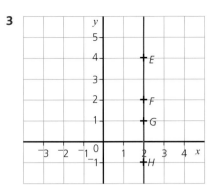

5

4

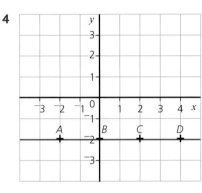

6

Now try to identify these two special lines. They are not parallel to either axis.

7

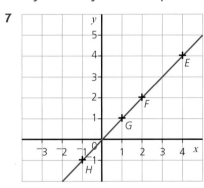

8

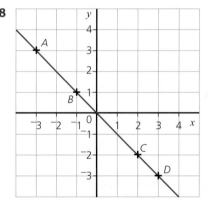

Points of intersection

A **point of intersection** is the point where two lines meet or cross.

Now that you know about the equations of lines you can draw some lines on a grid and consider points of intersection.

Exercise 15.3

Draw six co-ordinate grids with each pair of axes both numbered from ⁻4 to 4

Use one pair of axes for each of questions 1 to 6

1 Draw the lines given by the equations $x = 3$, $y = ⁻1$

Write down the co-ordinates of the point where the two lines intersect.

2 Draw the lines given by the equations $x = ⁻2$, $y = 0$

Write down the co-ordinates of the point where the two lines intersect.

3 Draw the lines given by the equations $x = 4$, $y = 1$

Write down the co-ordinates of the point where the two lines intersect.

4 Draw the lines given by the equations $x = ⁻2$, $y = x$

Write down the co-ordinates of the point where the two lines intersect.

5 Draw the lines given by the equations $x = 0$, $y = 3$

Write down the co-ordinates of the point where the two lines intersect.

6 Draw the lines given by the equations $x = 2$, $y = ⁻x$

Write down the co-ordinates of the point where the two lines intersect.

Drawing shapes on grids

You can draw more than one line on the same co-ordinate grid.

When you draw lines that intersect, the area between them is a **region**.

Sometimes the lines you draw will intersect in such a way as to form a **closed shape**.

Example

Draw a co-ordinate grid with both axes numbered from ⁻4 to 4

Draw the four lines given by the equations $x = ⁻2$, $y = 1$, $x = 2$, $y = ⁻3$

Name the shape enclosed by the four lines and find its area.

The shape is a square.

Area $= 4 \times 4$

$= 16$ square units

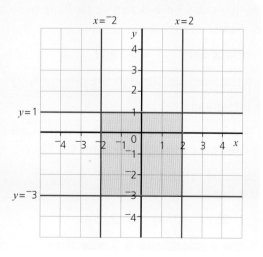

1 Draw a co-ordinate grid and number both axes from ⁻3 to 3

   Draw the four lines given by the equations $x = {}^-2, y = {}^-1, x = 1, y = 2$

   Work out the area of the square formed by the four lines.

2 Draw a co-ordinate grid and number both axes from ⁻4 to 4

   Draw the four lines given by the equations $x = 4, y = {}^-2, x = {}^-3, y = 3$

   Name the shape formed by the four lines and work out its area.

3 Draw a co-ordinate grid and number both axes from ⁻4 to 4. Draw the four lines given by the equations $x = 3, y = {}^-1, x = {}^-2, y = 4$

   Name the shape formed by the four lines and work out its area.

4 Draw a co-ordinate grid and number both axes from ⁻3 to 3. Draw the three lines given by the equations $x = {}^-2, y = {}^-1, y = x$

   Calculate the area of the triangle formed by the three lines.

5 Draw a co-ordinate grid and number both axes from ⁻5 to 5. Draw the three lines given by the equations $x = {}^-1, y = 4, y = {}^-2$

   Draw a fourth line so that the four lines form the outline of a rectangle of area 30 square units. Write down the equation of the fourth line.

6 Draw a co-ordinate grid and number both axes from ⁻4 to 4. Draw the three lines given by the equations $x = 3, y = {}^-2, x = {}^-3$

   Draw a fourth line so that the four lines form the outline of a square. Write down the equation of the fourth line and calculate the area of the square.

Graphs that are not parallel to the axes

Almost all the lines you have drawn so far have been parallel to the x-axis or the y-axis.

The two exceptions were $y = x$ and $y = {}^-x$

Both of these the lines ran through the origin (0, 0)

Now look at this graph.

The sloping line is straight; it does not pass through the origin but it does pass through the point (0, 3)

To find the equation for this line, start by looking at points that lie on the line.

(⁻3, 0)   (⁻1, 2)   (0, 3)   (2, 5)

In each case, the y-co-ordinate is 3 more than the x-co-ordinate.

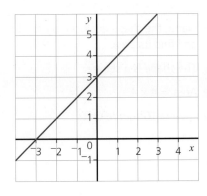

From this information, you can work out the equation for the line.

The equation of the line is $y = x + 3$

Any straight line can be described by an equation.

If you know the equation of a line, you can calculate points on the line.

For the line $y = x + 3$

- when $x = 0$, then $y = 0 + 3$

$$= 3$$

- when $x = 2$, then $y = 2 + 3$

$$= 5$$

- when $x = 4$, then $y = 4 + 3$

$$= 7$$

Now you can plot the points (0, 3), (2, 5) and (4, 7) and draw a line through them to represent the graph of the equation $y = x + 3$

Before you do this, though, practise some substitution.

Example

Given the equation $y = 2x$, find the value of y when x is 2

When $x = 2$

$$y = 2 \times 2$$

$$= 4$$

Exercise 15.5

1 Given the equation $y = 3x$, find the value of y when x is:

(a) 2   (b) 4   (c) 1   (d) 0

2 Given the equation $y = x + 5$, find the value of y when x is:

(a) 3   (b) 0   (c) 7   (d) 2

3 Given the equation $y = 7 - x$, find the value of y when x is:

(a) 4   (b) 2   (c) 0   (d) 3

4 Given the equation $y = 2x + 3$, find the value of y when x is:

(a) 1   (b) 3   (c) 7   (d) 0

5 Given the equation $y = \frac{x}{2}$, find the value of y when x is:

(a) 4   (b) 2   (c) 0   (d) 1

Substituting negative numbers

The values of unknowns such as x may be negative. Just remember the rules for negative numbers.

$$(^-2) \times (^+2) = {}^+4 \qquad (^+2) \times (^-2) = {}^-4$$

$$(^-2) \times (^+2) = {}^-4 \qquad (^-2) \times (^-2) = {}^+4$$

$$+ (^+2) = 2 \qquad + (^-2) = {}^-2 \qquad - (^+2) = {}^-2 \qquad - (^-2) = {}^+2 \text{ or } 2$$

> Always use brackets round negative numbers, so that you do not confuse the signs associated with the numbers with the operators +, −.

Example

Given the equation $y = 3x + 3$, find the value of y when x is $^-2$

$$y = 3 \times (^-2) + 3$$

$$= (^-6) + 3$$

$$= {}^-3$$

> You can do this in your head. You do not need to write down the calculation.

Exercise 15.6

1 Given the equation $y = {}^-x$, find the value of y when x is:

(a) $^-1$ (b) $^-4$ (c) 2   (d) 0

2 Given the equation $y = 3x - 2$, find the value of y when x is:

(a) $^-2$ (b) 0   (c) $^-3$ (d) 1

3 Given the equation $y = 3 + x$, find the value of y when x is:

(a) $^-4$ (b) $^-1$ (c) 0   (d) $^-3$

4 Given the equation $y = 2 - x$, find the value of y when x is:

(a) $^-1$ (b) $^-3$ (c) 0   (d) 1

5 Given the equation $y = 1 - 3x$, find the value of y when x is:

(a) $^-1$ (b) 0   (c) $^-3$ (d) 2

Drawing the graph of an equation

To draw a graph from an equation, you need to plot at least two points. It is sensible to plot at least three points, though, to make sure that you have not made a mistake.

Step 1: First write down the equation.

Step 2: Next choose at least three values for x and write them in a table.

Step 3: Then calculate and write down the corresponding values of y, in the same table.

Step 4: Finally, draw the graph. Plot each point with a dot or (better) a cross.

Step 5: Join the dots or crosses to draw the graph of the line.

Example

Draw a graph of the equation $y = x + 2$

x	$^-2$	$^-1$	0	1	2
y	0	1	2	3	4

Plot the points $(^-2, 0)$, $(^-1, 1)$, $(0, 2)$, $(1, 3)$, $(2, 4)$

Then draw the line and label it.

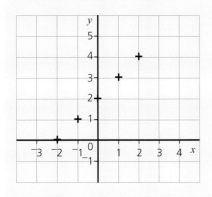 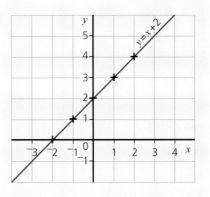

Finding other values

When you have drawn a line, you can find other values of x and y that lie on that same line. To do this, draw a dotted line from the value you are given to the line you have just drawn. When you reach the line, draw another dotted line back to the other axis. This gives you the value you are looking for.

Example

From the graph of $y = x + 2$, find:

(i) the value of y when $x = 2.5$

(ii) the value of x when $y = 1.5$

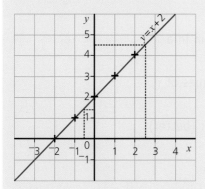

(i) When $x = 2.5$, $y = 4.5$

(ii) When $y = 1.5$, $x = {}^-0.5$

Exercise 15.7

For each equation, copy and complete this table of values for x and y.

x	$^-2$	$^-1$	0	1	2
y					

1 Draw a graph of $y = x - 2$

2 (a) Draw a graph of $y = 2x + 1$

   (b) From your graph find:

      (i) the value of y when $x = 1.5$

      (ii) the value of x when $y = 2$

3 (a) Draw a graph of $y = 3 - x$

   (b) From your graph find:

      (i) the value of y when $x = {}^-0.5$

      (ii) the value of x when $y = 2.5$

4 (a) Draw a graph of $y = 1 + 3x$

   (b) From your graph find:

      (i) the value of y when $x = 2.5$

      (ii) the value of x when $y = 5$

For more complicated equations you may find that an extra row of working helps you to calculate the value of y.

5 (a) Copy and complete this table of values for the equation $y = 2x - 3$

x	⁻2	⁻1	0	1	2
$2x$	⁻4	⁻2	0	2	4
y	⁻7				

(b) Draw a graph of $y = 2x - 3$

(c) From your graph find:

   (i) the value of y when $x = 1.5$

   (ii) the value of x when $y = ⁻2$

6 (a) Copy and complete this table of values for the equation $y = 4 - 2x$

x	⁻2	⁻1	0	1	2
$2x$	⁻4	⁻2	0	2	4
y	8				

(b) Draw a graph of $y = 4 - 2x$

(c) From your graph find:

   (i) the value of y when $x = ⁻1.5$

   (ii) the value of x when $y = 5$

7 (a) Draw up a table of values for the equation $y = 2 - \frac{x}{2}$ with values of x from ⁻3 to 3

(b) Draw a graph of $y = 2 - \frac{x}{2}$

(c) From your graph find:

   (i) the value of y when $x = 1.5$

   (ii) the value of x when $y = ⁻0.75$

8 (a) Draw up a table of values for the equation $y = \frac{x}{2} - 3$ with values of x from ⁻3 to 3

(b) Draw a graph of $y = \frac{x}{2} - 3$

(c) From your graph find:

   (i) the value of y when $x = 1.5$

   (ii) the value of x when $y = ⁻1.5$

Before you move on, look again at this graph to remind yourself of some of the things it tells you and how you can work out the equation for the line.

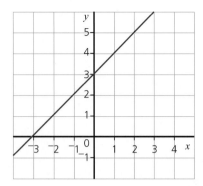

The sloping line is straight, but does not pass through the origin.

Points that lie on the line include (⁻3, 0), (⁻1, 2), (0, 3) and (2, 5)

In each case, the y-co-ordinate is 3 more than the x-co-ordinate.

The equation of the line is $y = x + 3$

Extension Exercise 15.8

1 Look at this graph.

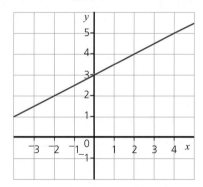

Write down the co-ordinates of the points that lie on the line.

From your list of points decide whether the line is:

(a) $y = 2x + 3$

(b) $y = \frac{x}{2} + 3$

(c) $y = x + 3$

Look at the graphs in the next four questions. In the same way as you treated the one in question 1. Write out the co-ordinates of several points and then write down the equation of the line.

2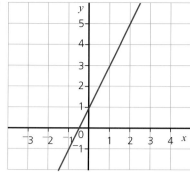

4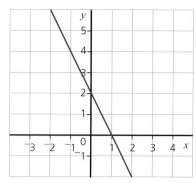

3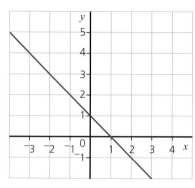

5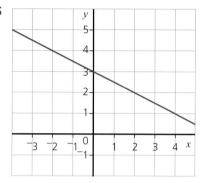

6 Look again at the lines in questions 1–5 and your answers.

Can you see any connection between your equations and the points where the lines cut the y-axis?

7 Look again at the lines in questions 1–5 and your answers.

Can you see any connection between your equations and whether the lines slope up to the right or up to the left?

8 Look again at the lines in questions 1–5 and your answers.

Can you see any connection between your equations and the steepness of the lines?

9 (a) Draw a co-ordinate grid with values of x and y from $^-5$ to 5

(b) Draw graphs of these equations.

    (i) $y = 0$ **(ii)** $y = 2x - 1$ **(iii)** $x = ^-1$

(c) Calculate the area of the triangle formed by the three lines.

10 (a) Draw a co-ordinate grid with values of x and y from $^-5$ to 5

(b) Draw graphs of these equations.

    (i) $y = ^-3$ **(ii)** $y = 1 - x$

(c) Draw a third line so that the three lines form an isosceles triangle.

(d) Calculate the area of the triangle.

(e) Write down the equation of the third line.

11 (a) Draw a co-ordinate grid with values of x and y from $^-5$ to 5

(b) Draw graphs of these equations.

    (i) $y = x$ **(ii)** $y = 2x - 4$

(c) Draw a third line so that the three lines form a triangle of area 9 square units.

(d) Write down the equation of the third line.

Summary Exercise 15.9

1 (a) Given the equation $y = x + 5$, find the value of y when x is 4

(b) Given the equation $y = x - 3$, find the value of y when x is $^-2$

(c) Given the equation $y = 2x + 3$, find the value of y when x is 2

(d) Given the equation $y = 2x + 1$, find the value of y when x is $^-1$

(e) Given the equation $y = 1 - x$, find the value of y when x is 4

(f) Given the equation $y = 3 - x$, find the value of y when x is $^-3$

(g) Given the equation $y = \frac{x}{2} + 5$, find the value of y when x is 4

2 Copy the graph and label each line.

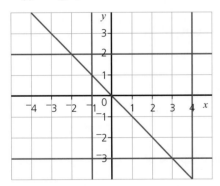

3 (a) Copy and complete this table of values for the equation $y = 2x - 4$

x	$^-2$	$^-1$	0	1	2
$2x$	$^-4$	$^-2$	0	2	4
y	$^-8$				

(b) Draw a co-ordinate grid and number the x-axis from $^-2$ to 2 and the y-axis from $^-8$ to 2. On your grid, draw the graph of the equation $y = 2x - 4$

(c) Where does this graph cross:

    (i) the x-axis   (ii) the y-axis?

(d) From your graph find:

    (i) the value of y when x is 1.5

    (ii) the value of x when y is $^-0.5$

Activity: Real-life graphs

Many companies use graphs to try to sell their products. This is an example of a bar graph about a brand of herbal bubble bath.

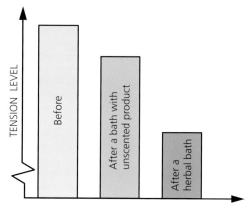

It appears from the graph that the herbal bath has a wonderful effect on tension levels.

But look carefully at the vertical axis. That little zig-zag means that the scale is not continuous. Notice also that there are no values given on the tension level axis, so you don't know how tension is measured.

The full graph could actually look like this: or this: or even this:

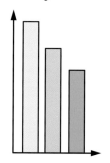 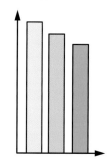 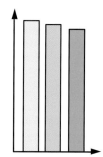

It could be that the herbal bath makes very little difference at all. It is important to remember that the company is interested in selling lots of the product and wants you to feel as though their herbal bath is great at reducing stress levels, even if it does probably exaggerate the real effect and is a bit misleading.

1 Make a class collection of all the graphs and charts you can find that are used to promote or advertise products. You will need to look in newspapers and magazines, in product information and on packaging.

2 Divide the graphs into two groups, **accurate and informative graphs** and **misleading graphs**. Write a short report on how the graphs are misleading.

3 Look again at the first group. Are you sure they are accurate? See if any of them could be sneakily misleading after all.

4 In a small group, decide on a product you would like to market. Draw up two graphs showing the wonderful properties or incredible popularity of your product. One graph should be accurate, the other misleading. How sneaky can you be?

16 Handling data

Information is what mathematicians call **data**. They often find it as the result of an experiment, a survey or by a series of measurements. Data, just after it has been collected, is called **raw data** and is not very useful. To make sense of it, you need to look at it in more detail and form an **analysis**. It often helps to put the data into a chart or table. The collection and analysis of data is known as **statistics**.

◯ What do you know?

You should already know about various ways of collecting and studying data.

Here is a quick review.

The range
The **range** is the difference between the highest and the lowest values in the set of data.

Range = highest value − lowest value

The mean
The **mean** is what most people think of as the average. To find the mean of n items of data you add up all the values and divide by n.

Adding up all values is called **finding the sum**.

$$\text{Mean} = \frac{\text{sum of all values}}{\text{number of values}}$$

$$\text{The mean of 5, 6, 10, 11 and 13} = \frac{5+6+10+11+13}{5}$$
$$= \frac{45}{5}$$
$$= 9$$

The mode

The **mode** is another average. It is the value that occurs most often, or most frequently, in the set of data.

The number of times a value occurs in a set of data is called its **frequency**.

The mode of the data set 1, 1, 2, 2, 2, 3, 4, 5, 5, 6, 7 is 2

The mode is the only average that you can use for data that is non-numeric, such as favourite colours or shoe sizes.

The median

This is the third type of average. If you list all the data values in order, the **median** is the one that lies exactly in the middle.

Example

Find the median of the data set 3, 7, 2, 5, 7, 9, 4, 6, 8, 3, 7

Step 1: Write the numbers in order.

2, 3, 3, 4, 5, 6, 7, 7, 7, 8, 9 There are 11 numbers.

Step 2: Work out the middle number.

The median is the sixth (middle) number.

The median is 6

If there is an even number of items then the median will be the **mean** of the two middle items.

Example

Find the median of the date set 3, 9, 8, 5, 1, 5, 7, 6

Step 1: Put the numbers in order.

1, 3, 5, (5, 6,) 7, 8, 9   There are 8 numbers.

Step 2: The median is the mean of the fourth and fifth numbers.

The median is $\frac{5+6}{2} = 5.5$

Now think about how you might use these calculations to analyse results in an experiment.

The pupils in Monty's class have been growing bean plants.

These are the heights, in centimetres, of the pupils' plants.

74	56	42	68	56
63	45	71	43	62
56	56	54	70	67
64	52	61	48	62

Monty's plant is 68 cm tall.

How does it compare with those of the rest of the class?

You can see that, when it is presented as an array of numbers, the information doesn't help Monty much.

Try finding the range, mean, mode and median of the heights of the plants.

The range is the highest value − the lowest value = 74 − 42

$$= 32\,cm$$

The mean height $= \dfrac{\text{the sum of all the heights}}{\text{the number of plants}}$

$$= \frac{1170}{20}$$

$$= 58.5\,cm$$

To find the mode, it is helpful if you put all the values in order. You could just count them up, by eye, but then you might miss out some values.

42	43	45	48	52	54	**56**	**56**	**56**	**56**
61	62	62	63	64	67	68	70	71	74

Now you can see that the number with the greatest frequency is 56

The mode is 56 cm.

To work out the median, you need the middle value. As there are 20 data items this will be the mean of the 10th and 11th when they are put in order.

The values are already in order, from the calculation of the mode.

The 10th and 11th values are 56 cm and 61 cm.

So the median is $\dfrac{56+61}{2} = \dfrac{117}{2}$

$$= 58.5\,cm$$

Monty can now see that his plant, at 68 cm, is well above the mean and median heights of 58.5 cm and, in fact, is very close to being the tallest.

The range is quite large, so the plants were probably treated in different ways, since some are much larger than others.

Those plants with heights that are considerably below the mean and median may not have had enough light or nutrients. Those with heights that are far above the mean and median may have had some special fertiliser.

Finding missing values

Sometimes you are given the average figure and a number of items, and are asked to calculate the total of the values.

Then you need to rearrange the equation you use for calculating the mean.

$$\text{Mean} = \frac{\text{sum of all values}}{n} \qquad \text{(where } n \text{ is the number of values being added)}$$

To calculate the total, rearrange the equation to get:

mean × number of items = sum of all items or total

Exercise 16.1

1 Find the range, mean, median and mode of each set of numbers.

   (a) 3, 4, 5, 6, 6, 6, 7, 8, 9

   (b) 1, 2, 3, 3, 3, 3, 4, 5

   (c) 17, 19, 20, 20, 24, 25, 29

   (d) 16, 18, 13, 15, 13, 18, 19

   (e) 2.2, 2, 2.22, 2.22, 2.2, 0.22, 0.2, 2.22

2 Find the range, the mean, the median and the mode of each set of numbers.

   (a) 98, 46, 65, 42, 38, 46

   (b) 4.2, 5.2, 4.6, 5.0, 4.4, 4.9, 4.2, 4.6, 5.0, 4.2

   (c) 100, 112, 104, 106, 108, 111, 104, 111

3 Find the range and the mean, median and mode for each set of numbers.

   (a) $\frac{1}{2}, \frac{3}{4}, \frac{1}{4}, \frac{1}{8}, \frac{3}{8}, \frac{1}{2}, \frac{1}{8}, \frac{5}{8}$

   (b) $2\frac{1}{4}, 2\frac{1}{4}, 2\frac{3}{4}, 1\frac{3}{4}, 2\frac{1}{4}, 2\frac{1}{4}$

   (c) $7\frac{1}{5}, 6\frac{1}{4}, 5\frac{2}{5}, 7\frac{1}{5}, 6\frac{3}{4}$

4 Every week my class has a mental maths test. These are my marks so far this term.

14   18   15   17   16   18   14

These are my friend Sam's marks. He was away last week and so he has one fewer mark than I do.

12   18   19   14   18   15

Who has the higher mean?

5 These are the ages of six pupils.

10 years 10 months, 11 years 5 months, 10 years 7 months, 10 years 8 months, 11 years 1 month, 10 years 5 months

What is the mean age of the pupils?

6 I sat six exams and my average mark was 63%. What was the total of all my marks?

7 In science I weigh samples of five compounds. The mean mass of these is 253 g. What do they weigh altogether?

8 The seven players in our netball team have a mean mass of 43 kg.

(a) What is the total mass of the team?

(b) Our substitute weighs 39 kg. What is the total mass of the team, including the substitute?

(c) What is the mean mass of the team if we include the substitute?

9 I have 10 numbers. Their range is 3. Their mode is 4, their mean is 5.5 and the median is 6. What are the numbers?

10 The mean age of a class of 15 pupils is 12 years and 3 months.

(a) What is the sum of all our ages?

(b) A new boy joins the class. The teacher recalculates the mean to include him and finds that it is now 12 years 2.5 months. What is the new boy's age?

Frequency tables and frequency diagrams

It is often more helpful to look at a picture than to read a table of numbers. In mathematics, you will use **tables**, **diagrams** and **charts** to display data.

In a **bar chart** or **frequency diagram**, each bar represents a data value or other piece of information and the height of the bar is the **frequency** of that data value. A bar chart may also represent a range of numbers, depending on what sort of information you are illustrating.

Before you can draw the chart, you need to sort the data to make it easy to represent. You can do this by using **tallies** in a frequency table. You will revise this technique in the next exercise.

1 These are marks out of 25 for a recent French vocabulary test.

16	20	19	23	18	24	18	17
20	21	18	16	22	24	19	16
22	19	17	17	20	25	21	16

(a) Copy and complete this frequency table to show the distribution of the marks.

Mark	Tally	Frequency
16		
17		
18		
19		
20		
21		
22		
23		
24		
25		
Total		

(b) What is the range of marks?

(c) What are the mean, the mode and the median?

(d) What, if anything, does this tell you about the marks?

2 Our class has been growing bean plants from seed. These are the heights, in centimetres, of the plants we have grown.

14	15	12	13	16	15
17	17	13	16	15	14
15	15	14	15	16	18

(a) Copy and complete this frequency table to show the information above.

Height (cm)	Tally	Frequency
12		
13		
14		
15		
16		
17		
18		
Total		

(b) What is the mean height of the plants?

(c) What is the range of heights?

3 This frequency table shows the distribution of marks for a French vocabulary test.

Mark	Frequency
12	1
13	2
14	4
15	2
16	7
17	3
18	1
Total	20

(a) What was the range of the marks?

(b) What was the mode?

(c) (i) How many pupils are there in the class?

    (ii) If the marks are put in order, which two would give you the median?

    (iii) What is the median? (It is not 15!)

(d) To find the mean you need to find the total of all 20 marks. What is the total? (It is not 95!)

(e) Calculate the mean.

4 Here is a table showing another set of marks.

Score	Frequency
17	2
18	0
19	1
20	2
21	5
22	6
23	3
24	0
25	1
Total	20

(a) Calculate the range, mode, median and mean of this set of data.

(b) Draw a frequency diagram to show this information.

(c) Could you find the range, mode, median and mean from the frequency diagram only? Explain your answer.

5 This frequency diagram shows the distribution of marks out of 10 for our Latin test. My class is not very good at Latin!

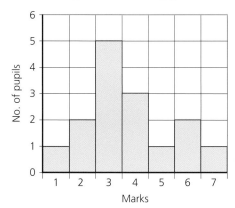

(a) What was the range of the marks?

(b) What was the mode?

(c) What was the median?

(d) Calculate the mean.

6 I did a traffic survey for prep. I stood outside my house for 20 minutes and filled in a tally chart to show how many vehicles passed me. Here are my results.

Type of vehicle	Tally	Frequency
Car	JHT JHT JHT JHT III	
Van	JHT II	
Lorry	I	
Motorbike	III	
Bicycle	IIII	
Total		

(a) Copy the table and complete the frequency column, then calculate the total. What was the modal type of vehicle?

(b) Why can you not work out a median and a mean?

Grouping data

Sometimes the data you collect will have so many different values that it would be difficult to represent it. In such a case, you can **group** data together into ranges of values.

Look at the statistics about rainfall in the first two questions in the next exercise. It would not be sensible to have a frequency for each value, to the nearest millimetre (mm). In this type of example, you should collect the individual data values together and put them into sensibly sized groups.

When data is grouped, you cannot find a mode. Instead, you refer to the group with the greatest frequency as the **modal group**.

Exercise 16.3

1 These figures record the daily rainfall, in centimetres, during April.

2.2	0	3.4	0.2	0	2.8	1.6	2.5	3.5	2.4
3	6.7	1.7	2.9	0	1.5	2.6	3.1	1.7	0.6
2.7	0.6	3.2	1.1	5.6	3.4	2.3	0	2.4	1.3

(a) Copy and complete this frequency table.

Rainfall (cm)	Tally	Frequency
0–0.9		
1.0–1.9		
2.0–2.9		
3.0–3.9		
4.0–4.9		
5.0–5.9		
6.0–6.9		
Total		30

(b) Draw a frequency diagram to show the daily rainfall during April.

2 This data shows the daily rainfall, in centimetres, over the month of June. Draw a frequency table and then a frequency diagram to display this information. Group the data as you did in question 1.

1.6	0	3.1	0	0.2	2.8	1.6	2.5	3.2	2.5
1.4	0	0.6	2.6	1.4	1.9	2.3	0	0	0.4
2.3	0	0.3	1.2	0.8	3.1	2.3	0	1.7	1.3

3 (a) Using the information in question 1 and question 2, find the range and the mean rainfall for each of the months of April and June.

(b) Identify the modal group for each month.

(c) What do all your results tell you about the two months?

4 Pupils in my year were asked to hold their breath for as long as possible. This frequency table shows the results.

Time (seconds)	Tally	Frequency
24.5–34.4	JHT	5
34.5–44.4	JHT II	7
44.5–54.4	JHT JHT I	11
54.5–64.4	JHT III	8
64.5–74.4	JHT I	6
74.5–84.4	III	3

(a) How many pupils are there in the year?

(b) Draw a frequency diagram to illustrate this information.

(c) What is the modal group?

(d) I pick one of the class at random. What is the probability that this pupil held their breath for between 44.5 and 54.4 seconds?

(e) Do the same experiment with your class. Draw a frequency diagram to show your results.

(f) Compare your results with those above. What are the differences?

5 These are the percentage marks of 32 boys who took a maths exam.

56	64	78	58	90	72	55	90
62	63	75	68	83	94	52	81
86	67	87	73	78	82	66	74
63	76	81	70	67	78	71	79

(a) What is the mean percentage? What is the median mark?

Because most of the marks are different, finding the mode for this set of data is not sensible, nor is it sensible to draw a bar chart from these results. Instead, you need to group the marks together to get a better picture of the distribution.

(b) Work out the groups that you need and draw a frequency table.

(c) What is the modal group?

(d) Draw a frequency diagram of this distribution.

(e) These are percentage marks for another set of 16 papers.

| 55 | 62 | 58 | 71 | 52 | 80 | 64 | 50 |
| 71 | 60 | 72 | 74 | 62 | 66 | 58 | 61 |

Draw another frequency table to show all 48 marks, and then draw another frequency diagram.

(f) What are the differences in the frequency diagrams?

(g) What are the new mean, median and modal group?

(h) If the new set of 16 papers come from another class, what does that tell you about the two classes?

◯ Pie charts

A **pie chart** is a circular diagram that is divided into slices, hence the name.

Pie charts show the proportions of the various categories of data that make up the whole data set. For example, local government may provide households with a breakdown of how the money taken in local taxes is spent on education, housing and services such as transport and waste disposal.

This is an example from North Lanarkshire.

Council Budget 2015/2016 (Net)

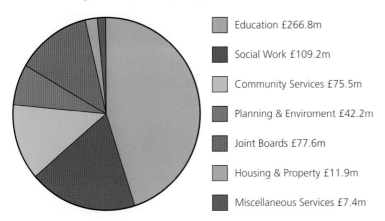

- Education £266.8m
- Social Work £109.2m
- Community Services £75.5m
- Planning & Enviroment £42.2m
- Joint Boards £77.6m
- Housing & Property £11.9m
- Miscellaneous Services £7.4m

This is the breakdown of another council's expenditure.

Education	£400 million
Social work	£80 million
Community services	£120 million
Planning and environment	£70 million
Other	£50 million
Total	£720 million

Can you remember how to display this information as a pie chart?

You need to work out the fraction of the whole 'pie' that each slice represents and then work out the angle for each sector.

The total is £720 million. Remember there are 360° in a full turn.

Therefore each £1 million will be represented by an angle of $\frac{360°}{720} = \frac{1}{2}°$

Now work out the angles that will represent the categories being represented. You can use a calculator to work out the angles, but record the calculations and the answers in a table, like this.

Expenditure	Amount (£m)	Calculation	Angle
Education	400	$\frac{360}{720} \times 400$	200°
Social Work	80	$\frac{360}{720} \times 80$	40°
Community Services	120	$\frac{360}{720} \times 120$	60°
Planning and Environment	70	$\frac{360}{720} \times 70$	35°
Other	50	$\frac{360}{720} \times 50$	25°
Total	720		360°

Always check that the total of the angles is 360° before you start to draw the pie chart.

Draw a circle, add a radius and then use your protractor to measure the angles. Then draw the pie chart. If you have drawn it correctly, the pie will be full. There should be no empty spaces and no sectors should overlap.

The first council had a budget of £590.6 million and the second had £720 million. Although the two councils allocated their money in different ways, the pie charts make it easy to see that the second council spent a higher proportion than the first on education.

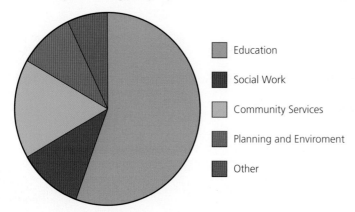

- Education
- Social Work
- Community Services
- Planning and Enviroment
- Other

Pie charts can also be used to present the data in terms of percentages.

This is the breakdown of votes in a local election.

Party	Percentage of poll
Labour	40%
Conservatives	36%
Lib Dems	20%
Others	4%
Total	100%

This time you need to find the **percentages** of 360°

Again, you should record your working in a table.

Party	Calculation	Angle
Labour	$\frac{40}{100} \times 360°$	144°
Conservatives	$\frac{36}{100} \times 360°$	129.6 ≈ 130°
Lib Dems	$\frac{20}{100} \times 360°$	72°
Others	$\frac{4}{100} \times 360°$	14.4 ≈ 14°
Total		360°

This table shows fractions, but you can also use decimals, in which case the first calculation would be $0.4 \times 360 = 144$

Always check that the angles add up to 360°. In this case:

$144° + 130° + 72° + 14° = 360°$

but the check is important because some of the angles may have been rounded to the nearest whole degree. When this happens, the total may be 361° or 359° and you will need to make further adjustments.

Now you can draw the pie chart.

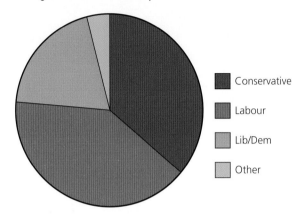

Conservative

Labour

Lib/Dem

Other

Exercise 16.4

1 A year group of 36 pupils carried out a survey to look at the number of brothers and sisters that they all had. They are going to draw a pie chart to show the results of their survey.

(a) Copy and complete this table to work out the angles.

Number of brothers and sisters	Frequency	Calculation	Angle
0	9	$\frac{360}{36} \times 9$	
1	12		
2	9		
3	5		
4	1		10°
Total	36		360°

(b) Draw a pie chart to show this information.

2 I conducted a survey of my class of 30 pupils to find out approximately how many hours of television they watched each week. These are my results.

0–2 hours	1 pupil
2–4 hours	3 pupils
4–6 hours	5 pupils
6–8 hours	12 pupils
8–10 hours	6 pupils
More than 10 hours	3 pupils

(a) Draw up a frequency table like the one in Q1 to display this information.

(b) Complete the table by calculating the angles.

(c) Display the information on a pie chart.

3 A market research company asked the pupils at my school about their favourite television programmes. These are their results as percentages of the total number of pupils at the school.

Star Factory	43%
The Dance Factor	35%
Bake it!	9%
The News	5%
Other	8%

(a) Copy and complete this table.

Programme	Percentage	Calculation	Angle
Star Factory	43%	0.43 × 360	155°
The Dance Factor	35%		
Bake it!	9%		
The News	5%		
Other	8%		
Total	100%		360°

(b) Show this information on a pie chart.

4 220 children were asked how they preferred to spend their free time. These were their first choices.

Watching television	53	Reading	12
Playing computer games	46	Art/modelling/pottery	8
Sport (football/rugby)	35	Music (listening/playing)	6
Sport (tennis/badminton)	22	Other	24
Riding	14		

(a) Draw up a table like the one in question 1 and calculate the angles.

(b) Construct a pie chart to illustrate these results.

(c) What percentage of children chose tennis or badminton as their first choice?

(d) What percentage of children chose watching television or computer games as their first choice?

(e) If a child were chosen at random, what is the probability that riding would be their first choice?

Interpreting pie charts

Consider these two pie charts. They compare the activities that pupils in Year 4 and Year 8 like doing after school.

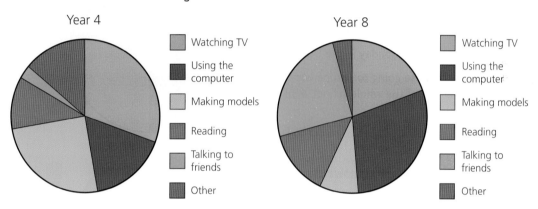

The charts show that the older pupils enjoy using the computer and talking to friends more than the younger children do. Although the pie charts do not give exact figures, you can see that about a quarter of the Year 4 pupils like making models, but only about a tenth of the Year 8 pupils do.

Exercise 16.5

1 A teacher asked the pupils in his class what they were doing at 7 p.m. the previous evening. This chart shows the answers.

(a) What fraction of them were watching TV?

(b) What fraction of them were doing their homework?

(c) What would be the probability that a pupil picked at random was eating supper at 7 p.m?

(d) Given that six pupils were reading, how many pupils were in the class?

(e) How many were walking the dog?

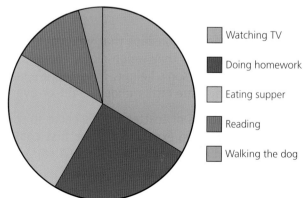

2 The parents conducted a survey of how pupils come to school in the morning. This pie chart shows the results.

(a) Roughly what fraction come to school by car?

(b) Given that 40 come by bicycle, how many pupils took part in the survey?

The school introduced a school minibus service and now one half of those who used to come by car use the school minibus.

(c) Sketch another pie chart showing the new breakdown of morning transport.

3 This pie chart shows where the pupils in the school went on holiday last year.

(a) What was the most popular destination?

(b) What fraction spent their holiday in the USA?

(c) In fact a quarter of those going to Europe went to France. What fraction of the whole school went to France?

(d) 60 pupils stayed in the UK. How many went to Europe?

4 My class did a survey in the local park to find out what people did there. This pie chart shows the various activities.

Write a report about these results. Include as much detail as you can. Think what time of day we might have asked the questions. Would we have found the same results at a different time?

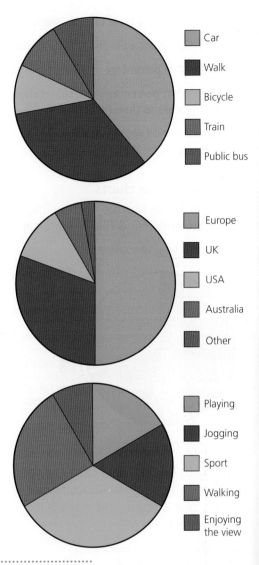

Car
Walk
Bicycle
Train
Public bus

Europe
UK
USA
Australia
Other

Playing
Jogging
Sport
Walking
Enjoying the view

◯ Scatter graphs

A **scatter graph** is a way of comparing two sets of data, to find out if they are related. For example, you may want to find out if people with big feet can swim faster than those with small feet, or whether people who like dogs also like cats.

There are some relationships that you would expect; for example, as people get taller they weigh more. There is a range of ideal mass according to a person's height. If someone's mass is outside that range, then they are either underweight or overweight.

Other applications of scatter graphs occur in science. Look at the results of these two experiments. The first compares the amount of fertiliser used on six identical plants (A to F) against the height of those plants after four weeks.

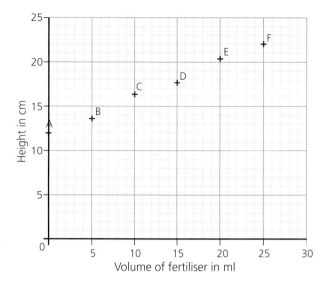

This scatter graph shows that as the amount of fertiliser (in millilitres) that is used increases, so the height of the plant (measured in centimetres) increases. The graph demonstrates **positive correlation**.

The second experiment compares the amount of insecticide applied to six identical plants (G to L) against the height of those plants after four weeks.

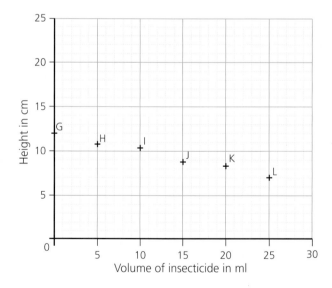

In this case, as the amount of insecticide increases, the height decreases. This graph demonstrates **negative correlation**.

When you have plotted all the points, you can sometimes draw a **line of best fit**. There should be the same number of points above the line as there are below it and it should be as close to them as possible.

Here are the graphs from the two experiments, with lines of best fit added.

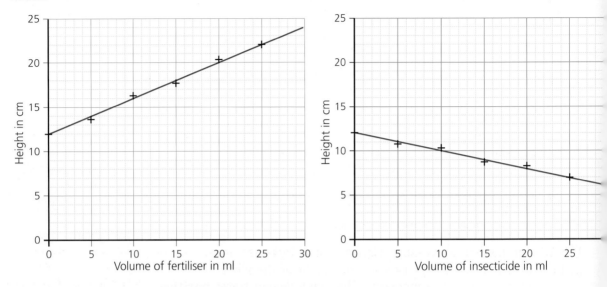

You can often use the line of best fit to make some deductions about the data. Although there is no plotted point for a plant that is 21 cm high, by drawing a horizontal line from 21 cm to the line of best fit and then a vertical line down to the axis you can deduce that you would need about 23 ml of fertiliser. You should do this only for values within the scales on the axes.

Exercise 16.6

1 This table of values shows the shoe sizes and heights (in metres) of 10 pupils.

Height (m)	1.42	1.55	1.63	1.35	1.59	1.60	1.51	1.38	1.72	1.50
Shoe size	36	38	40	33	39	41	36	35	43	35

(a) Draw a scatter graph to show the relationship between the two sets of data.

(b) Draw a line of best fit.

(c) What type of correlation does this show?

2 This table shows the percentage marks scored in maths and English exams by 14 pupils.

Mathematics	56	63	72	68	80	76	45	90	81	73	62	65	76	84
English	61	67	74	65	85	67	56	83	78	80	70	58	80	75

(a) Draw a scatter graph to show the relationship between the two sets of data.

(b) Draw a line of best fit

(c) What type of correlation does this show?

3 Our class sat two mathematics papers. This table shows the results.

Paper 1	81	65	71	90	55	63	74	75	77	52	62	68
Paper 2	45	34	42	48	26	40	19	43	43	27	30	36

(a) Draw a scatter graph to compare the two sets of results.

(b) Fred was not feeling well when he took Paper 2. Circle the point on the scatter graph that you think might show Fred's marks.

(c) Draw a line of best fit.

(d) Mary was away for Paper 2 but scored 85 on Paper 1. Use the line of best fit to predict what Mary might have scored on Paper 2

Extension Exercise 16.7

In this exercise you will use algebra to explore answers to questions on statistics.

When you are answering them, you may need to use the formula:

total = mean × number of items

> An **expression** is a collection of **terms**. It cannot be solved but may be simplified.
>
> An **equation** is made up of two expressions separated by an equals sign and can be solved.

1 The average age of a class of 20 is x months. Write an expression in terms of x for the sum of their ages.

2 The average age of a class of x children is 10 years 5 months. Write an expression in terms of x for their total age in months.

3 There are x pupils in the class and the sum of their ages is 1980 months.

(a) Write an expression in terms of x for their average age in months.

(b) What is their average age, in years, in terms of x?

4 I have £x, India has £2 more and Archie has £5 less.

(a) Write an expression for the total amount of money that we have.

(b) The mean amount of money we have is £12. Form an equation and solve it to find the value of x.

5 This table shows the ages of a group of pupils.

Age	9	10	11	12
Number of pupils	4	6	x	2

(a) What is the value of x, given that the mean age of the pupils is 10 exactly?

(b) What is the maximum number of pupils, and hence the maximum value of x, if the median age is 10?

(c) What is the maximum value of x, and hence the maximum number of pupils, if the modal group is 10?

6 This table shows the ages of a group of children.

Age	4	5	6	7
Number of pupils	$2x$	$x - 1$	x	$x + 3$

(a) Given that the mean age is 6, what is the value of x?

(b) How many five-year-olds are there?

7 This bar chart shows the numbers of patients that visited Dr Bone's evening surgery last week.

Dr Bone cannot remember how many patients he saw last Friday, but the bar chart shows the mean number of patients he saw in the evenings over the five days. Calculate the number of patients he saw on Friday evening. Let x be the number of patients that he saw on Friday evening.

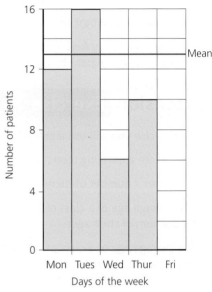

8 There are x pupils at a school. A quarter of them walk to school, two-thirds come by car and the rest by bus.

(a) Write an expression in x for the number of pupils who come to school by bus.

(b) If the number that come to school by bus is 19, form an equation in x and solve it to find the number of pupils in the school.

9 There are x employees in the SunLite Factory, and they are rarely ill. In fact, the mean number of days that they have taken off this last year is 1.75

(a) How many working days have been lost over the year?

(b) Three times as many employees have been ill as have not been ill at all. Write an expression in x for the number of employees who have been ill.

(c) No-one has had more than five days off and the number of people who have had two days off is the same as the number who have had four days off. Half of this number have had five days off.

Twice as many as the number that had two days off have had one day off. No-one was off for exactly three days. What fraction of the people who had any days off had five days off?

(d) Write expressions in x for the number of people who had 0, 1, 2, 3, 4 and 5 days off. Make sure that the total adds up to x.

(e) 24 more people than the number who took 5 days off were never ill. Write an equation in x and solve it to find the total number of employees.

Summary Exercise 16.8

1 Work out the range, mean, median and mode of each set of numbers.

(a) 3   4   4   4   5   6   7   7   8

(b) 2.1   1.8   1.6   2.3   1.8   2.1   1.4   2.1   1.9

(c) 14.1   12.4   13.2   14.1   12.8   13.8

2 These are the ages of five pupils, in years and months.

11 years 6 months, 10 years 4 months, 10 years 6 months, 11 years 4 months, 10 years 11 months

(a) What is the mean age of the pupils?

(b) A sixth pupil joins the group and the mean age of all six pupils is 11 years and 1 month. What is the age of the sixth pupil?

3 These are the marks, out of 20, for a recent mental arithmetic test.

15   16   14   13   15   17

11   15   17   12   16   14

13   19   14   16   18   15

(a) Draw a tally or frequency table to show the results.

(b) Work out the mean, mode and median of the marks.

(c) Show the results on a frequency diagram.

4 This frequency diagram shows how many people there are in each car that comes to my school in the morning.

(a) How many cars had three people in them?

(b) How many more cars carried four people than carried two?

(c) How many cars were there altogether?

(d) How many people were there in all the cars?

(e) What was the mode?

(f) What was the mean number of people in the cars?

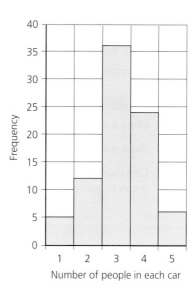

5 These numbers show the daily rainfall (in cm) for the month of September.

5.1	1.9	5.3	0	0.4	2.5	5.5	6.3	0	3.8
3.1	0.7	2.6	3.9	0	1.2	0	0	0	0.6
3.2	2.7	0.3	0	0	0	2	0.6	1.9	3.3

(a) Collect these results in a frequency table. You will need to group the data suitably.

(b) Illustrate the information on a frequency diagram.

(c) Find the range and the mean rainfall.

6 A headteacher asked 175 pupils how many books they had read this term. These were the results.

Number of books	Frequency
More than 10	17
8 or 9	25
6 or 7	20
4 or 5	58
2 or 3	43
Fewer than 2	12

(a) Make a table to calculate the angles you will need, to show these results in a pie chart.

(b) Draw a pie chart to illustrate these results.

(c) What percentage of the pupils had read more than 10 books?

7 This table shows the heights and masses of pupils in my class.

Height (cm)	155	160	158	143	135	150	163	157	152	146	139	151
Mass (kg)	44	52	45	37	28	40	55	43	43	40	30	42

(a) Draw a scatter graph to compare the two sets of results.

(b) Draw a line of best fit.

(c) One pupil was away on the day of the survey. He is 154 cm tall. Use your graph to estimate his mass.

Activity: A traffic survey

Many statistical investigations are about traffic and travelling. Here are some ideas for conducting your own surveys. You will be able to practise what you have learnt in this chapter and have some fun at the same time.

Traffic

There are many questions that you might like to ask about the traffic that runs past your school.

- What type of vehicle?
- What colour of vehicle?
- How many buses?
- When is the traffic at its busiest?

Before you start, you need to prepare by following these steps.

1 Decide what it is that you want to know about the traffic.

2 Make up a recording sheet so that you can record your observations.

3 Decide when you are going to make your observations and for how long. For example, you might want to do it at two different times of day.

When you are fully prepared, follow these steps.

4 Find somewhere safe to stand and start recording. Make sure that an adult knows where you are and what you are doing.

5 When you have your results, you can make your report. Use any of the charts and tables that you have studied in this chapter to make your report more interesting.

Travelling to or from school

Several other questions you will have seen were about how pupils travelled to and from school, and how many people were in a car.

Here's how you could conduct your own survey.

1 Ask your class how they came to school in the morning.

2 Ask anyone who travelled by car how many people were in it. Remember to ask your teacher too!

3 Ask people where they came from. You might find a pattern.

4 Put together a questionnaire for other classes. When you are happy with it, ask your teacher to give it out.

5 When you have your results, think about what sort of things you want to find out. It might be the sort of information we have already mentioned, or it might be that you want to see if there is a difference as pupils get older, or you might want to compare travel to different destinations.

6 Write a report about the results of your survey. Try to use many of the things you have learnt from this chapter to make your report interesting.

17 Transformations

A **transformation** is a change. In mathematics, a transformation changes the position or **orientation** of an object but maintains its basic shape. This does not necessarily mean it stays the same size. If the transformation is an enlargement, the shape and its image will be **similar** but not **congruent**.

Two or more shapes are congruent if they are the same shape and the same size. Two or more shapes are similar if they have the same shape but are not the same size. Their angles are the same and their sides are in the same ratio.

○ Reflections

Many mathematical shapes and patterns have **lines of symmetry**. Sometimes you may be asked to draw a pattern that is symmetrical about a line, sometimes you may be given a shape or a pattern and asked to find the line of symmetry. If your pattern is drawn on a co-ordinate grid, then it can be simpler to describe the exact position of the line of symmetry, of the **object** being reflected and its **image**.

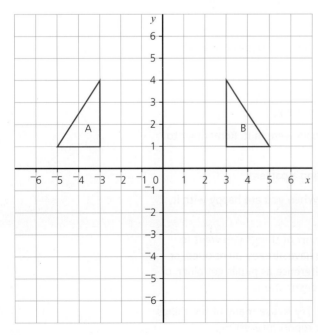

In this example, triangle B is the image of triangle A after a **reflection** in the y-axis (the line $x = 0$)

Exercise 17.1

For each question in this exercise, draw a co-ordinate grid and mark the values of x and y from $^-6$ to 6, as in the earlier diagram on the previous page.

1 Copy triangles A and B (above) on to your grid. Draw the reflections of A and B in the x-axis.

2 Draw square P with vertices at (3, 3), (3, 5), (5, 5) and (5, 3). Draw the line $y = 2$, Draw the square Q, which is a reflection of P in $y = 2$

3 Draw triangle X with vertices at (3, $^-1$), (3, $^-4$) and (5, $^-1$). Draw the line $x = 1$ and then draw triangle Y, which is the image of X after a reflection in $x = 1$

4 Draw triangle R with vertices at ($^-1$, 3), ($^-4$, 1) and ($^-4$, 3). Draw the line $y = ^-1$ and then draw triangle S, which is the image of R after a reflection in $y = ^-1$

5 Draw square A with vertices at ($^-1$, 1), ($^-2$, $^-1$), ($^-4$, 0) and ($^-3$, 2). Draw the line $x = 1$ and then draw square B, which is the image of A after a reflection in $x = 1$

6 Draw trapezium P with vertices at (2, 4), (1, 1), (5, 1) and (4, 4). Draw the line $x = 2$ and then draw trapezium Q, which is the image of P after a reflection in $x = 2$

7 Look at this grid.

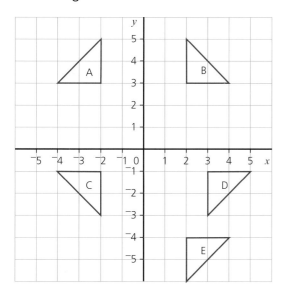

Describe the reflection that maps:

(a) A to B   (b) A to C   (c) C to D   (d) B to E

8 Look at this grid.

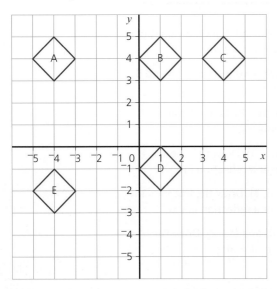

Describe the reflection that maps:

(a) A to B   (c) B to C   (e) D to B

(b) A to C   (d) E to A

◯ Rotations

In a **rotation**, an **object** is turned round a fixed point to form the **image.** To draw a rotation on a co-ordinate grid, you need **three** pieces of information:

● the centre of rotation

● the angle of rotation

● the direction of rotation.

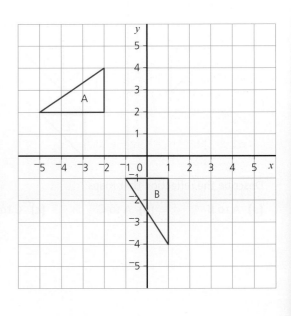

B is the image of A after a **rotation of 90° anticlockwise** about the point **(1, 2)**

A is the image of B after a **rotation of 90° clockwise** about the point **(1, 2)**

Tracing paper is very useful when you are studying rotations, especially when you need to check the centre of rotation. First trace over the object, and then put the point of your pencil on the centre of rotation to hold the tracing paper in place. Then you can rotate the tracing paper to check the position of the image.

17 Transformations

Exercise 17.2

For each question in this exercise, draw a co-ordinate grid and mark the values of x and y from ⁻6 to 6. You will also need some tracing paper.

1 Draw triangle A with vertices at (2, 1), (5, 1) and (2, 3)

    (a) Draw triangle B, a rotation of A through 90° clockwise about the origin.

    (b) Draw triangle C, a rotation of A through 180° about the origin.

    (c) Draw triangle D, a rotation of A through 270° clockwise about the origin.

2 Draw triangle P with vertices at (2, 2), (3, 4) and (1, 4)

    (a) Draw triangle Q, a rotation of P through 90° clockwise about the point (1, 0)

    (b) Draw triangle R, a rotation of P through 180° about the point (1, 0)

    (c) Draw triangle S, a rotation of P through 270° clockwise about the point (1, 0)

3 Draw triangle W with vertices at (1, 2), (1, 5) and (0, 5)

    (a) Draw triangle X, a rotation of W through 90° clockwise about the point (1, 2)

    (b) Draw triangle Y, a rotation of W through 180° about the point (1, 2)

    (c) Draw triangle Z, a rotation of W through 270° clockwise about the point (1, 2)

4 Draw rhombus A with vertices at (2, 0), (1, 2), (2, 4) and (3, 2). Draw image B, a rotation of A through 90° anticlockwise about the point (2, ⁻1). Draw image C, a rotation of B through 90° anticlockwise about the point (2, ⁻1)

5 Draw trapezium P with vertices at (0, 0), (2, 1), (2, ⁻3) and (0, ⁻2). Draw image Q, a rotation of P through 180° about the point (⁻1, 1)

6 Draw kite Y with vertices at (⁻3, 5), (⁻1, 4), (⁻3, ⁻1) and (⁻5, 4). Draw image Z, a rotation of Y through 90° clockwise about the point (0, 1)

7 Look at this grid.

Describe the rotation that maps:

    (a) B to C   **(d)** B to A

    (b) D to E   **(e)** B to F.

    (c) A to E

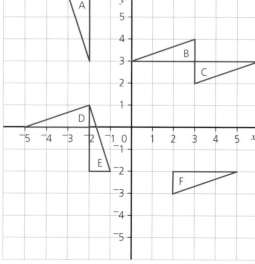

8 Look at this grid.

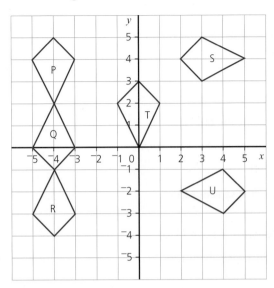

Describe the rotation that maps:

(a) P to Q   **(c)** Q to T   **(e)** S to U

(b) P to R   **(d)** T to U

9 An object A is rotated 90° clockwise about a point to an image B, then B is rotated 90° clockwise about the same point to an image C. What single transformation will map A to C?

10 Look again at the diagram for question 8. What **reflection** will map P to Q?

◯ Translations

After a reflection the image is in a different place from the object and is flipped over. After a rotation the image is in a different place from the object and is a different way round. Sometimes you just want an image to be in a new place, but the **same** way round. To do this you need to **slide** the object across the page. Such a slide is called a **translation**.

A translation is described as a **move in two directions**, first in the x-direction and then in the y-direction.

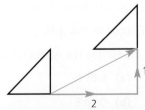

The translation in the diagram is: 2 to the right, 1 up.

Example

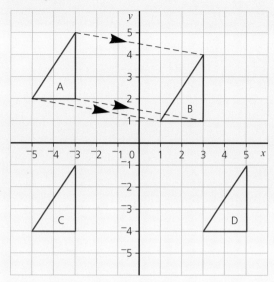

The translation of A to B is 6 units to the right, 1 unit down.

The translation of A to C is 6 units down.

The translation of C to D is 8 units to the right.

The translation of D to B is 2 units to the left, 5 units up.

Exercise 17.3

1 Look at this grid.

Describe the translation that maps:

(a) A to B

(b) C to B

(c) C to D

(d) B to D

(e) D to A.

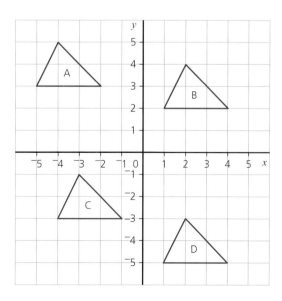

2 Look at this grid.

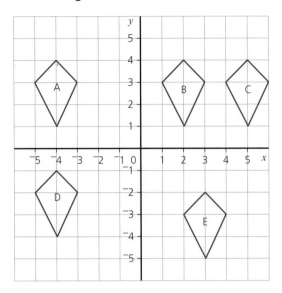

Describe the translation that maps:

(a) A to B

(b) B to C

(c) D to B

(d) A to D

(e) D to E

(f) E to A.

3 Draw a co-ordinate grid and mark the values of x and y from $^-6$ to 6. Draw triangle A with vertices at (5, 5), (5, 3) and (2, 4)

(a) Draw triangle B, the image of A after a translation of 4 units to the left, 3 units down.

(b) Draw triangle C, the image of B after a translation of 2 units to the left, 1 unit up.

(c) Draw the triangle D, the image of C after a translation of 5 units to the right, 4 units down.

(d) Describe the translation that will map triangle D to triangle A.

4 Draw a co-ordinate grid and mark the values of x and y from $^-6$ to 6
Draw kite K with vertices at ($^-4$, $^-4$), ($^-3$, $^-5$), ($^-2$, $^-4$) and ($^-3$, $^-2$)

(a) Draw kite L, the image of K after a translation of 4 units to the right, 3 units up.

(b) Draw kite M, the image of L after a translation of 3 units to the left, 2 units up.

(c) Draw kite N, the image of M after a translation of 5 units to the right, 4 units down.

(d) Describe the translation that will map kite M to kite L.

○ Mixed or combined transformations

You know that a transformation transforms the original object into its image. A transformation may be a rotation, a reflection, a translation or an enlargement.

Sometimes a transformation may be described in more than one way.

B is the image of A after any one of:

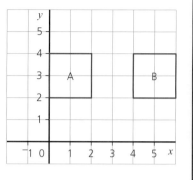

● a reflection in the line $x = 3$

● a rotation through 180° about the point (3, 3)

● a rotation through 90° clockwise about the point (3, 1)

● a rotation through 270° anticlockwise about the point (3, 5)

● a translation, 4 units right, 0 units up.

Remember:

● **reflection** needs a **mirror line**

● **rotation** is a turn through an **angle** in a stated **direction** about a **fixed point**

● **translation** is a move to the **right or left** followed by a move **up or down**

● **enlargement** requires a **scale factor** and a **centre of enlargement**.

Look back to Chapter 11 and review the topic of enlargement, if you need to, before you start the next exercise.

Exercise 17.4

1 Look at this grid.

   Describe the transformation that maps:

   (a) A to C   (c) D to B

   (b) C to D   (d) E to B.

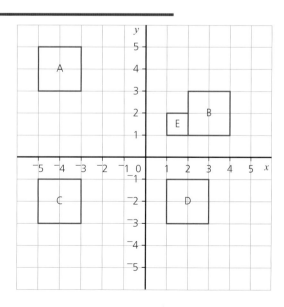

2 Look at this grid.

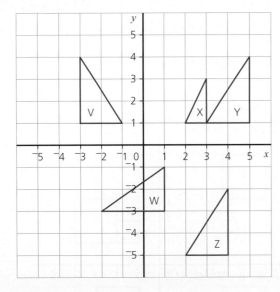

Describe the transformation that maps:

(a) triangle P to triangle R

(b) triangle R to triangle S

(c) triangle P to triangle Q

(d) triangle R to triangle Q.

3 Look at this grid.

Describe the transformation that maps:

(a) triangle V to triangle Y

(b) triangle X to triangle Y

(c) triangle V to triangle W

(d) triangle Y to triangle Z.

4 Look at this grid.

Describe the transformation that maps:

(a) triangle A to triangle B

(b) triangle B to triangle C

(c) triangle B to triangle D

(d) triangle C to triangle E

(e) triangle D to triangle E

(f) triangle B to triangle E

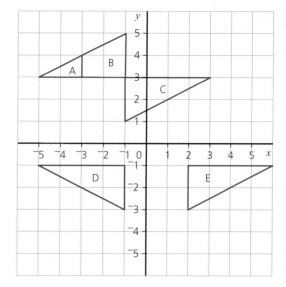

For questions 5–10, draw a co-ordinate grid and mark the values of x and y from $^-6$ to 6. You will also need some tracing paper.

5 Draw triangle A with vertices at (3, 5), (3, 3) and (5, 3)

(a) Draw image B, the reflection of A in the y-axis.

(b) Draw image C, the rotation of A through 90° clockwise about the origin.

(c) Draw D, the image of A after a translation of 6 units to the left, 5 units down.

(d) Describe a single transformation that will map B to C.

6 Draw triangle W with vertices at (1, 2), (3, 2) and (3, 3)

(a) Draw image X, the rotation of W through 90° anticlockwise about the point (1, 2)

(b) Draw image Y, the enlargement of W by scale factor 2, centre of enlargement (1, 2)

(c) Draw image Z, the reflection of W in the line $x = ^-1$

7 Draw rhombus P with vertices at (2, 4), (4, 3), (6, 4) and (4, 5)

(a) Draw image Q, the reflection of P in the line $x = 1$

(b) Draw image R, the reflection of P in the line $y = 2$

(c) Draw S, the image of P after a translation of 6 units left, 4 units down.

(d) Describe the rotation that maps Q to R.

(e) Describe the translation which maps S to Q.

8 Draw trapezium A, with vertices at ($^-5$, 3), ($^-4$, 4), ($^-3$, 4) and ($^-2$, 3)

(a) Draw image B, the reflection of A in the line $y = 1$

(b) Draw image C, the rotation of B of 180° about the point (0, 2)

(c) Draw D, the image of C after a translation of 4 units left, 2 units down.

(d) Describe the reflection that maps D to A.

(e) Describe the rotation that maps B to D.

9 Kite K has vertices at $(^-3, 0)$, $(^-2, 1)$, $(^-3, 4)$ and $(^-4, 1)$. Draw K.

(a) Draw image L, the reflection of K in the line $y = 1$

(b) Draw image M, the rotation of K through 180° about the point $(^-2, 1)$

(c) Describe a transformation that could map L to M.

(d) Draw image N, the rotation of K through 90° clockwise about the point $(^-3, ^-2)$

(e) Draw image P, the reflection of L in the y-axis.

(f) Describe the transformation that maps N to P.

10 Draw triangle W with vertices at $(^-3, 1)$, $(^-2, 0)$ and $(^-2, 2)$

(a) Draw image X, the reflection of W in the line $x = 1$

(b) Draw Y, the image of W after a translation of 2 units right.

(c) Draw image Z, the rotation of Y through 90° anticlockwise about the point $(0, 2)$

Extension Exercise 17.5

1 You can see some interesting transformations by reflecting objects in the lines $y = x$ and $y = ^-x$. Copy this diagram and reflect triangles A and B in $y = x$ and $y = ^-x$

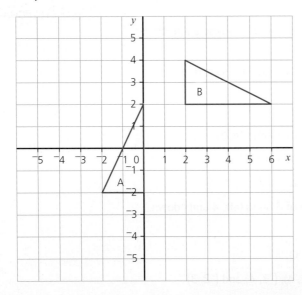

Copy and complete this table, which gives the co-ordinates of the six vertices of the two triangles.

Triangle	Co-ordinates	Image after reflection in $y = x$	Image after reflection in $y = {}^-x$
A	(0, ⁻2)		
	(0, 2)		
	(⁻2, ⁻2)		
B	(2, 4)		
	(2, 2)		
	(6, 2)		

What do you notice about the co-ordinates after the reflections?

2 Sometimes you need to apply two transformations to map an object to its image.

(a) Explain why you cannot map A to B in a single transformation.

(b) Given that the first transformation of A is a reflection in the x-axis, what is the second?

(c) Given that the first transformation is a reflection, and the second is a translation, write down the exact transformations.

(d) Can you find another pair of transformations?

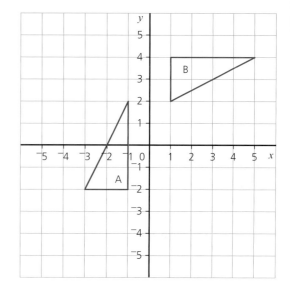

3 Sometimes there is more than one transformation that takes an object to its image.

Work out all the possible single transformations that will map:

(a) A to B

(b) C to D

(c) E to F

Which pair has the most possibilities and which the least? Try to explain your answer.

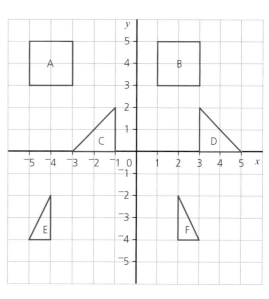

4 Copy this diagram.

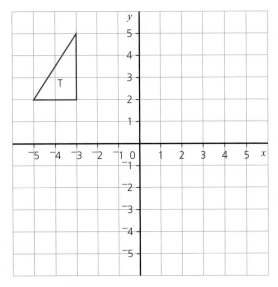

Rotate triangle T through 90° clockwise about (⁻3, ⁻1) to give image R.

A certain reflection of R will give the same image as a certain reflection of T.
Draw this image and clearly mark the two lines of symmetry.

5 The hexagon *ABCDEF* is divided into
12 congruent triangles.

(a) Describe the **single** transformation that
maps triangle X on to triangle Y.

(b) Describe the **single** transformation that
maps triangle Y on to triangle Z.

(c) Describe **as many other pairs** of
consecutive transformations that map
triangle X on to triangle Z.

(d) How many of the other triangles, N, P, Q,
R, S, T, U, V and W, can be filled by a single
transformation of triangle X? Describe each
transformation carefully.

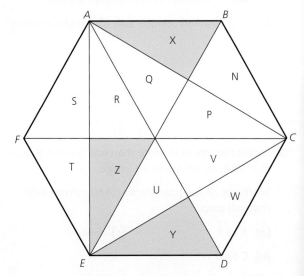

Summary Exercise 17.6

1 Look at this grid.

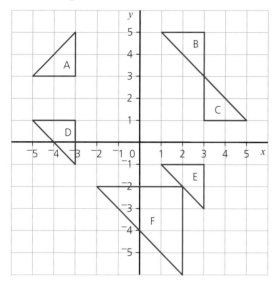

Describe any single transformations that map:

(a) A to D   (d) E to C

(b) E to F   (e) E to B

(c) B to C   (f) B to D.

2 Copy this co-ordinate grid and triangle A.

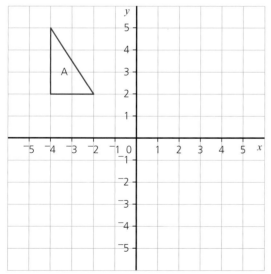

(a) Reflect the triangle in the *x*-axis. Label this image B.

(b) Rotate A through 180° about the origin. Label this image C.

(c) Translate A 3 units right, 2 units down. Label this image D.

3 Copy this co-ordinate grid and triangle P.

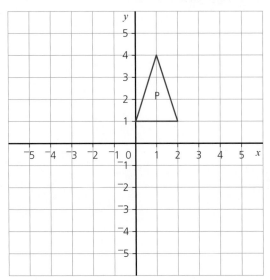

(a) Reflect P in the line $x = 2$. Label the image Q.

(b) Rotate P through 90° clockwise about the point (2, 1). Label the image R.

(c) Translate P 4 units right, 3 units down. Label the image S.

4 Copy this co-ordinate grid and shape W.

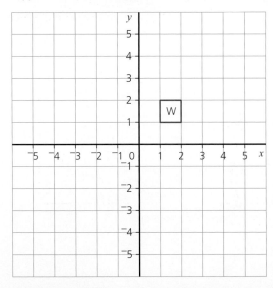

(a) Enlarge W by scale factor 3 with centre of enlargement the origin. Label this image X.

(b) Translate X 2 units left, 4 units down. Label this image Y.

(c) Describe the enlargement that maps W to Y.

5 Draw a co-ordinate grid and mark the values of x and y from $^-6$ to 6
Draw kite K with vertices at ($^-2$, $^-1$), ($^-1$, $^-3$), ($^-2$, $^-5$) and ($^-5$, $^-3$)

   (a) Reflect K in the line $y = ^-1$ and label the image L.

   (b) Reflect L in the line $x = ^-1$ and label the image M.

   (c) Describe the transformation that maps K to M.

6 Draw a co-ordinate grid and mark the values of x and y from $^-6$ to 6
Draw triangle Z with vertices at (4, $^-1$), (3, 2) and (1, 0)

   (a) Draw image Y, the reflection of Z in the line $y = 1$

   (b) Draw image X, the rotation of Y through 180° about the point (0, 2).

   (c) Draw image W, the translation of X 2 units down.

   (d) Describe the transformation that maps W to Z.

Activity: The four-colour problem

The four-colour problem is famous and was unsolved for many years.

An outline of the problem

Ever since mapmakers began making the sort of maps that show distinct regions (such as countries or states), they have known that, if they plan well enough, they will never need to use more than four colours.

The basic rule for colouring a map is that no two regions that share a boundary can be the same colour.

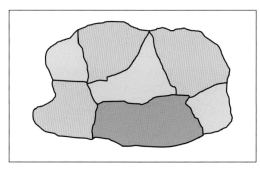

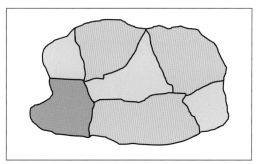

This map is coloured correctly.
No two adjacent regions are coloured the same.
It is fine for regions meeting at a point to be the same colour.

This map is not coloured correctly.
Two adjacent regions are coloured the same.

How many different colours must you have if you want to colour a map so that countries that share a boundary are not coloured in the same colour?

Look at the 'maps' below. Can you colour these with only four colours? Which ones need fewer colours? Draw some maps of your own and try out some theories. Try to suggest some theories about why some need fewer colours than others.

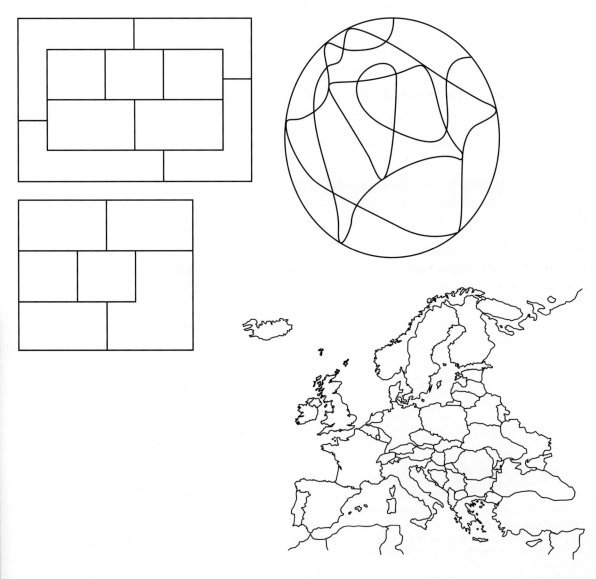

18 3D shapes

A **two-dimensional** (**2D**) shape is flat; it has a perimeter and an area.

A **three-dimensional** (**3D**) shape is a solid; it has a surface area and volume.

Units of volume and capacity

1000 cubic centimetres (cm^3) = 1 litre (l)

1000 millilitres (ml)   = 1 litre (l)

100 centilitres (cl)   = 1 litre (l)

Capacity is the amount a container can hold. **Volume** is the amount of space taken up by a substance. A jug may have capacity of one litre but contain a lesser volume of milk.

In this chapter you will learn more about surface area and volume, the amount of space taken up by a solid.

Surface area

The **surface area** of a 3D shape is the **total area** of **all its surfaces**.

To find the surface area you need to consider each of the faces of the 3D shape.

One way is to draw the **net** of the 3D shape.

Here are some nets that you should recognise.

To fold this net into a solid, you join the sides: red to red, blue to blue, orange to orange and green to green.

Net of a cube

Here are some more nets.

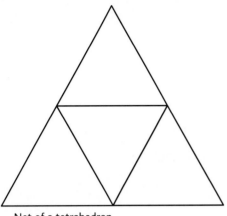

Net of a tetrahedron

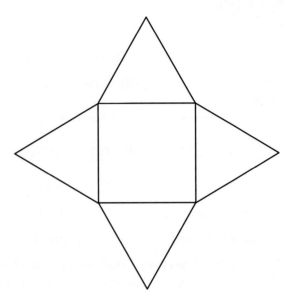

Net of a a square-based pyramid

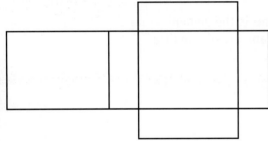

Net of a cuboid

Calculating surface area

To calculate the surface area of a 3D shape, you need to calculate the area of each 2D shape in the net and then add these areas all together. This is not as difficult as it may seem because in most shapes, some of the faces are the same shape and size.

You know how to calculate the surface area of a **cuboid**.

> Remember always to check that the dimensions are in the same units.

Example

Calculate the surface area of a cuboid with length 35 cm, width 95 mm and height 20 cm.

$l = 35\,\text{cm}$ $w = 9.5\,\text{cm}$ $h = 20\,\text{cm}$

Surface area $= 2 \times$ area A $+ 2 \times$ area B $+ 2 \times$ area C

$= 2 \times (20 \times 35) + 2 \times (9.5 \times 20) + 2 \times (35 \times 9.5)$

$= 2 \times 700 + 2 \times 190 + 2 \times 332.5$

$= 1400 + 380 + 665$

$= 2445\,\text{cm}^2$

> Even when you use a calculator it is sensible to write down your working, stage by stage, and check it as you go.

Exercise 18.1

Give any non-exact answers correct to 1 decimal place.

1 Copy the diagram of the net of a cuboid. Colour the sides to indicate which ones will meet when the net is folded up.

2 Copy the diagram of the net of a tetrahedron. Colour the sides of the triangles to indicate which ones will meet when the net is folded up.

3 Copy the diagram of the net of the square-based pyramid. Colour the sides of the shapes that make up the net, to indicate which ones will meet when the net is folded up.

4 Calculate the surface area of a cube with sides of:

(a) 5 cm

(b) 1.2 m.

5 Calculate the surface areas of each cuboid.

(a) 4 m by 1.2 m by 5 m

(b) 25 cm by 20 cm by 35 cm

(c) 1.2 m by 45 cm by 0.9 m

> Draw the net first and label the sides A, B and C.

6 A tetrahedron is made from four equilateral triangles with sides of 6 cm.

   (a) Construct the equilateral triangle accurately.

   (b) Construct a line that runs from the top of the triangle to meet the base at 90°

   (c) Measure the length of the line to find the height of the triangle.

   (d) Work out the area of the triangle.

   (e) What is the surface area of the tetrahedron?

You can remind yourself about this construction by looking back at Chapter 14

7 The length of the base of a square-based pyramid is 6 cm. All the triangular sides are equilateral triangles. Use some of your answers from question 6 to calculate its surface area.

8 Another square-based pyramid has a base of length 10 cm and its sides are triangles with sides of 10 cm, 8 cm and 8 cm. Construct a triangle, drop a perpendicular and measure its length, to find the height of the triangle. Then calculate the surface area of the square-based pyramid.

9 A cuboid has a total surface area of 126 cm². The base of the cuboid is 5 cm by 6 cm. Draw its net and give a possible value for the height of the cuboid.

10 I have a roll of paper 3 m long and 60 cm wide. I need to cut out as many nets of a 10 cm by 8 cm by 5 cm cuboid as possible.

   (a) What is the maximum number of nets I can cut from the roll of paper?

   (b) What percentage of the total roll is wasted?

◯ Volume

Volume is measured in **cubic** units: cubic millimetres (mm³), cubic centimetres (cm³), cubic metres (m³) and cubic kilometres (km³) for oceans.

You may also meet cubic imperial units: in³, ft³, yd³ but use of these is now unusual.

Cubes and cuboids

You can find the volume of a cuboid by multiplying its length by its width and then multiplying the result by its height. If you think of volume as a series of layers, you should be able to see why this works.

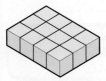

1 layer
12 cubic centimetres (cm³)

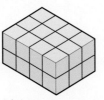

2 layers
24 cubic centimetres (cm³)

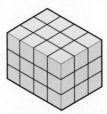

3 layers
36 cubic centimetres (cm³)

The formula for the volume of a cuboid is:

volume of cuboid (V) = length (l) × width (w) × height (h)

$$V = l \times w \times h$$

When all the sides are the same length, the cuboid is a cube.

The formula for the volume of a cube is:

volume of cube = length³

$$V = l^3$$

When you are writing down the formula for the volume of a shape, make sure that you specify what shape it is, for example, *volume of a cube*. This is because formulae for volumes of different shapes are different. It is always important to use the correct formula.

In questions you may find other words are used for length, width and height, such as **breadth** or **base**. You can still use the formula and substitute the correct value.

Before you do any calculations, remember to make sure that measurements are all expressed in the same units.

Example

Find the volume of a cuboid of length 4 m, width 3.2 m and height 0.9 m.

In this example, the units are all given in metres.

$l = 4\,$m $w = 3.2\,$m $h = 0.9\,$m

Volume of cuboid $= l \times w \times h$

$$= 4 \times 3.2 \times 0.9$$

$$= 11.52\,\text{m}^3$$

In the next example the units are different. This is why it is sensible to write out the dimensions you are given first and check they are in the same units. If you are not told which units to use, then work with units that give you the fewest decimal places.

Example

Find the volume of a wooden plank of length 32 cm, width 22 mm and height 1.2 m.

$l = 1.2\,$m $= 120\,$cm $w = 32\,$cm $h = 22\,$mm $= 2.2\,$cm

Volume of cuboid $= l \times w \times h$

$$= 120 \times 32 \times 2.2$$

$$= 8448\,\text{cm}^3$$

Remember the steps for using a formula: write the **formula, substitute, calculate**, write the **answer** with correct **units**.

1 Find the volume of each cuboid.

   (a) 3 cm by 5 cm by 7 cm

   (b) 5 m by 10 m by 12 m

   (c) 1.6 m by 1.2 m by 0.8 m

2 Find the volume of a cube of side:

   (a) 5 cm   **(b)** 50 cm   **(c)** 0.5 cm.

3 Find the volume of each cuboid.

   (a) length 1.2 m, breadth 90 cm and height 12 cm

   (b) length 4.8 cm, breadth 8 mm and height 1.4 cm

   (c) length 3.2 m, breadth 75 cm and height 0.9 m

4 A water tank is 1 m long, 1.5 m wide and 80 cm deep. How many litres of water does it contain when it is full?

> Remember
> that 1000 cm^3 is equivalent to 1 litre.

5 A fish tank is 30 cm wide, 20 cm deep and 20 cm tall. How many litres of water does it contain when it is three-quarters full?

6 Find out which of these has the greatest volume.

   (a) a 125-litre water tank

   (b) a water tank in the shape of a cube of side 50 cm

   (c) a cuboid water tank with sides of 25 cm, 50 cm and 1 m

> Remember that
> 1000 ml = 1 l and that
> 1 ml = 1 cm^3.

7 **(a)** How many millilitres are there in 5 litres?

   (b) How many millilitres are there in 500 cubic centimetres?

   (c) How many cubic centimetres are there in 50 millilitres?

8 What is the volume of a plastic cuboid with sides of length 4 cm, 7 cm and 8 cm. Give your answer in millilitres.

9 Which volume is largest, a cube of side 8 cm, half a litre or a cuboid with sides of length 5 cm, 9 cm and 11 cm?

10 **(a)** I have 24 centimetre cubes. If I use all 24, how many different cuboids can I make?

   (b) I have 36 centimetre cubes. If I use all 36, how many different cuboids can I make?

   (c) I have 35 centimetre cubes. If I use all 35, how many different cuboids can I make?

   (d) I have 37 centimetre cubes. If I use all 37, how many different cuboids can I make?

Finding the height or depth of a 3D shape

By carefully substituting the correct values into the formula and then treating the result as an equation, you can work out unknown lengths.

Example

Work out the height of a cuboid of length 4 cm, breadth 3 cm and volume 60 cm³.

Volume of cuboid = 60 cm³, l = 4 cm, b = 3 cm

Volume of cuboid = $l \times w \times h$	Formula
$60 = 4 \times 3 \times h$	Substitute
$60 = 12h$	Calculate
$(\div 12)$	
$h = 5$ cm	Answer and units

Exercise 18.3

1 This cuboid has a base of area 12 cm² and a volume of 60 cm³. What is the height of the cuboid?

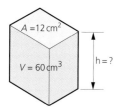

2 Find the height of each cuboid.

(a) base area 9 cm², volume 63 cm³

(b) base area 20 cm², volume 150 cm³

(c) base area 40 cm², volume 24 000 cm³

3 (a) A cube has a volume of 125 cm³. What is the length of one side?

(b) A cube has a surface area of 96 cm². What is the length of one side?

4 This cuboid is 5 cm wide and 12 cm long. The volume of the cuboid is 7.2 litres. What is the height of the cuboid?

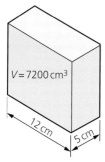

5 Work out the heights of these cuboids.

    (a) volume 1 litre, length 10 cm and width 10 cm

    (b) volume 5 litres, length 25 cm and width 8 cm

    (c) volume 300 litres, length 2.5 m and width 1.2 m

6 (a) A jug contains 500 ml of water. Water is poured from the jug into an empty cuboid of base area 25 cm^2. What is the depth of the water in the cuboid?

    (b) A jug contains 2 litres of water. Water is poured from the jug into an empty cuboid of length 40 cm and width 20 cm. What is the depth of the water in the cuboid?

7 A hollow cube of side 5 cm is repeatedly filled with water, which is then poured into a cuboid 25 cm by 10 cm by 15 cm. How many cubefuls of water does it take to fill the cuboid?

8 (a) How many cubes of side 2 cm will fit into a larger cube of side 8 cm?

    (b) How many cubes of side 2 cm will fit into a larger cube of side 7 cm?

9 A brick with sides of length 5 cm, 10 cm and 15 cm is dropped into a rectangular bowl of water. If the rectangular bowl has sides of length 30 cm and 40 cm, by how much does the water level go up?

10 A child has a set of three hollow cubes that fit one inside another. The largest cube has sides of 8 cm, the next has sides of 7 cm and the smallest has sides of 6 cm.

The child decides to fill all the cubes with water from a litre bottle. He fills the two smallest cubes but there is not quite enough to fill the largest. What is the depth of water in the largest cube (to the nearest mm)?

Problem solving

What do you understand by the word 'per'? When you were learning about percentages, you took the term 'per cent' to mean 'per hundred'. So what does 'cost per millilitre' or 'mass per cubic metre' mean?

In mathematics, you can take 'per' to mean that you have to divide something by something else.

For example, suppose you were comparing the prices of different bottle of shampoo. The best way would be to work out the cost **per** millilitre, by **dividing** the price of the bottle by the total volume of shampoo inside the bottle. The best value is the one that gives you most millilitres per pound or penny.

Example

Which is better value, 125 ml of orangeade for £1.20, or 175 ml of lemonade for £1.61?

Cost of orangeade $= \frac{120}{125}$ Cost of lemonade $= \frac{161}{175}$

$\qquad\qquad\quad = 0.96\text{p per ml}$ $\qquad\qquad\quad = 0.92\text{p per ml}$

The lemonade is better value, as long as you like lemonade and orangeade equally.

> Remember that when you use a calculator, you must first write down the calculation that you are going to do, then check your answer to make sure it is sensible.

Exercise 18.4

1 I buy half a litre carton of milk for 52p. What is the cost per litre?

2 I buy a 225 ml can of energy drink for 99p. What is the price of the drink per litre?

3 A carton of juice is 15 cm by 10 cm by 6 cm.

   (a) What is this in litres?

   (b) If the carton costs £1.35, what is the price per litre?

4 Which is better value, 225 ml of banana milkshake for £1.35p, or 175 ml of raspberry smoothie for £1.05p?

5 I can buy one shampoo that costs £1.20 for 750 ml, and another shampoo for £1.50 per litre. Which one is better value?

6 A box of muesli measuring 5 cm by 15 cm by 30 cm costs £1.80. Is this better value than a litre bag of the same muesli costing £1?

7 I have a water tank that holds 400 litres. So that it will fit through my loft door, it must have a maximum height of 1 m and a maximum width of 50 cm. What must the minimum length of the tank be?

8 A cereal packet has a base of 10 cm by 24 cm and a height of 30 cm. It contains 750 g of Wheeties. What is the mass per cubic centimetre (cm^3) of Wheeties?

9 A pot of 1.25 litres of emulsion paint costs £22.50. The same paint is sold in 1.75 litre pots at £24.15. Which size is the better value?

10 I have to paint the walls of a room that is 8 m by 6.5 m and 2.2 m high. One litre of paint covers 15 m^2.

   (a) How much paint do I need? Ignore any doors and windows in the room.

   (b) How much will it cost me if I buy the paint described in question 9?

   (c) There is a special offer on the 1.75-litre pots – 'Buy one and get the second half price!' How much money can I save by using the special offer?

1 This is the net of a hollow cuboid.

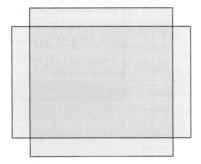

It is a rectangle with a square cut from each corner.

What size of square will give the maximum volume of the cuboid?

To find out, let the length of the side of each square be x. The rectangle is 10 cm by 8 cm.

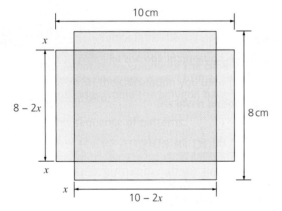

Then the lengths of the sides of the cuboid are x, $(8 - 2x)$ and $(10 - 2x)$

Copy and complete this table to find the value of x that would give a cuboid with the greatest possible volume.

x	$8 - 2x$	$10 - 2x$	Volume
1	6	8	48
1.5			
2			
2.5			
3			
3.5			

2 Repeat question 1 but this time base it on the net of a box made from a square 20 cm by 20 cm. You will need more rows in your table.

3 Repeat question 1 but this time base it on the net of a box made from a rectangle 15 cm by 20 cm. You will need more rows in your table.

4 From your table in question 3 draw a graph of x against volume.

5 A4 is the name for the size of standard, everyday paper. It measures about 21 cm by 29 cm. What is the maximum volume of a hollow cuboid that you can make from a piece of A4 paper?

The questions so far have been about volume, but you could also look at the surface area. Look again at this net for a box.

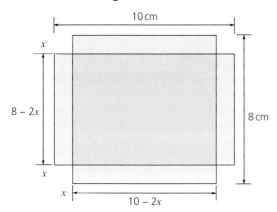

Make sure that you can identify the five rectangles that make up the net for the box.

The areas of these five rectangles are:

$x(8 - 2x)$ $x(8 - 2x)$ $x(10 - 2x)$ $x(10 - 2x)$ $(8 - 2x)(10 - 2x)$

and you could add them up.

However, it is quicker to look at the whole shape to calculate the surface area.

Start by calculating the area of the whole rectangle (10 cm by 8 cm) and then subtract the areas of the four cut-out squares ($4 \times x \times x$)

Then the surface area is $10 \times 8 - 4 \times x^2$ which is $80 - 4x^2$

6 Copy and complete the table below. Then draw a graph to show the change in the surface area, as x changes.

x	x^2	$4x^2$	$80 - 4x^2$
1	1	4	76
1.5			
2			
2.5			
3			
3.5			

If you can use a spreadsheet program, then you can do some further investigation into volumes and surface areas.

1 I have a cube of side 6 cm.

Calculate:

(a) its surface area

(b) its volume.

2 A cuboid is 8 cm long, 5 cm wide and 9 mm high.

(a) What is its surface area? Give your answer in square centimetres (cm^2).

(b) What is its volume? Give your answer in cubic centimetres (cm^3).

3 By construction, measuring and calculation find the surface area of a tetrahedron with sides of 8 cm.

4 (a) The volume of a cube is 64 cm^3.

    (i) What is the length of one side of the cube?

    (ii) What is the volume of the cube, in litres?

(b) The surface area of a cube is 294 cm^2.

    (i) What is the length of one side of the cube?

    (ii) What is the volume of the cube, in litres?

5 This cuboid is 50 cm wide, 2.5 m long and 4 m high. Give its volume in:

(a) cm^3 **(b)** m^3.

> Work the answer out first in cm^3 and then in m^3.

6 The area of the base of a cuboid is 15 cm^2 and its volume is 60 cm^3. What is the height of the cuboid?

7 Which is better value, 1.2 litres of OZO washing powder at £2.25 per litre or 2 litres of DAX at £3.10 per litre?

8 I need two 2.5-litre pots of paint. The local DIY store is selling it for £24 per pot.

(a) What is the cost per litre?

(b) The next week the paint store had a special offer: 'Buy one pot, get one free!' I buy two pots. What is the cost per litre?

(c) What is my percentage saving?

9 An empty water tank measuring 2 m by 1.2 m by 80 cm is filled by means of a 4-litre bucket. How many bucketfuls does it take to fill the water tank?

10 A square hole 2 cm wide is cut through a cube of edge 5 cm. What is the volume of the solid, once the hole has been made?

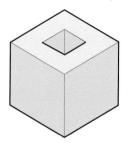

Activity: Euler's theorem

More polyhedra

If you have access to a polygon construction kit, you will find it very useful for this investigation.

A **polyhedron** is a 3D or solid shape with faces that are planes.

There are five **platonic solids** with faces that are all the same regular polygon.

  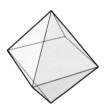  

| Tetrahedron: 4 equilateral triangles | Cube: 6 squares | Octahedron: 8 equilateral triangles | Dodecahedron: 12 regular pentagons | Icosahedron: 20 equilateral triangles |

There are many other solids with faces that may be different shapes.

  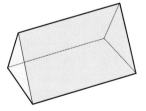

These solids have plane faces and have straight edges that join together at points or vertices. A cuboid has 6 faces, 12 edges and 8 vertices.

Do you think that there might be some relationship between these three values?

The answer is: 'Yes!' Try to find what it is.

1 Count the faces, edges and vertices of the cube, tetrahedron, pyramid and triangular prism shown on the previous page.

2 Make a table like this and fill it in.

Solid	Faces	Edges	Vertices
Cube	6	12	8

3 Look at the remaining three platonic solids. Add them to the table.

4 Now make some more solids and add them to the table.

5 With all this information can you now find the relationship between F (the number of faces), E (the number of edges) and V (the number of vertices)?

This relationship was proved by the mathematician Leonhard Euler (1707–1783). He opened up many new areas of mathematics and was the originator of the Konigsburg Bridge problem, which may be familiar to your parents and even your grandparents. Ask your teacher about this puzzle.

19 Algebra 3: More equations

You already know how to solve simple equations. Now it is time to look at more complicated examples.

◯ Forming and solving equations

I am ordering trophies for the school football tournament. When I asked my maths teacher for help, she told me that the cost of one trophy plus £50 was the same as the cost of three trophies plus £2

I decided to let 🏆 represent the cost of one trophy, and wrote down an equation.

🏆 + 50 = 🏆 + 🏆 + 🏆 + 2

To find the cost of one trophy, I need to solve the above equation.

My teacher then told me this was not a very mathematical approach, and that it would be easier to use algebra as I know some rules.

Taking c as the cost of one trophy, the equation is:

$$c + 50 = 3c + 2$$

We can solve this equation in the same way as we solved earlier equations. By doing the same operation to both sides (to keep everything balanced) we can simplify the equation until we find a numeric value for c

$$c + 50 = 3c + 2$$
$$(-c)$$
$$50 = 2c + 2$$
$$(-2)$$
$$48 = 2c$$
$$(\div 2)$$
$$24 = c$$
$$c = 24$$

The cost of the trophy is £24

Check: $24 + 50 = 74$ and $3 \times 24 + 2 = 74$ ✓

Remember to take the equation step by step. If you have brackets or more than one unknown term on one or both sides then you must multiply out the brackets and simplify before you start.

Step 1   Subtract the smaller unknown term from both sides.
Step 2   Subtract the remaining number term from both sides.
Step 3   Finally divide by the coefficient of the unknown.

(The **coefficient** of x is the number that multiplies x.)

Align the equals signs in your working and always write down what you are doing to both sides of the equation, as a commentary down the right-hand side.

If you are confident in recording every step in a calculation, you can use the shorter method, as shown in the next example.

Example

Solve the equation: $4x + 20 = x + 29$

$$4x + 20 = x + 29$$
$$(-x)$$
$$3x + 20 = 29$$
$$(-20)$$
$$3x = 9$$
$$(\div 3)$$
$$x = 3$$

Check: $12 + 20 = 32$ $3 + 29 = 32$ ✓

Exercise 19.1

Solve these equations.

1   $2a + 4 = a + 8$

2   $2b + 14 = 3b + 8$

3   $4c + 12 = 5c + 5$

4   $6x + 10 = 7x + 6$

5   $7x + 9 = 8x + 4$

6   $3y + 2 = y + 8$

7   $4x + 2 = x + 11$

8   $2p + 14 = 5p + 8$

9   $2q + 12 = 6q + 8$

10   $7z + 4 = 5z + 8$

Add or subtract?

So far you have been subtracting the numbers, to solve the equations.

Sometimes you will need to add them.

Example

Solve the equation: $4a + 12 = 7a - 6$

$4a + 12 = 7a - 6$

$\qquad\qquad (-4a)$

$12 = 3a - 6$

$\qquad\qquad (+6)$

$18 = 3a$

$\qquad\qquad (\div 3)$

$6 = a$

$a = 6$

Check: $4 \times 6 + 12 = 36$ and $7 \times 6 - 6 = 36$ ✓

Exercise 19.2

Solve these equations.

1 $2a - 4 = a + 1$

2 $4b - 7 = 3b + 3$

3 $5c - 3 = 4c + 2$

4 $3x + 3 = 2x + 7$

5 $4y + 1 = 5y - 6$

6 $7z + 9 = 9z - 5$

7 $8p - 5 = 5p + 1$

8 $2q + 1 = 4q - 9$

9 $2r - 3 = 15 + 4r$

10 $7x - 7 = x + 11$

Negative numbers or coefficients

Sometimes, when you remove one term, you will be left with a negative number.

It is very important to write down your working clearly. If you do, you should be able to work with the negative numbers. Alternatively, you can avoid having a negative unknown term if you always subtract the smaller term.

Example

Solve the equation: $6 + 8b = 4b - 10$

$6 + 8b = 4b - 10$

$\qquad\qquad (-4b)$

$6 + 4b = {}^-10$

$\qquad\qquad (-6)$

$4b = {}^-16$

$\qquad\qquad (\div 4)$

$b = {}^-4$

Check: $6 + ({}^-32) = {}^-26$ and ${}^-16 - 10 = {}^-26$ ✓

> Do not ignore the negative signs, they change the value of the number, but do take great care. It is easy to be careless with negative numbers.

Now you know how to solve equations with the unknown on both sides, and those in which the answers are whole numbers, positive or negative. In some equations, the answer may be a fraction, positive or negative.

Examples

(i) Solve the equation: $3 + 4x = x - 1$

$$3 + 4x = x - 1$$
$$(-x)$$
$$3 + 3x = {}^-1$$
$$(-3)$$
$$3x = {}^-4$$
$$(÷3)$$
$$x = \frac{{}^-4}{3}$$

Turn your improper fraction into a mixed number for your answer.

$$x = {}^-1\frac{1}{3}$$

(ii) Solve the equation: $5 + 11y = 7y - 9$

$$5 + 11y = 7y - 9$$
$$(-7y)$$
$$5 + 4y = {}^-9$$
$$(-5)$$
$$4y = {}^-14$$
$$(÷4)$$
$$y = \frac{{}^-14}{4}$$
$$= \frac{{}^-7}{2}$$
$$= {}^-3\frac{1}{2}$$

Remember that you should always write fractions in their lowest terms in your final answer.

Exercise 19.3

Solve these equations.

1 $3x + 1 = 2x - 4$

2 $3a - 1 = 4a - 5$

3 $5y + 7 = 4y - 4$

4 $4b - 1 = 5b - 7$

5 $7 + 6z = 5z - 3$

6 $6c + 2 = 4c - 4$

7 $2 + 4p = 7p - 7$

8 $5q + 7 = q - 1$

9 $7r + 1 = 2r - 4$

10 $3s - 1 = 7 + 5s$

11 $4x - 1 = x + 1$

12 $5y - 6 = 3y + 1$

13 $z - 1 = 2 + 3z$

14 $3 + 6a = a + 7$

15 $3b - 7 = 4 + 8b$

16 $3 + 2d = 4d - 2$

17 $7m - 1 = m + 4$

18 $3 + 2n = 8n + 9$

19 $3x - 10 = 7x + 4$

20 $5 + 6x = 3x - 2$

Finally, you need to be prepared for two special situations.

1 The vanishing term

Look at this equation.

$3x + 2 = x$

$\qquad\qquad (-x)$

$2x + 2 = ?$ $\qquad\qquad$ What is left on the RHS?

$2x + 2 = 0$ $\qquad\qquad$ You know that $x - x = 0$ so write 0

$\qquad\qquad (-2)$

$\quad 2x = {}^-2$

$\qquad\qquad (\div 2)$

$\quad\quad x = {}^-1$

2 The negative term

Look at this equation. Here are two possible solutions.

$2x + 2 = 4 + 3x$ $\qquad\qquad\qquad\qquad$ $2x + 2 = 4 + 3x$

$\qquad\quad (-3x)$ $\qquad\qquad\qquad\qquad\qquad\qquad (-2x)$

${}^-x + 2 = 4$ $\qquad\qquad\qquad\qquad\qquad\qquad\quad 2 = 4 + x$

$\qquad\quad (-2)$ $\qquad\qquad\qquad\qquad\qquad\qquad\qquad (-4)$

${}^-x = 2$ $\qquad\qquad\qquad\qquad\qquad\qquad\quad {}^-2 = x$

$\qquad\quad (\div {}^-1)$ $\qquad\qquad\qquad\qquad\qquad\qquad (\div {}^-1)$

$\quad x = {}^-2$ $\qquad\qquad\qquad\qquad\qquad\qquad x = {}^-2$

> The solution to the right avoids finishing on a negative x term.

Always try to avoid finishing with a negative x-term. If you look carefully at the equation, you can identify the smaller x-term and eliminate it. Just take care with signs, and check whether to add or subtract to eliminate the smaller term.

Sometimes you need to simplify equations before you start to solve them. Use the abbreviation (S) on the right to show that the stage is simplification.

Example

Solve the equation: $5b - b + 13 = b + 4 - 2b$

$5b - b + 13 = b + 4 - 2b$

$\qquad\qquad\qquad\qquad (S)$

$\quad 4b + 13 = 4 - b$

$\qquad\qquad\qquad (+b)$

$\quad 5b + 13 = 4$

$\qquad\qquad\qquad (-13)$

$\qquad 5b = {}^-9$

$\qquad\qquad\qquad (\div 5)$

$\qquad\quad b = {}^-\dfrac{9}{5}$

$\qquad\quad b = {}^-1\dfrac{4}{5}$

Solve these equations.

1 $7c - 4 + 4c = 8$

2 $3x = 3 - 2x + 6$

3 $2 = 6 - 8z - z$

4 $3 - 2a + a = 8 + 3a - 4$

5 $4x - 1 + 3x = 3x - 6 - x$

6 $12b = 3b + 1 - 7b$

7 $11 - 2t = 3 + 2t - 9$

8 $5(2 + 2z) = 7 - 3z$

9 $7 - a = 4a - 3(a - 3)$

10 $3(5 - 4c) = 2(1 + 5c)$

You have now solved equations in various different forms. See how quickly you can do the next 20 questions – time yourself.

Exercise 19.5

Solve these equations.

1 $4 + a = 6$

2 $2 = 5 - b$

3 $9c = 15$

4 $\frac{x}{4} = 5$

5 $2y + 1 = 7$

6 $9 - 3z = 3$

7 $3(s + 1) = 2$

8 $7 = 2(t - 3)$

9 $\frac{1}{8}(v + 4) = 2$

10 $7 = \frac{x - 5}{3}$

11 $3(y - 2) = 1$

12 $3z + 3 = 2z + 7$

13 $5p - 5 = 6p + 9$

14 $3q - 1 = 4 + q$

15 $7m + 4 = 5 + 2m$

16 $5n + 3 = 2n$

17 $8 - x + 4x = 5$

18 $4 - 3y - 7 = 5y + 12 - 2y$

19 $5(1 - 3z) = 7(2 - z)$

20 $7 - 4x = 3(3 + 2x)$

◯ Using algebra to solve problems

Now that you are good at solving equations, you can put what you know into practice, by solving real problems. When you do, make sure you know what you are representing by the letters you choose. It could be a quantity, for example cost, mass, age or just an unknown number.

Example

I am given the same amount of pocket money each week. One week
I bought four tennis balls and had 27p left over. The next week I bought
two tennis balls and had £1.45 left over. How much do the tennis balls
cost and how much pocket money do I get each week?

Let one tennis ball cost x pence.

Week 1: $4x + 27$

Week 2: $2x + 145$

I had the same amount of money each week, so:

$4x + 27 = 2x + 145$

$\qquad\qquad\qquad (-2x)$

$2x + 27 = 145$

$\qquad\qquad\qquad (-27)$

$\qquad 2x = 118$

$\qquad\qquad\qquad (\div 2)$

$\qquad x = 59$

Check $4 \times 59 + 27 = 263$; $2 \times 59 + 145 = 263$ ✓

Tennis balls cost 59 pence each and I get £2.63 pocket money each week.

> Always start
> by defining what
> unknown numerical
> value the letter
> represents.

> Write your answer
> as a sentence.

Exercise 19.6

1 I have just enough money to buy *either* four packets of Jellos *or* two packets
   of Jellos and 15 sticks of liquorice at 2p per stick.

   (a) A packet of Jellos costs x. What is the cost of four packets, in terms of
       x?

   (b) What is the cost of two packets of Jellos and the 15 sticks of liquorice,
       in terms of x?

   (c) Form an equation in terms of x and solve it.

   (d) How much does a packet of Jellos cost and how much money did I have
       to start with?

2 Buns cost 24p each. The cost of four cakes and six buns is the same as the
   cost of three buns and five cakes.

   (a) Cakes cost c pence each. Write an expression in terms of c for the cost
       of four cakes and six buns.

   (b) Write an expression in terms of c for the cost of 3 buns and 5 cakes.

   (c) Write an equation in terms c and solve it.

   (d) What is the cost of five cakes?

3 Here are two angles on a straight line.

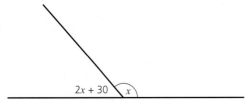

Form an equation in terms of x and solve it to find the sizes of the two angles.

4 (a) What is the angle sum of a triangle?

(b) Form an equation in terms of x for the angle sum of this triangle. Solve your equation to find the sizes of the three angles in the triangle.

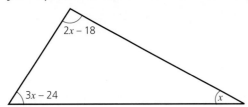

5 I have three pieces of string. The second piece is 5 cm shorter than the first piece and the third piece is 10 cm longer than the first piece.

(a) The length of the first piece of string is s. Write an expression in terms of s for the length of the second piece.

(b) Write an expression in terms of s for the length of the third piece.

(c) The first and second piece together are the same length as the third piece. Write an equation in terms of s and solve it.

(d) What is the total length of all three pieces of string?

6 My grandfather gave me some money. He gave my elder brother £10 more than he gave me and he gave my younger sister £2 less than he gave me.

(a) If my grandfather gave me £m, how much, in terms of m, did he give my brother and my sister?

(b) How much did my grandfather give us altogether?

(c) The total amount that my grandfather gave us was four times the amount that I received. How much, in terms of m, did my grandfather give us altogether?

(d) Form an equation in terms of m and solve it to find out how much we each received.

7 Louis baked x cakes and India baked three times as many as Louis did. Archie baked 15 cakes more than Louis did.

(a) How many cakes did India bake?

(b) How many cakes did Archie bake?

(c) Archie baked the same number of cakes as Louis and India together. Form an equation in terms of x and solve it to find out how many cakes each of them baked.

8 On Mother's Day my son gave me one red rose for each year of his age, and my daughter gave me two white roses for each year of her age. My son is four years older than my daughter and I received 28 roses altogether.

 (a) My son is s years old. How many roses did he give me?

 (b) How old is my daughter, in terms of s?

 (c) How many roses did my daughter give me, in terms of s?

 (d) Form an equation in terms of s and solve it to find the ages of my two children.

9 The perimeter of this rectangle is 52 cm.

3x + 1

 Form an equation in terms of x and solve it to find the length and width of the rectangle.

10 For our maths homework I worked out that the length of the side of this square must be $2x + 9$. My friend worked out that it was $3x - 1$

 As it happened, we were both correct!

 Form an equation in terms of x and solve it, then find the area of the square.

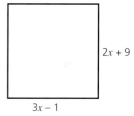

11 I have to write a 1000-word essay. I have written most of it and now I just have to write one third of the amount that I have already written, plus 20 words. How many words have I already written?

12 Kola Cola costs 6p more per can than Perli Cola. I can buy four tins of Perli Cola for the same price as I can buy three cans of Kola Cola. What is the cost of each brand of cola?

Extension Exercise 19.7

New operations

In the exercises on algebra and arithmetic you did not need to define the symbols. They all had a known meaning.

It can be quite interesting to set up your own special code. You may wish to define some new symbols with meanings that only you know about.

The new symbols should represent a new sequence of +, −, × or ÷, or other operations.

Example

The symbol # means 'is 4 more than'.

So 12 # 8   4 # 0 2^3 # 2^2 (as $8 = 4 + 4$)

Find the value of x when: (i) x # 7   (ii) 20 # x^2

(i) If x # 7 then $x = 4 + 7$

$\qquad\qquad\qquad = 11$ 11 is 4 more than 7

(ii) If 20 # x^2 then $20 = 4 + x^2$

$\qquad\qquad\qquad 16 = x^2$

so $x = 4$ or $^-4$

---

1 (a) Given that # means 'is 4 more than', which of these statements is true?

    (i) 10 # 6   **(ii)** 3 # 7   **(iii)** 4^3 # 4^2

  (b) Find a value of x that makes each of these statements true.

    (i) 7 # x **(iii)** $2x$ # x **(v)** $\frac{20}{x}$ # 0

    (ii) x # 15   **(iv)** 5 # $\frac{1}{x}$ **(vi)** $\frac{24}{x}$ # $\frac{x}{2}$

> You may find that it helps to turn the operation into an equation in order to find the value of x.

Example

Given that # means 'is 4 more than' and 6 # $\frac{1}{x}$, find the value of x

$6 = 4 + \dfrac{1}{x}$

$2 = \dfrac{1}{x}$

$x = \dfrac{1}{2}$

---

2 Given that ‡ means 'is 3 less than' then:

    1 ‡ 4   1 is 3 less than 4

    $^-1$ ‡ 2 $^-1$ is 3 less than 2

  (a) Which of these statements are true?

    (i) 5 ‡ 2   **(ii)** $^-5$ ‡ $^-2$ **(iii)** 2×3 ‡ 3^2

  (b) Find a value of x that makes each of these statements true.

    (i) 39 ‡ x **(iii)** $4x$ ‡ x **(v)** $\frac{1}{2x}$ ‡ $\frac{2}{x}$

    (ii) x ‡ $^-5$ **(iv)** x ‡ $2x$

3 If the symbol △ between two numbers means 'is one more than half of', then 5 △ 8 (5 is one more than 4 which is half of 8).

(a) Which of these statements is true?

(i) 4 △ 6   (ii) 3 △ 1   (iii) $\frac{1}{2}$ △ ⁻1

(b) Find a value of x that makes each of these statements true.

(i) x △ 1   (iii) $\frac{3}{2}$ △ x (v) $\frac{1}{x}$ △ ⁻4

(ii) 6 △ x (iv) x △ $\frac{1}{2}$ (vi) x △ 3x

4 If the symbol ◇ means 'the remainder when the second number is divided by 9', then 3 ◇ 21, since 21 ÷ 9 = 2 remainder 3

(a) Which of these statements are true?

(i) 1 ◇ 19   (ii) 5 ◇ 13   (iii) 3 ◇ 3

(b) If x ◇ y, are there any values of x and y such that x is greater than y?

(c) Write a value of x, between 20 and 30, that makes each of these statements true.

(i) 0 ◇ x (ii) 8 ◇ x (iii) 5 ◇ x

(d) Find as many values of x as you can to make the statement x ◇ 4x true.

Summary Exercise 19.8

1 Solve these equations.

(a) $3x + 8 = 2x + 5$ (d) $4 - 3x = 5 + x$

(b) $x + 8 = 2x - 3$ (e) $5(x + 1) = 2(x + 5)$

(c) $5 - 2x = 2x + 1$ (f) $9 - x + 8 = 2x - 3 + 7x$

2 Jamie, Henry, Charlie and Oliver have been on the school ski trip. When they return, they compare how much money they have left. Jamie has twice as many euros left as Charlie does. Henry has 10 euros more than Charlie does. Oliver has €7. Together Jamie, Charlie and Oliver have the same number of euros as Henry.

(a) Charlie has x euros. How many has:

(i) Jamie   (ii) Henry?

(b) Form an equation in terms of x and solve it to find how many euros Charlie has.

(c) How much money do the four of them have altogether?

3 For the same amount of money, I can buy either five sticks of liquorice and eight penny sweets or four sticks of liquorice and 12 penny sweets.

(a) If the cost of a stick of liquorice is x pence, what is the cost, in terms of x, of five sticks of liquorice and eight penny sweets?

(b) What is the cost, in terms of x, of four sticks of liquorice and 12 penny sweets?

(c) Write an equation in terms of x and solve it to find the cost of a stick of liquorice.

4 Mia won the school mathematics prize and received a book token to spend. When she went to the book shop, she found that they have some special-offer books at half price. She could buy either five books at the normal price and have £1.50 change or 11 special-offer books and have 55p change.

(a) If the special offer price is x pence, what will the normal price be?

(b) Write an equation in terms of x and solve it to find the normal price of books.

(c) What was the value of Mia's book token?

20 Sequences

A **sequence** is a set of numbers or shapes that follow a pattern.

◯ Recognising sequences

Look at these sequences of numbers.

2, 4, 6, 8, 10, 12, 14, ...

1, 3, 5, 7, 9, 11, 13, 15, ...

3, 6, 9, 12, 15, 18, 21, ...

The first is the sequence of **even numbers**, the second is the sequence of **odd numbers** and the third is the **three-times table**, or the sequence of **multiples of three**.

These are familiar sequences. If you were asked to find the 100th even number, odd number or multiple of three, you could do that quite easily.

● 100th even number is 200 2×100

● 100th odd number is 199   1 less than the 100th even number

● 100th multiple of three is 300 3×100

It is not so easy to recognise other sequences, or to calculate their 100th terms.

If a sequence goes up in regular steps, you can compare it to a times table.

Example

Work out the next two terms in this sequence and write down the 100th term.

3,   8,   13,   18,   ...,   ...

The difference between the terms is $13 - 8 = 5$

The next terms are:

$18 + 5 = 23$ $23 + 5 = 28$

The times table that goes up in 5s is the 5 times table.

This sequence is the 5 times table less 2

The 100th term is $5 \times 100 - 2 = 498$

> Check this is the same for every term.

1 (a) Write out the next three terms of each sequence.

    (i)   5, 10, 15, 20, 25, ..., ..., ...

    (ii) 6, 11, 16, 21, 26, ..., ..., ...

  (b) Write down the 100th term of each of the sequences in part (a). Show your calculations clearly.

2 (a) Write out the next three terms of each sequence.

    (i)   4, 8, 12, 16, 20, ..., ..., ...

    (ii) 3, 7, 11, 15, 19, ..., ..., ...

  (b) Write down the 100th term of each of the sequences in part (a). Show your calculations clearly.

3 (a) Write out the next three terms of each sequence.

    (i)   6, 12, 18, 24, 30, ..., ..., ...

    (ii) 9, 15, 21, 27, 33, ..., ..., ...

  (b) Write down the 100th term of each of the sequences in part (a). Show your calculations clearly.

Did you notice that the sequences in the last three questions went in pairs? If you did, you may also have seen a connection between the first and second terms in each pair.

Now try these. They are like the second sequence in each pair above.

4 (a) Write out the next three terms of each sequence.

    (i)   2, 5, 8, 11, 14, ..., ..., ...,

    (ii) 5, 12, 19, 26, 33, ..., ..., ...

    (iii) 4, 9, 14, 19, 24, ..., ..., ...

  (b) Write down the 100th term of each of the sequences in part (a). Show your calculations clearly.

For other sequences it may be harder to find the pattern. See if you can recognise these. You have met them before. Look carefully at the pattern of differences.

5 (a) Write out the next three terms of each sequence.

    (i)   1, 4, 9, 16, 25, ..., ..., ...

    (ii) 1, 3, 6, 10, 15, ..., ..., ...

    (iii) 1, 1, 2, 3, 5, 8, 13, ..., ..., ...,

  (b) Write down the 10th term in each sequence above, showing your calculations clearly.

Sequences and patterns

Many sequences are generated by geometrical patterns. Drawing patterns can help you to work out the rule behind a particular sequence.

Exercise 20.2

1 Look at this sequence of patterns.

(a) Draw the next two patterns.   (b) Copy and complete this table.

Number of white rectangles	1	2	3	4	5	100
Number of green rectangles						

(c) Write down the calculation you used to find the number of green rectangles in the 100th pattern.

2 Look at this sequence of patterns.

  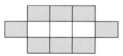

(a) Draw the next two patterns.   (b) Copy and complete this table.

Number of white rectangles	1	2	3	4	5	10	20
Number of green rectangles							

(c) Write down the calculation you used to find the number of green rectangles in the 20th pattern.

3 Look at this sequence of patterns.

(a) Draw the next two patterns.   (b) Copy and complete this table.

Number of white rectangles	1	2	3	4	5	20	100
Number of green rectangles							

(c) Write down the calculation you used to find the number of green rectangles in the 100th pattern.

(d) What is the name of the sequence of numbers you have generated in the green rectangles row?

4 Look at this sequence of patterns, drawn on square spotted paper.

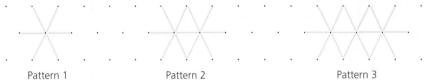

Pattern 1   Pattern 2   Pattern 3

(a) Draw the next two patterns.   **(b)** Copy and complete this table.

Pattern number	1	2	3	4	5	10	20	100
Number of lines								

(c) Write down the calculation you used to find the number of lines in the 100th pattern.

5 Look at this sequence of patterns, drawn on triangular spotted paper.

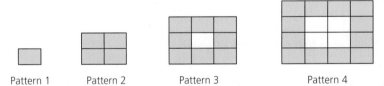

Pattern 1   Pattern 2   Pattern 3

(a) Draw the next two patterns.

(b) Draw a table like the one in question 4 and fill it in.

(c) Write down the calculation you used to find the number of lines in the 100th pattern.

6 Look at this sequence of patterns.

Pattern 1   Pattern 2   Pattern 3   Pattern 4

(a) Draw the next two patterns in the series.   **(b)** Copy and complete this table.

Pattern number	Number of green rectangles	Number of white rectangles	Total number of rectangles
1	1	0	1
2	4	0	4
3			9
4			
5			
6			
10			

(c) Add an extra row for the 100th pattern number and explain how you calculate each of your answers.

7 Look at this sequence of patterns.

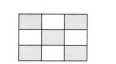 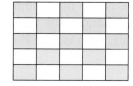

Pattern 1   Pattern 2   Pattern 3

(a) Draw the next two patterns in the series.

(b) Copy and complete a table like the one in question 6

(c) Add an extra row for the 100th pattern number and explain how you calculate each of your answers.

8 (a) Make up a pattern of your own. Use squared paper.

(b) Draw up a table like those you have used earlier.

(c) Calculate the numbers in your 100th pattern, showing your calculations clearly.

Equations for sequences

In the last exercise, the patterns helped you to understand the relationship between the pattern number and the rule. You can also use algebra to help understand the rule.

Consider an equation, such as $y = 2x + 1$

There is one value of y for each value of x

Taking the values of x as 1, 2, 3, 4, 5, ... gives the values of y as 3, 5, 7, 9, 11, ...

You can write this in a different way, taking the y numbers as a sequence. Then the values of x tell you the number of the term in the sequence that you are looking at.

It is common to use the letter n in sequences, rather than x and y. Then n stands for the pattern or term number in the sequence.

- for the first term $n = 1$
- for the second term $n = 2$
- for the third term $n = 3$
- for the kth term $n = k$

So the rule for the nth term of the sequence above is $2n + 1$

When you are considering sequences, you can also use the 'What's in the box?' technique, as in Book 1. The boxes represent **function machines.** Each function machine changes the number that goes in so that a new number comes out. Here is a '× 2' machine.

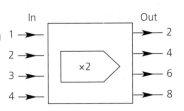

Exercise 20.3

1 The nth term of a sequence is given by the formula: nth term $= n + 4$
  Write down:

  (a) the first term

  (b) the second term

  (c) the third term

  (d) the fourth term.

2 The nth term of a sequence is given by the formula: nth term $= n - 1$
  Write down:

  (a) the first term

  (b) the second term

  (c) the third term

  (d) the fourth term.

3 The nth term of a sequence W is given by the formula: nth term $= 3n + 2$
  Write down:

  (a) the first term

  (b) the second term

  (c) the seventh term

  (d) the tenth term.

4 The nth term of a sequence S is given by the formula: nth term $= 3 + 2n$
  Write down:

  (a) the first term

  (b) the third term

  (c) the fifth term

  (d) the eighth term.

5 The nth term of a sequence T is given by the formula: nth term $= 5 + n$
  Write down:

  (a) the first term

  (b) the second term

  (c) the sixth term

  (d) the ninth term.

6 The nth term of a sequence V is given by the formula: nth term $= 5n + 1$
  Write down:

  (a) the first term

  (b) the fifth term

  (c) the 20th term

  (d) the 100th term.

Finding the rule

Another useful method for finding the rules behind patterns of numbers is a relationship diagram. These are like the tables you used when you drew the patterns, or the 'In' and 'Out' lists on the function machines.

20 Sequences

Example

Find the next three terms and the rule for the nth term for this sequence.

4, 7, 10, 13

The difference between consecutive terms is 3

The next terms will be:

$13 + 3 = 16 \qquad 16 + 3 = 19 \qquad 19 + 3 = 22$

Draw a relationship diagram for these terms and add three more rows.

n	$\rightarrow$	nth term	$\rightarrow$	$3n$
1	$\rightarrow$	4	$\rightarrow$	3
2	$\rightarrow$	7	$\rightarrow$	6
3	$\rightarrow$	10	$\rightarrow$	9
4	$\rightarrow$	13	$\rightarrow$	12
5	$\rightarrow$	16	$\rightarrow$	15
6	$\rightarrow$	19	$\rightarrow$	18
7	$\rightarrow$	22	$\rightarrow$	21

> From the nth term column it is clear that the numbers go up in threes. The three-times table goes up in threes, and each of these numbers is just one more than a number in the three-times table. So from this the rule must be:
>
> nth term $= 3n + 1$

> The three-times table is written as $3n$ in a third column so you can check this.

Exercise 20.4

1 Work out the next three terms in the series and hence find the rule for the nth term.

2, 5, 8, 11

Draw a relationship diagram to help!

2 Work out the next three terms in the series and hence find the rule for the nth term.

6, 11, 16, 21

3 Work out the next three terms in the series and hence find the rule for the nth term.

2, 6, 10, 14

4 Find the next three terms in the series and hence the rule for the nth term.

5, 12, 19, 26

5 Work out the next three terms in the series and hence find the rule for the nth term.

3, 9, 15, 21

6 Find the rules for the nth term for each of the sequences in questions 1–5 of Exercise 20.2

A different rule

You have been considering sequences in which the difference between two consecutive terms was the same. For example, the sequence 1, 5, 9, 13, ... has a constant difference of 4 and so is based on the four-times table or $4n$.

Other sequences may be based on different patterns. You should recognise this sequence of square numbers.

1, 4, 9, 16, 25, ...

The differences have their own pattern.

$$1 \xrightarrow{+3} 4 \xrightarrow{+5} 9 \xrightarrow{+7} 16 \xrightarrow{+9} 25$$

Can you see the pattern in those differences? You should recognise that the nth term is based on the square numbers (n^2)

Example

Find the next three terms and hence the rule for the nth term for this sequence.

3, 6, 11, 18

The pattern of differences is 3, 5, 7

The next three differences will be 9, 11, 13

This is the pattern of differences for the square numbers.

Draw up a relationship diagram and add three more rows.

n	$\rightarrow$	nth term	$\rightarrow$	n^2
1	$\rightarrow$	3	$\rightarrow$	1
2	$\rightarrow$	6	$\rightarrow$	4
3	$\rightarrow$	11	$\rightarrow$	9
4	$\rightarrow$	18	$\rightarrow$	16
5	$\rightarrow$	27	$\rightarrow$	25
6	$\rightarrow$	38	$\rightarrow$	36
7	$\rightarrow$	51	$\rightarrow$	49

The rule is $T_n = n^2 + 2$

Exercise 20.5

1 Work out the next three terms in the series and hence find the rule for the nth term.

1, 4, 9, 16

2 Work out the next three terms in the series and hence find the rule for the nth term.

2, 5, 10, 17

3 Work out the next three terms in the series and hence find the rule for the nth term.

0, 3, 8, 15

4 Work out the next three terms in the series and hence find the rule for the nth term.

4, 7, 12, 19

5 Work out the rule for the nth term of each of the sequences in questions 6 and 7 of Exercise 20.2

Extension Exercise 20.6

There were a couple of sequences in the first exercise that did not fit either the constant difference pattern or the square number pattern. Take another look at them.

Sequence 1

1, 3, 6, 10, 15, ..., ..., ...,

Consider the differences.

$1 \xrightarrow{+2} 3 \xrightarrow{+3} 6 \xrightarrow{+4} 10 \xrightarrow{+5} 15$

These differences go up by one each time. Where have you seen this before? This diagram should give you a clue.

Whichever way you arrange the dots, they make the same number sequence.

$T_1 = 1 = 1$

$T_2 = 1 + 2 = 3$

$T_3 = 1 + 2 + 3 = 6$

Do you recognise them now? They are the **triangular numbers**.

Is there a rule for the nth triangular number?

Look at this diagram.

$2 \times T_1$	$2 \times T_2$	$2 \times T_3$	$2 \times T_4$
$= 1 \times 2$	$= 2 \times 3$	$= 3 \times 4$	$= 4 \times 5$
$= 2$	$= 6$	$= 12$	$= 20$

Then it follows that:

$2 \times T_n = n \times (n + 1)$

$\qquad\quad = n(n + 1)$

And therefore the formula for the nth triangle number must be:

$T_n = \frac{1}{2} n(n + 1)$

1 Write down the next three terms and then the rule for the nth term of each sequence.

(a) 0, 2, 5, 9, 14, ...

(b) 0, 1, 3, 6, 10, 15, ...

(c) 2, 6, 12, 20, 30, ...

2 Draw a circle and divide it into a number of regions.

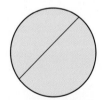 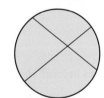 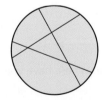

(a) Copy the diagrams and then draw the next three in the sequence. Every line must cross every other line.

(b) Copy and complete this table.

Number of lines	1	2	3	4	5	6
Number of regions						

(c) From your table, write a formula for R_n the number of regions when you have n lines.

(d) Draw a circle divided up by eight lines and check that your formula works when $n = 8$

Sequence 2

1, 1, 2, 3, 5, 8, 13, ..., ..., ...,

Consider the differences.

1 $\xrightarrow{+0}$ 1 $\xrightarrow{+1}$ 2 $\xrightarrow{+1}$ 3 $\xrightarrow{+2}$ 5 $\xrightarrow{+3}$ 8 $\xrightarrow{+5}$ 13

The sequence of differences is the same as the original sequence. You have met this pattern before. It is known as the **Fibonacci sequence**. There are other sequences that are formed in the same way.

3 Write down the next three terms of each sequence.

    (a) 2, 5, 7, 12, 19, ..., ..., ...

    (b) 1, 3, 4, 7, 11, 18, ..., ..., ...

    (c) 0, 2, 2, 4, 6, 10, ..., ..., ...

4 Copy these sequences and fill in the missing numbers.

    (a) 2, ..., 5, 8, 12, ..., 23, ...

    (b) 1, 5, ..., 11, ..., 28, ...

    (c) ..., 7, 17, ..., 49, 71, ...

    (d) 50, 32, 18, ..., 2, ..., 4, ...

Summary Exercise 20.7

1 (a) Write out the next three terms of each sequence.

    (i) 8, 16, 24, 32, 40, ..., ..., ...

    (ii) 5, 13, 21, 29, 37, ..., ..., ...

  (b) Write down the 100th term in each sequence in part (a). Show your calculations clearly.

2 (a) Write out the next three terms of each sequence.

    (i) 9, 19, 29, 39, 49, ..., ..., ...

    (ii) 7, 12, 17, 22, 27, ..., ..., ...

  (b) Write down the 100th term for each sequence in part (a). Show your calculations clearly.

3 Look at this series of patterns.

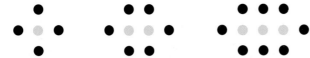

(a) Draw the next three patterns in the series.

(b) Copy and complete this table.

Number of green dots	1	2	3	4	5	6
Number of black dots						

(c) How many black dots will there be if there are 10 green dots?

(d) How many green dots will there be if there are 100 black dots?

4 The nth term of a sequence is given by the formula $20 - 3n$. Write down:

(a) the first term

(b) the third term

(c) the sixth term

(d) the 12th term.

5 Write down the next three terms and then the rule for the nth term in this sequence.

1, 5, 9, 13

Draw a relationship diagram if it helps.

6 Write down the next three terms and then the rule for the nth term in this sequence.

3, 6, 11, 17

Activity: Pentagonal and hexagonal numbers

You have looked at the patterns of triangles and squares, produced by dots, and have seen that they give the triangular numbers and square numbers.

Copy and complete this table for the number of dots in each pattern number below.

Number	First	Second	Third	Fourth	Fifth	nth
Triangular	1	3	6			
Square	1	4				

The two next shapes in this sequence are pentagons and hexagons. Look at the patterns that they produce.

Pentagonal

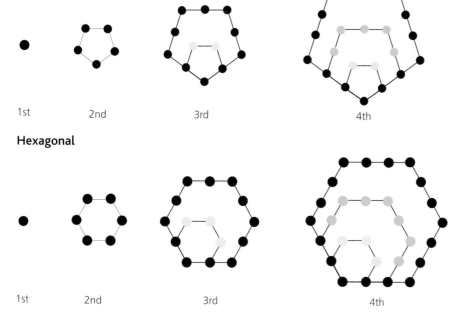

1st 2nd 3rd 4th

Hexagonal

1st 2nd 3rd 4th

Now add these to your copy of the table above and record these numbers.

Number	First	Second	Third	Fourth	Fifth	nth
Triangular	1	3	6			
Square	1	4	9			
Pentagonal	1	5	12			
Hexagonal	1	6				

Try to work out the rule for the nth number.

Without drawing patterns, can you extend the table for heptagonal and octagonal numbers? Have a go!

Glossary

2D Two-dimensional: a plane (flat) shape such as a rectangle or circle.

3D Three-dimensional: a solid object such as a cube or sphere.

Acute angle An angle that is between 0° and 90°

Alternate angles Equal angles formed when a transversal crosses parallel lines, found in a Z-shape.

Area The amount of space inside a 2D shape such as a rectangle or circle, measured in square units such as square centimetres (cm^2).

Axes The plural of axis; the horizontal and vertical number lines on which a co-ordinate grid is based, they tell you the values of the data.

Bisect Divide a line or an angle into two equal parts.

Cancel Divide the top and bottom of a fraction by one or more common factors to reduce it to its lowest terms.

Circumference The line round the outside, or the perimeter, of a circle.

Chord A line across a circle which does not pass through the centre.

Coefficient The number multiplying an algebraic variable in a term.

Co-interior angles Angles formed when a transversal crosses parallel lines, inside a C-shape, which add up to 180°

Co-ordinates The horizontal and vertical distances from the origin (the point where the axes cross), used to plot a point on a grid; for example, the point (3, 5) is 3 units along and 5 units up from the origin.

Corresponding angles Equal angles formed when a transversal crosses parallel lines, found in an F-shape.

Common factors Numbers that are factors of two or more other numbers; for example, 5 is a common factor of 20 and 25

Common multiples Numbers that are multiples of two or more other numbers; for example, 100 is a common multiple of 20 and 25

Congruent Exactly the same shape and the same size.

Co-ordinate grid The grid on which the horizontal and vertical axes and the graph are drawn.

Cube number A number multiplied by itself and by itself again; for example, $3 \times 3 \times 3 = 3^3 = 27$

Cube root of a number is a value that when cubed gives the original number. Cube root of 27 is 3 and 3 cubed is 27

Cube A 3D shape with 6 faces that are all identical squares.

Cuboid A 3D shape that has 6 faces that are all rectangles, although some of the rectangles may be squares.

Data A set or piece of information, for example, highest daily temperatures; data may refer to a group of values that can be analysed and recorded in a table or plotted on a chart or graph.

Decimal fraction A number less than one, written after a decimal point.

Decimal place The position in a number of a digit that occurs to the right of the decimal point; they include tenths, hundredths, thousandths, etc.

Denominator The bottom number in a fraction, showing the number of parts into which the whole is divided.

Diagonal A line joining non-adjacent vertices in a 2D or 3D shape.

Diameter A line joining two points on the circumference of a circle and passing through the centre; the diameter is twice the radius.

Difference   The result of subtracting a smaller number from a larger number; for example, the difference between 5 and 11 is 6 (11 − 5)

Digit   One of the symbols 0, 1, 2, 3, 4, 5, 6, 7, 8, 9 used to make numbers; for example, 45 is a two-digit number.

Equation   A mathematical sentence that includes an equals sign; equations frequently contain at least one unknown term and may be solved.

Equivalent fractions   Fractions that have the same value although their numerators and denominators are different; for example, $\frac{3}{4} = \frac{9}{12}$

Equivalent fractions, decimals and percentages   Fractions, decimals and percentages that are equal; for example, $20\% = 0.2 = \frac{1}{5}$

Equivalent units   The approximate comparison between metric and imperial units.
1 foot ≈ 30 cm, 1 metre ≈ 3 ft 3 in or 3.25 feet
8 kilometres ≈ 5 miles
1 lb ≈ 450 g and 1 kg ≈ 2.2 lb
1 pint ≈ 600 ml, 1 gallon ≈ 4.5 litres, 1 litre ≈ 1.7 pints
10 litres ≈ 2.2 gallons

Estimate   Make an approximation, often by calculating with rounded numbers.

Evaluate   Calculate the answer to

Expression   A mathematical phrase, with no equals or inequality signs, which may comprise numbers, unknown terms or variables (such as x) and operators. An expression could also be a fraction and may contain brackets. An expression may be simplified but cannot be solved.

Factor   A number that divides exactly into another number; for example, 1, 2, 3 and 6 are factors of 6 and $6 = 2 \times 3 = 1 \times 6$

Factor pair   Two factors that when multiplied together give the number being considered; for example, factor pairs of 6 are 1 and 6, 2 and 3

Formula   A rule used to calculate a specific value, often written in letters or words; for example, the formula for the
volume of a cuboid = length (l) × width (w) × height (h) or $V = lwh$

Fraction   A number less than one, written with a numerator and a denominator, such as $\frac{3}{4}$

Highest common factor (HCF)   1, 2, 3 and 6 are factors of both 12 and 18. The HCF of 12 and 18 is 6

Imperial units   Non-metric units in common use in Britain and America.
Mass (weight)
16 ounces (oz) = 1 pound (lb)
14 pounds (lb) = 1 stone (st)   1 ton (t) = 2240 pounds (lb)
Length
12 inches (in) = 1 foot (ft)   3 feet (ft) = 1 yard (yd)
1760 yards (yd) = 1 mile
Capacity or volume
2 pints (pt) = 1 quart (qt)   8 pints (pt) = 1 gallon (gall)

Improper fraction   A fraction in which the numerator (top number) is larger than the denominator (bottom number), such as $\frac{7}{4}$

Index number   The number of times a number or unknown is multiplied by itself.

Inequality   A relationship between two values that are not equal, using one of the symbols < (less than), > (more than), ≤ (less than or equal to) or ≥ (more than or equal to), ≠ not equal too.

Integer   A whole number, positive or negative; for example, 4, ⁻3 and 17 are all integers.

Inverse   An opposite calculation; addition is the inverse of subtraction, division is the inverse of multiplication.

Isosceles triangle   A triangle with two equal sides and two equal angles.

Line graph   A line that represents the relationship between two variables, such as distance and time; it may be straight or curved.

Line of symmetry   The line that divides a shape into two congruent parts, one being a reflection of the other.

Long division   Division by a number with two or more digits, showing each stage of the calculation and working down the page.

Long multiplication   Multiplication by a number with two or more digits, showing each stage of the calculation; multiplication by first the units, then the tens, and so on, with the sum of the multiplications at the bottom.

Lowest common multiple   The lowest multiple two numbers have in common. For example: the lowest common multiple of 2 and 3 is 6

Lowest terms   A fraction or ratio in which the components (numerator and denominator) have no common factors.

Mean   The average that is the sum of all the values divided by the number of values, often referred to simply as the 'average'; for example, the mean of 3, 5, 7 and 9 $= \frac{3+5+7+9}{4} = \frac{24}{4} = 6$

Median   The middle value in a row of numbers arranged in numerical order; for an even number of numbers, the median is the mean of the middle two numbers.

Metric units   Units of mass (weight), length and capacity (volume) that are in use in Britain and in Europe as well as many other countries.
Mass
1000 milligrams (mg) = 1 gram (g)   1000 grams (g) = 1 kilogram (kg)
1000 kilograms (kg) = 1 metric tonne (t)
Length
10 millimetres (mm) = 1 centimetre (cm)   100 centimetres (cm) = 1 metre (m)
1000 millimetres (mm) = 1 metre (m)   1000 metres (m) = 1 kilometre (km)
Capacity (volume)
1000 millilitres (ml) = 1 litre (l)

Mixed number   A combination of a whole number and a proper fraction; for example, $2\frac{3}{4}$

Mode   The value that occurs most often in a set of data; this is the only average that may apply to non-numeric data.

Multiple   A number that is a product (result of a multiplication) of a factor; for example, 6 is a multiple of 2

Negative numbers   Numbers less than zero (0); for example, ⁻4, called 'negative 4'

Net   A 2D shape that can be folded up to form a 3D shape.

Numerator   The top number on a fraction; it tells you how many parts of the whole you have.

Obtuse angle   An angle between 90° and 180°

Order of operations   The order in which a calculation should be done: brackets, index numbers or other calculation then divide, multiply, add, subtract (BIDMAS).

Parallel   Lines that are the same distance apart and will never meet, however far they are extended.

Parallelogram   A quadrilateral with two pairs of equal and parallel sides.

Percentage   A fraction expressed as hundredths of a whole, written with a percentage sign; for example, $25\% = \frac{25}{100}$

Perimeter   The line around the outside of a 2D shape.

Pie chart   A chart in the shape of a circle, in which quantities are represented as proportions of the whole, according to the angle at the centre of each sector.

Polygon   A 2D shape with sides that are straight lines.

3 sides – a triangle	4 sides – a quadrilateral
5 sides – a pentagon	6 sides – a hexagon
7 sides – a heptagon	8 sides – an octagon
9 sides – a nonagon	10 sides – a decagon
12 sides – a dodecagon	20 sides – an icosagon

Powers of 10   The numbers that result from multiplying 10 by itself: $10^0 = 1$, $10^1 = 10$, $10^2 = 100$, $10^3 = 1000$, $10^4 = 10\,000$, $10^5 = 100\,000$, $10^6 = 1\,000\,000$, $10^{-1} = \frac{1}{10} = 0.1$

Prime factor   A factor that is a prime number; for example, 2 and 3 are prime factors of 6

Prime number   A number that has exactly two factors, itself and 1; for example, 2, 3, 5 and 7 are prime numbers, but 1 is not.

Product   The result of a multiplication; for example, the product of 3 and 4 is 12

Proper fraction   is where the numerator (the top number) is less than the denominator (the bottom number); for example, $\frac{3}{4}$

Protractor   A transparent circular or semi-circular scale used to measure angles.

Quadrant   1 A quarter of a circle.
2 One of the four sections of a co-ordinate grid between the horizontal and vertical axes.

Quotient   The whole number part of the result of a division calculation; for example, for $25 \div 2 = 12$ remainder 1, 12 is the quotient.

Radius   1 The distance from the centre of a circle to the circumference.
2 A line from the centre of a circle to the circumference.
All radii are the same length in any one circle.

Range   The difference between the highest and lowest values.

Ratio   A relationship between two or more parts of a whole, expressed in the form 'a to b' or $a : b$

Rectangle   A quadrilateral with four right angles and two pairs of equal sides.

Reciprocal   The result of dividing 1 by a number; for example, the reciprocal of 2 is $\frac{1}{2}$ and the reciprocal of $\frac{3}{4}$ is $\frac{4}{3}$

Reflection   A shape as seen in a mirror; the original shape is the object and the reflected shape is its image.

Reflex angle   An angle between 180° and 360°

Remainder   The part that is left over in a division calculation; for example, $25 \div 2 = 12$ remainder 1

Rhombus   A quadrilateral with four equal sides.

Right angle   An angle that is equal to 90°

Root   A number that, multiplied by itself one or more times, gives the number of which it is the root; for example, 3 is the square root of 9 ($\sqrt{9} = 3$), 2 is the cube root of 8 ($\sqrt[3]{8} = 2$). Roots may not be exact; for example, on a calculator the square root of 2 is 1.4142... but the exact value is written as $\sqrt{2}$

Rotation   A turn of an object through a number of degrees, clockwise or anti-clockwise, about a centre of rotation.

Round   Approximate a number to a given accuracy, such as to:

the nearest whole number

the nearest ten, hundred, thousand, ...

one, two, three or more decimal places (d.p.)

one, two, three or more significant figures (s.f.).

Scale factor   The ratio of the length of the enlargement to the length of the original object, or with its representation on a map or plan.

Sector   Part of a circle enclosed by an arc and two radii.

Segment   The part of a circle between a chord and an arc.

Significant figures   The numbers that show the magnitude of a number that has been rounded to a degree of accuracy; for example, 34 567 = 34 600 to 3 s.f. When 3046 is rounded to 3 s.f., it is written as **305**0 and the three digits in bold are significant.

Similar   Exactly the same shape but not the same size.

Simplest form   See lowest terms

Simplify   Reduce (a fraction or ratio) to its lowest terms or an expression to its simplest form.

Square number   A number that can be expressed as one of its factors multiplied by itself; for example, $4 \times 4 = 16$, 4 is the square root of 16 and 16 is a square number.

Square root   (see root)

Standard index form   A way of writing a number as a number between 1 and 10 multiplied by a power of 10; very large and very small numbers may be displayed on a calculator in standard index form; for example, 34 000 may be shown as 3.4×10^4

Statistics   The process of collecting and analysing numerical data.

Substitution   Means replacing letters in a formula with numerical values.

Sum   The answer to an addition calculation; for example, the sum of 3 and 4 is 7

Supplementary angles   Two angles which add up to 180°

Transformation   A change to a 2D shape, may be a translation, reflection, rotation or enlargement, that changes the position or size of a shape (the object) to form its image.

Translation   A movement of an object, first parallel to the horizontal axis, then parallel to the vertical axis, to produce its image.

Triangular number   A number that can be represented in the form of a triangle. Triangle numbers can be calculated on the sum of consecutive numbers starting with 1

Variable   An unknown value, usually represented by a letter such as x.

Venn diagram   A diagram representing mathematical sets pictorially as circles or closed curves with common elements of the sets being represented by intersections of the circles.

Vertically opposite   The angles formed when two straight lines cross. At every such point, there are two pairs of equal vertically opposite angles.

Index